NEURO-OPHTHALMOLOGY

NEURO-OPHTHALMOLOGY

Associate Editors
THOMAS L. SLAMOVITS, MD
Professor and Vice-Chairman
Department of Ophthalmology and Visual Sciences
Montefiore Medical Center
Bronx, New York

RONALD BURDE, MD
Professor and Chairman
Department of Ophthalmology and Visual Sciences
Montefiore Medical Center
Bronx, New York

VOLUME 6

TEXTBOOK OF OPHTHALMOLOGY
EDITED BY
STEVEN M. PODOS, MD, FACS
Professor and Chairman
Department of Ophthalmology
Mt. Sinai School of Medicine
New York, NY

MYRON YANOFF, MD, FACS
Professor and Chairman
Department of Ophthalmology
Hahnemann University
Philadelphia, PA

Mosby

London St. Louis Baltimore Boston Chicago Philadelphia Sydney Toronto

For full details of all Mosby-Year Book Europe Limited titles, please write to Mosby-Year Book Europe Limited, Lynton House, 7–12 Tavistock Square, London, WC1H 9LB, England.

LIBRARY OF CONGRESS CATALOGING-IN-PUBLICATION DATA
(Revised for volume 6)

Textbook of ophthalmology.

    Includes bibliographical references and indexes.
    Contents: v. 1. Optics and refraction / David Miller—
v. 2. The uvea / Narsing A. Rao, David J. Forster, James J. Augsburger—[etc.]—
v. 6. Neuro-ophthalmology / associate editors, Thomas L. Slamovits, Ronald Burde.
    1. Ophthalmology. 2. Ophthalmology. I. Podos, Steven M.
II. Yanoff, Myron.
RE46.T26 1991   617.7   91-34425
ISBN 1-56375-011-2 (v. 1)

BRITISH LIBRARY CATALOGUING-IN-PUBLICATION DATA:
A catalogue record for this book is available from the British Library.

ISBN Volume 6: 1-56375-099-6
ISBN Set: 0-397-44692-6

10 9 8 7 6 5 4 3 2 1

Editorial Director: LEAH KENNEDY
Project Manager: DIMITRY POPOW
Editors: DIMITRY POPOW, SHARON RULE
Art Director and Cover Design: KATHRYN GREENSLADE
Interior Design: NANCY BERLINER
Layout: THOMAS TEDESCO
Illustration Director: CAROL KALAFATIC
Illustrators: WENDY JACKELOW AND CRAIG LUCE

Originated in Hong Kong by Bright Arts, Ltd.
Produced by Imago Productions, Pte., Ltd.
Printed and bound in Singapore, 1994.

EDITORS' PREFACE

A s we approach the twenty-first century it is apparent that the half-life of medical knowledge is continuing to shrink and the amount of current dogma is continuing to expand. Packaging today's relevant ophthalmic knowledge is a difficult chore, yet one that periodically demands doing. Every editor or author desires to accomplish this task in a new and unique fashion. This ten-volume series represents our vision of a *Textbook of Ophthalmology* for the 1990s: one that integrates the basic visual science and clinical information of each subspecialty in a separate volume that is edited or written by noted basic scientists and clinicians; one that is manageable, readable, and affordable for the ophthalmic expert as well as the neophyte; and one that contains original diagrams, figures, and photographs—all in full color—designed to depict the necessary knowledge we hope to impart.

We are grateful to our associate editors and authors for sharing their superb expertise in the compilation of this unique ophthalmic resourse, to our assistants Barbara Zoldessy and Roe Brennan for their unstinting efforts in organizing and coordinating this project, and to our wives Wendy Donn Podos and Karin L. Yanoff for their continued patience and encouragement throughout the many phases of this endeavor.

STEVEN M. PODOS, MD, FACS
DEPARTMENT OF
OPHTHALMOLOGY
MT. SINAI SCHOOL OF MEDICINE
NEW YORK, NY

MYRON YANOFF, MD, FACS
DEPARTMENT OF
OPHTHALMOLOGY
HAHNEMANN UNIVERSITY
PHILADELPHIA, PA

CONTRIBUTORS

Joseph M.R. Furman, MD, PhD
Associate Professor of Otolaringology, Neurology,
    and Electrical Engineering
University of Pittsburgh School of Medicine
Pittsburgh, Pennsylvania

William M. Hart, Jr., MD, PhD
Professor of Ophthalmology and Visual Sciences
Washington University School of Medicine
St. Louis, Missouri

Barrett Katz, MD
The Wayne and Gladys Valley Professor
Vice-Chairman, Department of Ophthalmology
California Pacific Medical Center
Senior Scientist
Smith-Kettlewell Eye Research Institute
San Francisco, California

Nancy J. Newman, MD
Assistant Professor in Ophthalmology and Neurology
Instructor in Neurosurgery
Emory University School of Medicine
Director, Neuro-Ophthalmology
The Emory Clinic
The Emory Eye Center
Atlanta, Georgia

Steven A. Newman, MD
Associate Professor of Ophthalmology
    and Neurological Surgery
University of Virginia Health Sciences Center
Charlottesville, Virginia

Jeffrey G. Odel, MD
Associate Clinical Professor of Ophthalmology
Columbia University
Edward S. Harkness Eye Institute
New York, New York

Alfredo A. Sadun, MD, PhD
Professor of Ophthalmology
University of Southern California School of Medicine
Doheny Eye Institute
Los Angeles, California

Lyn A. Sedwick, MD
Visiting Professor in Neuro-Ophthalmology
University of South Florida
Tampa, Florida
Neuro-Ophthalmologist
Central Florida Eye Associates
Orlando, Florida

Michael Wall, MD
Associate Professor of Neurology and Ophthalmology
The University of Iowa Hospitals and Clinics
Iowa City, Iowa

Joel M. Weinstein, MD
Associate Professor of Ophthalmology, Neurology,
    and Neurosurgery
Department of Ophthalmology
University of Wisconsin—Madison
Madison, Wisconsin

Jacqueline M.S. Winterkorn, MD, PhD
Associate Professor of Ophthalmology and Neurology
Department of Ophthalmology
North Shore University Hospital—
    Cornell University Medical College
Manhasset, New York

CONTENTS

Clinical Perimetry and Topographic Diagnosis in Diseases of the Afferent Visual System

William M. Hart, Jr.

A common goal in clinical neuro-ophthalmology is to make a distinction between primary diseases of the eye and those that affect the retrobulbar visual pathways. A clear understanding of the anatomic features of the visual system and its physiologic properties is fundamental for the diagnosis and management of patients who have visual loss. This chapter deals with the normal anatomy and physiology of the afferent visual system (from the retina back through the visual cortex), and with clinically important visual function tests, principally visual field testing, which are used in evaluating patients. Interspersed are examples of common clinical syndromes that affect the afferent visual system.

STANDARD NOMENCLATURE OF VISUAL FIELD DEFECTS

Using verbal descriptions alone, one should be able to describe accurately a visual field defect using generally accepted terms. A depression of sensitivity surrounded by areas of (relatively) preserved function is a *scotoma*. A scotoma is said to be *relative* when some visual sensation remains within its boundaries. A scotoma in which no visual sensation can be elicited by perimetry is said to be a very *dense*, or *maximal luminance scotoma*. A scotoma is said to be *absolute* when no visual sensation can be elicited within it by any stimulus, no matter how bright. (The physiologic blind spot is an absolute scotoma.) Scotomas can be classified by location, size, or shape: *central* (involving foveal function), *paracentral* (within 5 degrees of fixation), and *cecocentral* (involving both fixation and the area of the physiologic blind spot). A scotoma may be *round, sectoral,* or *arcuate* in shape. A restricted area of reduced sensitivity not surrounded by areas of higher sensitivity is a *localized depression*. Reduced visual sensitivity spread uniformly across the entire visual field is *gen-*

eralized depression. Loss of the entire peripheral visual field with relative preservation of the central portion is called *constriction* of the visual field.

Visual field defects that reach but do not cross either the vertical or horizontal meridian are said to *respect* the meridian. Arcuate scotomas arising from damage to temporal retinal nerve fiber bundles typically *respect* the nasal horizontal meridian (the so-called nasal step). Because there is a major decussation of nasal retinal/optic nerve fibers within the chiasm, damage to this structure characteristically produces defects in the visual field that respect the vertical meridian.

Visual field defects present in only one eye are said to be *monocular,* whereas those involving both eyes are *binocular.* Because of the major decussation of fibers at the chiasm, defects that do not respect the vertical meridian, whether monocular or binocular, are more likely to be caused by *prechiasmal* disease, whereas those that do respect the vertical meridian are typically found in *chiasmal* and *postchiasmal* disease. Binocular defects that respect the vertical meridian are said to be *homonymous* if they fall on the same side with respect to the vertical, and are said to be *heteronymous* when they fall on opposite sides of the vertical meridian. A common heteronymous form of binocular defect is the bitemporal hemianopia associated with chiasmal damage (Fig. 1.1).

Binocular homonymous defects that respect the vertical meridian are pathognomonic of postchiasmal damage to the afferent visual pathways. Homonymous defects that are equal or very similar in size, shape, and location (comparing right eye defect to left) are said to be *congruous,* whereas those that are substantially different from one another are *incongruous.* Finally, defects that cover an entire half of the visual field are *hemianopic. Altitudinal hemianopias* (those respecting the horizontal meridian) are common in *prechiasmal* disease of the retina and/or optic nerve. *Quadrantic* defects are those confined to a single 90-degree sector.

RETINA

A fundamentally important feature of the retina is the duplex nature of its structure and function. The rod and cone photoreceptors are spatially distributed in a pattern that takes full biologic advantage of their specialized functions.[1] The density distribution of cones peaks at the fovea, corresponding to the so-called "point of fixation" at the center of the visual field. The spatial density of cones falls off sharply at relatively small angular distances from the foveal center (the foveola). The distribution of rods, on the other hand, is densest at an eccentricity of approximately 2.5 degrees, and rods are effectively excluded from the photoreceptor mosaic at the foveola (Fig. 1.2). This accounts for the physiologic relative central scotoma at fixation in the dark-adapted eye.

Cones are the primary photoreceptors that mediate photopic vision, which in the human is characterized by a high degree of spatial acuity and color discrimination. Primary photoreceptor diseases that preferentially affect cone function characteristically produce defects in the center of the visual field, accompanied by reduced visual acuity and loss of color perception. On the other hand, primary photoreceptor degenerations that preferen-

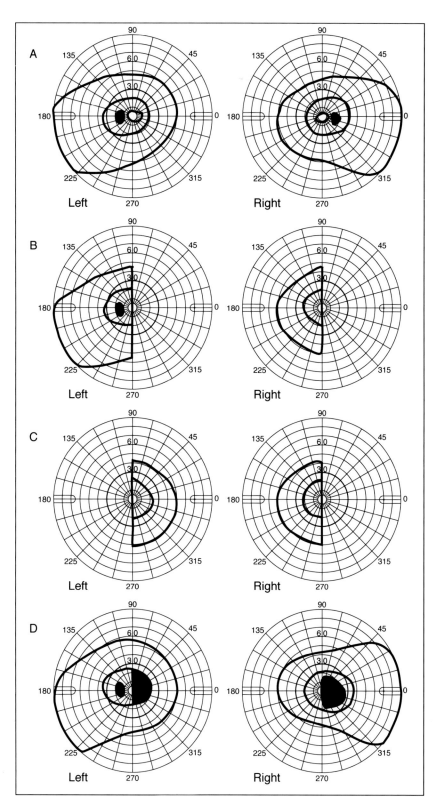

1.1 | General patterns of visual field loss in chiasmal/retrochiasmal disease. *A:* Normal. *B:* Complete homonymous hemianopia (total destruction of retrochiasmal afferent visual system on one side). *C:* Total, heteronymous bitemporal hemianopia (as in advanced chiasmal disease). *D:* Congruous, homonymous hemianopic scotomas (as in focal damage to primary visual cortex).

tially affect rod function produce impaired dark adaptation (nyctalopia) and broad areal defects in the peripheral visual field, where rod function accounts for a much greater proportion of retinal scotopic and mesopic activity.

The trichromacy of color vision is reflected in the tripartite division of cone function. There are separate populations of long-, middle-, and short-wavelength-sensitive cones in the photoreceptor mosaic. In the human and nonhuman primate retina, short-wavelength-sensitive (blue) cones have a spatial distribution analogous to that of rods, i.e., they are eliminated from the photoreceptor mosaic at the center of the foveola and have their highest density in the perifoveal macula.[2] Thus, the foveolar cone mosaic is a relatively pure mixture of long-wavelength-sensitive (red) and middle-wavelength-sensitive (green) cones.

An inference that can be drawn from this observation is that diseases affecting primarily the foveolar cone mosaic should be expected to impair preferentially red/green discrimination, with a simultaneous early reduction in spatial acuity. On the other hand, diseases preferentially affecting the perifoveal cone mosaic, although leaving foveal function relatively intact, should tend to spare central acuity and to preferentially depress blue/yellow hue discrimination. This has clinical importance because retinal and choroidal diseases have a common tendency to impair preferentially extrafoveal function in the central visual field, whereas most optic neuropathies do not. Therefore, as a general rule, retinal and choroidal diseases

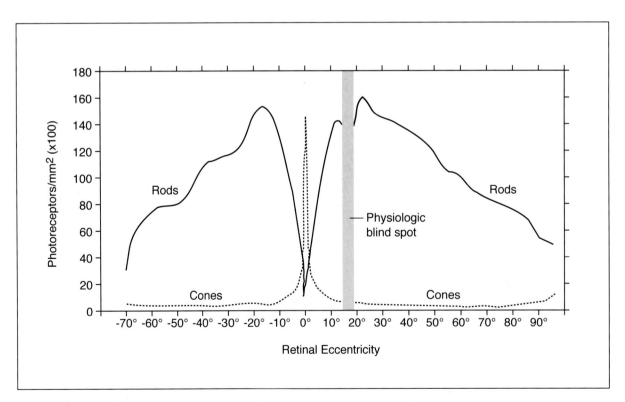

1.2 | Density distribution of rods and cones in human retina. (Adapted from Østerberg G: Topography of the layer of rods and cones in the human retina. *Acta Ophthalmol 1935;[suppl 6]:8.*)

are associated with loss of hue discrimination between blues and yellows (acquired tritanopia), and frequently cause loss of extrafoveal visual field while *relatively* preserving foveal function, such as visual acuity. Optic neuropathies, on the other hand, more readily impair foveal function, resulting in an acquired loss of red/green hue discrimination accompanied by a more profound loss of visual acuity.[3]

Photoreceptors in the foveal or perifoveal retina transmit their signals through synaptic contacts onto bipolar cells in a nearly one-to-one ratio. This high degree of parallelism in the foveal neural circuitry carries through to the ganglion cell level, resulting in a large number of ganglion cell axons per unit area of visual field representation at the fovea. On the other hand, in the extramacular retina there is a high degree of neural convergence in which hundreds of photoreceptors pool their input onto single ganglion cells. Therefore, the receptive fields of ganglion cells subserving the foveal or perifoveal portions of the visual field are quite small, whereas those of ganglion cells subserving extramacular portions of the visual field cover progressively larger areas, with increasing degrees of retinal eccentricity. The very large number of densely packed ganglion cells subserving the central visual field requires that these cells be relatively small. This large number of small-axoned ganglion cells subserving the macular representation of the visual field is densely bundled together as it approaches the temporal side of the optic disc to exit from the eye. This subset of optic nerve fibers is commonly referred to as the *papillomacular bundle*. Although this bundle comprises a relatively large proportion of the axons in the optic nerve, it serves a much smaller proportion of the total visual field.

The ten-layered structure of the retina (Fig. 1.3) is highly modified at the center of the macula. The foveola is an almost pure photoreceptor mosaic of cones with their associated synaptic contacts onto bipolar cells. The outer plexiform layer of the retina is replaced in this region by long axonal processes of the photoreceptors which are splayed outward in a radial fashion, like the spokes of a wheel radiating away from the center. The inner limiting membrane of the retina in this region lies directly over these axonal processes (called Henle's fibers) and their synaptic contacts with bipolar cells.[4] Proteinaceous deposits associated with chronic edema in this portion of the retina are commonly aligned along the radial pattern of Henle's fibers, resulting in the ophthalmoscopic appearance known as a "macular star." The bipolar cells, horizontal cells, amacrine cells, and ganglion cells subserving the foveolar cones are displaced to a perifoveal location, overlying approximately the same regions of the retina at which peak photoreceptor densities for blue cones and rods are found.

This radial displacement of inner retinal layers away from the foveola may be related to a common phenomenon found in macular diseases, in which the preponderance of damage to the retina appears to have a perifoveal distribution with relative sparing of foveal function (Fig. 1.4). This is seen ophthalmoscopically as a so-called "bull's-eye" or "target" lesion. This appearance, which is largely the result of damage to the pigment epithelium underlying the perifoveal retina, is seen in a variety of toxic retinopathies.[5] The target pattern is apparent during fluorescein angiography, in which the choroidal fluorescence is accentuated through the defects in the pigment epithelium in an annular pattern surrounding the fovea. Similarly, the characteristic pattern of fluid accumulation in the middle and inner layers of the

CONVERGENCE VS. PARALLELISM IN RETINAL NEURAL CIRCUITRY

retina in cystoid macular edema is described as "petaloid." This refers to the radiating pattern of teardrop-shaped cystoid macular lesions that are radially arranged around the foveola with their tapered apices pointed towards the center.

It is believed that these anatomic features are related to the phenomenon of preferential impairment of visual function in the perifoveal visual field which is observed in a wide variety of retinal diseases. This perifoveal depression of visual function is associated with a higher incidence of relative blue/yellow dyschromatopsias, annular depressions of the visual field surrounding the fovea, and relative preservation of foveal function (optotype acuity and red/green hue discrimination) until relatively late in the course of these diseases.

THE RETINAL NERVE FIBER LAYER

The retinal nerve fiber layer is formed by the unmyelinated portions of the axons of the retinal ganglion cells. The ganglion cells are the innermost cellular elements of the retina. Their somata lie in the ganglion cell layer and their axons comprise the nerve fiber layer, lying immediately beneath the internal limiting membrane. The latter is formed by interdigitating processes

1.3 | The ten-layered structure of the (extramacular) retina. The retina consists of two major parts: the pigment epithelium and the neurosensory retina. The latter is customarily divided into nine layers: 1, the photoreceptor outer segments; 2, the external limiting membrane (formed by zonula adherens attachment sites between adjacent photoreceptors and Müller cells; 3, the outer nuclear layer (containing the nuclei of the photoreceptors); 4, the outer plexiform layer; 5, the inner nuclear layer (containing nuclei of bipolar, amacrine and Müller cells); 6, the inner plexiform layer (containing synapses between bipolar and ganglion cells); 7, the ganglion cell layer; 8, the nerve fiber layer; and 9, the internal limiting membrane (formed by the basement membrane of the Müller cells). (From Yanoff M, Fine BS: *Ocular Pathology. A Color Atlas,* ed 2. New York: Gower Medical Publishing, 1992, 11.3.)

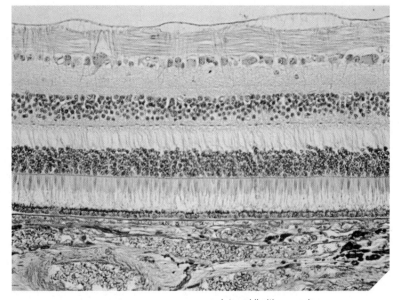

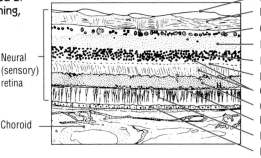

Neural (sensory) retina

Choroid

Internal limiting membrane
Nerve fiber layer
Ganglion cell layer
Inner plexiform layer
Inner nuclear layer
Middle limiting membrane
Outer plexiform layer
Outer nuclear layer
External limiting membrane
Photoreceptors
Retinal pigment epithelium

of Müller's cells. There are approximately 1–1.5 million ganglion cells in the adult human retina,[6,7] with one axonal process per cell body. These fibers sweep across the broad expanse of the retina to exit the eye at the optic disc. The pattern these fibers assume in their course towards the optic nerve determines much of the spatial anatomy of visual field defects that occur with damage to the fibers. The optic disc is a unique area in the eye, being a transitional structure interposed between the intraocular pressure, the intraorbital pressure, and the intracranial pressure. The optic disc is also a transitional zone for vascular supply, with capillaries in the prelaminar disc arising from vessels supplied by (a) the choroid, via the posterior ciliary arteries, and (b) the perineural plexus of vessels within the subarachnoid space of the optic nerve. In addition, the optic disc is frequently positioned within a watershed zone or region between areas supplied by adjacent posterior ciliary arteries. As a consequence of these anatomic features, the optic disc is a site of high potential for damage to ganglion cell fibers. Discrete damage to adjacent bundles of fibers results in characteristic patterns of visual damage.

Because all ganglion cell bodies subserving the central portions of the macula are radially displaced away from the center, the axonal fibers arising from them originate in an annular pattern and sweep in an arcuate fashion towards the optic disc such that they avoid the center of the macula (Fig. 1.5). Those fibers arising from cells positioned between the foveola and the disc pursue a direct, rectilinear course, whereas those arising from cell bodies located on the opposite side of the foveola (in the temporal portions of the macula) sweep in an arcuate pathway that avoids direct passage through the center. Fibers arising from ganglion cells located above the horizontal meridian uniformly pursue a course that lies superior to the fovea, and those arising from ganglion cell bodies situated below the horizontal meridian remain similarly segregated to the inferior half of the macula during their passage towards the optic disc.

The nerve fibers that cross the temporal border of the optic disc arise, for the most part, from the dense group of ganglion cells located in the central portions of the macula. These fibers are very small and are closely bundled together, making them extremely difficult to see by ophthalmoscopy.

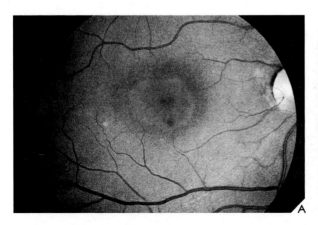
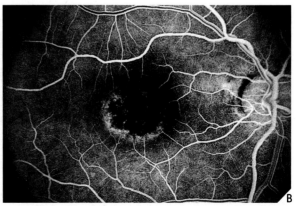

1.4 | Target or "bull's-eye" lesion in patient with toxic (hydroxychloroquine) retinopathy. *A:* Ophthalmoscopic appearance. *B:* Fluorescein angiography showing ring of "window" defects in pigment epithelium, accentuating choroidal fluorescence in annular pattern. Static perimetry often shows a similar pattern of perifoveal, annular depression of sensitivity.

Just above and below this temporal sector of the optic disc are the grouped axonal fibers, arising from the more temporal portions of the central retina, that have taken the indirect arcuate course around the center of the macula. The superior and inferior quadrants of the optic disc are largely filled with bundles of ganglion cell fibers that have originated from the temporal half of the extramacular retina (the portion subserving the nasal visual field). The nasal quadrant of the disc is largely populated by axon fibers arising from the nasal half of the retina and subserving the temporal visual field (Fig. 1.6).

Discrete pathologic lesions at various locations around the circumference of the optic disc lead to characteristic visual field defects that match exactly the geographic areas served by the nerve fiber bundles they have destroyed (Fig. 1.7). Inflammatory, vascular, degenerative, and traumatic diseases are all capable of producing these patterns. A discrete lesion at the temporal border of the optic disc produces a small, dense visual field defect that is located between fixation and the physiologic blind spot. Involving the papillomacular bundle, such a defect is commonly associated with poor color discrimination and a loss of visual acuity. A discrete lesion at either the supe-

1.5 | Common patterns of visual field damage in disease of the anterior optic nerve. *A:* Diagram depicting direct ophthalmoscopic view of area served by damaged nerve fiber bundles. *B:* Corresponding visual field defects. Damage to nerve fiber bundles commonly occurs at or close to the margin of the optic disc. Discrete lesions in this region produce characteristic visual field defects (nerve fiber bundle defects) and associated changes in opthalmoscopic appearance, such as grooving of the nerve fiber layer and sectoral disc atrophy (pallor). (From Spalton DJ: Neuro-ophthalmology, in Spalton DJ, Hitchings RA, Hunter PA (eds): *Atlas of Clinical Ophthalmology.* London: Gower Medical Publishing, 1984, 19.17.)

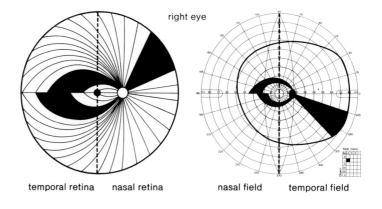

right eye

temporal retina   nasal retina   nasal field   temporal field

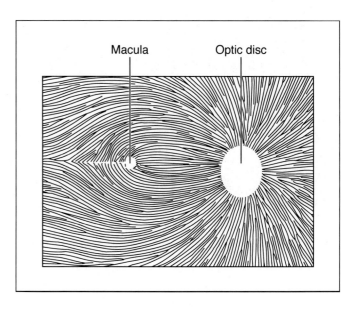

Macula   Optic disc

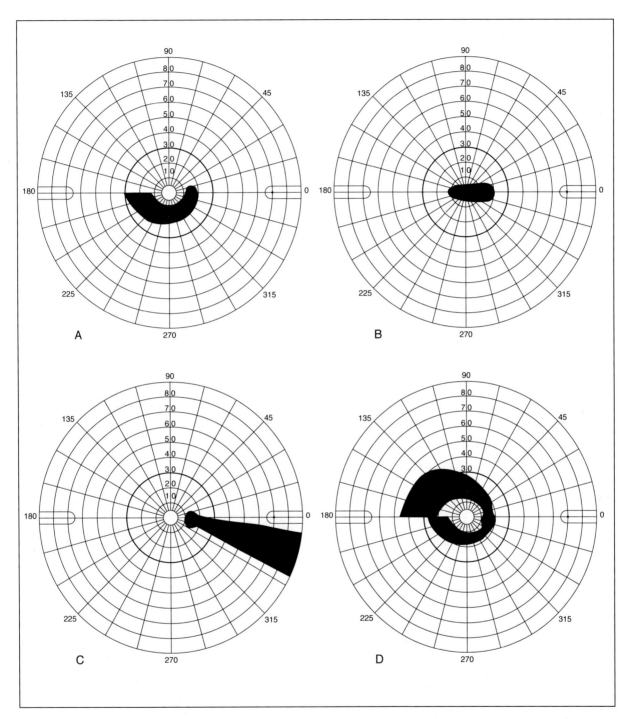

1.7 | Patterns of visual field defects associated with damage to nerve fiber bundles at or close to the margin of the optic disc (all examples are for a right eye). *A:* Arcuate scotoma in visual field of right eye, damage located at superior pole of optic disc (remember that the visual field is inverted with respect to the retina). *B:* Cecocentral scotoma from damage located at temporal border of optic disc, a pattern that also occurs with retrobulbar damage to the papillomacular bundle. *C:* Temporal wedge-shaped depression from focal damage located at the nasal border of the optic disc, a pattern that occurs in as many as 5% of patients with glaucoma. *D:* Double arcuate scotomas from extensive damage at both superior and inferior poles of optic disc, a common pattern found in late-stage glaucoma.

rior or inferior pole of the optic disc results in an arcuate visual field defect, or so-called nerve fiber bundle defect, shaped somewhat like a scimitar, obeying the nasal horizontal meridian and arcing around the center of the visual field in a progressively narrowing pattern to connect directly with the physiologic blind spot. Diseases that cause damage at the nasal border of the optic disc produce sector-shaped defects in the temporal visual field, with relatively straight sides that point directly towards the physiologic blind spot.[8]

It can be seen that these patterns involve visual field defects that respect the horizontal meridian in the nasal visual field and which have their apices directed at the physiologic blind spot. These must be distinguished from homonymous visual field defects resulting from retrochiasmal disease, which, although they may be wedge- or sector-shaped, have apices directed towards the center of the visual field (fixation) rather than towards the physiologic blind spot.

LARGE AND SMALL GANGLION CELL FIBERS

Neurobiologists have adopted a global view of the afferent visual system as being divided into two principal components: the magnocellular or "M-cell" and the parvocellular or "P-cell" pathways. These names arise from the relative sizes of cell bodies located in the lateral geniculate nucleus (LGN). As a

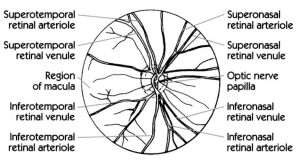
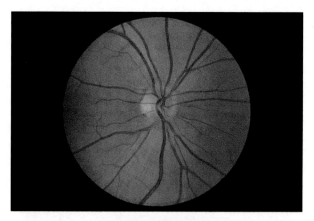

1.8 | Fundus photograph of posterior pole of right eye shows normal retinal vasculature. The line drawing reveals the major branches of central retinal vessels.

Superotemporal retinal arteriole — Superonasal retinal arteriole
Superotemporal retinal venule — Superonasal retinal venule
Region of macula — Optic nerve papilla
Inferotemporal retinal venule — Inferonasal retinal venule
Inferotemporal retinal arteriole — Inferonasal retinal arteriole

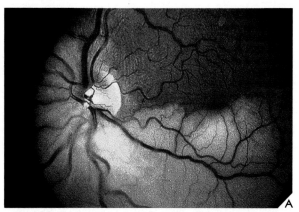
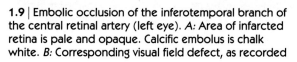
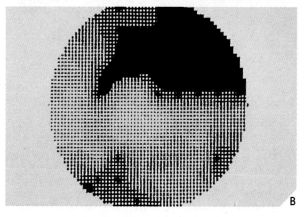

1.9 | Embolic occlusion of the inferotemporal branch of the central retinal artery (left eye). *A:* Area of infarcted retina is pale and opaque. Calcific embolus is chalk white. *B:* Corresponding visual field defect, as recorded by threshold static perimetry, appears as dense arcuate depression of visual sensitivity in superior half of visual field. Nasal horizontal border of defect respects the horizontal meridian.

general rule, the ganglion cells that synapse with large cells in the LGN have relatively large axons that conduct rapidly, while smaller ganglion cell fibers that conduct more slowly synapse with geniculate neurons that have small somata. The smaller, more slowly conducting fibers arise principally from the ganglion cells in the fovea, foveola, and perifoveal macula. Conversely, the larger, more rapidly conducting nerve fibers arise from ganglion cells located in the extramacular or peripheral portions of the visual field. The smaller, more slowly conducting axons have tonic firing patterns, small receptive fields, and synapse with LGN cells that have color-opponent receptive fields. On the other hand, the larger, more rapidly conducting fibers have phasic firing properties, large receptive fields, and synapse with cells that are insensitive to color contrast. However, the M-cells are exquisitely sensitive to luminance contrast at low spatial frequencies and to moving visual stimuli.[9]

The papillomacular bundle consists largely of the smaller (P-cell) nerve fibers, whereas the extramacular fibers are principally of the large, rapidly conducting variety. These properties conform to the known spatial distribution of visual function in which acuity and color discrimination (cone photoreceptor input) are functions largely concentrated in the macular representation of the visual field (the central 10 degrees of the visual field), whereas the highest levels of low spatial frequency contrast sensitivity, spatial summation, and motion detection are located in the peripheral visual field. Peripheral visual function is dominated by rod input and is characterized by extensive neural convergence onto a smaller number of large, rapidly conducting ganglion cell fibers.

VASCULAR SUPPLY OF THE RETINA

The outer layers of the retina, including the pigment epithelium, the photoreceptors, and the outer portions of bipolar cells, receive their supply of oxygen and nutrients by diffusion from the choriocapillaris lying beneath Bruch's membrane. The inner layers of the retina, including the inner portions of the bipolar cells, amacrine cells, and ganglion cells, receive their metabolic supplies through the vascular tree of the central retinal artery.

The central retinal artery is a branch of the ophthalmic artery that penetrates the dural sheath of the optic nerve to take up an axial position at the center of the optic nerve approximately 10 to 15 millimeters behind the globe. This vessel passes through the lamina cribrosa to appear on the surface of the optic disc inside the eye, where it divides into superior and inferior branches which, in turn, give rise to major vascular arterial branches that are ophthalmoscopically visible. There are characteristically four major branches: the superotemporal vascular arcade, the inferotemporal vascular arcade, and similar superior and inferior nasal branches (Fig. 1.8). In a pattern somewhat analogous to that adopted by the retinal nerve fibers, the vascular tree of the retina is displaced away from the center of the macula.

The major arcuate bundles of retinal nerve fibers that enter the superior and inferior quadrants of the optic disc lie directly beneath the superior and inferior temporal arcades of the retinal arterial tree. The anatomy of this pattern is important because embolic and thrombotic diseases of the retinal arterial tree produce areas of infarcted retina that have a sectoral shape corresponding to the regional distribution of the involved vessel (Fig. 1.9). Because this shape mimics to some extent that of the underlying nerve fiber bundles, visual field defects associated with branch retinal arteriolar occlusions can be very similar to those seen in retinal nerve fiber diseases. Such a field defect is likely to be very dense, with sharply defined borders and a sectoral shape with its apex directed towards the physiologic blind spot.

OPTIC NERVE

The nerve fiber layer of the retina is thickest at the margin of the optic disc. The unmyelinated nerve fibers make a sharp right-angled turn immediately after crossing the optic disc margin to enter the neuroglial tissue of the prelaminar optic disc. The nerve fibers become segregated into a series of fascicles or bundles separated from one another by columns of glial cells. Not until these glially supported nerve fiber bundles pass through the lamina cribrosa do the nerve fibers subsequently become invested by a myelin sheath. The columns of glial cells surrounding the nerve fascicles in the prelaminar disc are composed entirely of astrocytes. The lamina cribrosa is a series of collagenous trabeculae contiguous with the scleral coat of the eye. The criss-cross pattern of the trabeculae forms a series of pores through which the nerve fiber fascicles pass. The retrolaminar myelinated portion of the

1.10 | The normal optic nerve. *A* and *B*: Longitudinal sections (gross and microscopic, respectively) of the optic nerve (ON) show its intraocular (within the scleral canal) and retrobulbar portions. The intraocular portion is divided into three parts or layers: the inner retinal layer anteriorly, the middle choroidal layer where white myelination of the ON begins *(A)*, and the outer scleral layer posteriorly. The anterior surface of the retinal layer (the optic disc or ON head) measures about 1.5 mm; as the ON exits the scleral canal posteriorly to form the retrobulbar portion, it measures 3 to 4 mm; the increased width mainly is caused by the addition of myelin (seen as white within the ON in *A*). (*A*, courtesy of Dr. RC Eagle, JR. From Yanoff M, Fine BS: *Ocular Pathology. A Color Atlas*, ed 2. New York: Gower Medical Publishing, 1992, 13.2.)

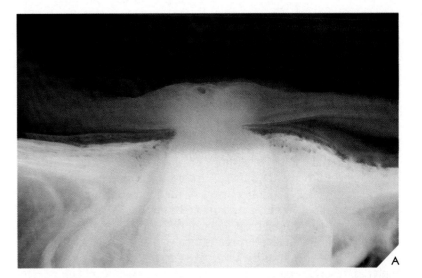

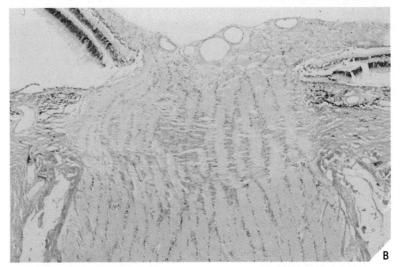

optic nerve is embryologically and anatomically more like a tract of the brain than a true cranial nerve (Fig. 1.10). It is invested by dural and arachnoidal membranes from the external scleral surface all the way to the optic canal, where the dura becomes fused with the periosteum of the sphenoid bone.

The subarachnoid space of the optic nerve is contiguous with that of the intracranial contents. Therefore, an elevation in intracranial pressure is directly transmitted to the subarachnoid space surrounding the optic nerve and contained within its dural sheath. The most anterior portion of the optic nerve is that which lies across the ocular wall from the disc surface to the retrolaminar position, where myelin first becomes apparent. This portion of the nerve, approximately 2 mm in length, is a critically important location for disease. It passes through a region of a relatively high pressure gradient and receives a complex, bipartite vascular supply at the capillary level.

The extraocular or retrobulbar portion of the optic nerve, extending from the posterior wall of the eye to the anterior end of the optic canal, is approximately 3 cm long and takes a somewhat sinuous course, the length of the nerve being greater than the distance from eye to canal (Fig. 1.11). The

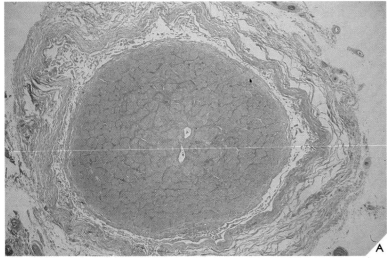

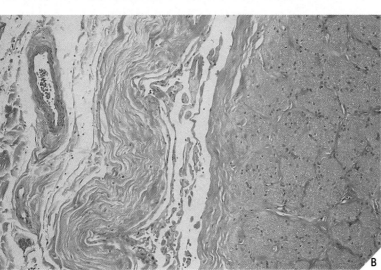

1.11 | The normal optic nerve. *A* and *B*: Cross sections (low and medium magnification, respectively) of the ON show the central parenchyma that contains axons, central retinal artery and vein, other blood vessels, astrocytes, oligodendrocytes, and pial septa. This is surrounded by pia mater, subarachnoid "space," arachnoid matter, subdural "space," and dura. (Courtesy of Dr. MG Farber. From Yanoff M, Fine BS: *Ocular Pathology. A Color Atlas,* ed 2. New York: Gower Medical Publishing, 1992, 13.2.)

floppy, redundant folds of the nerve allow freedom of rotation of the globe without placing any tension along the length of the nerve. At the apex of the orbit, the dural sheath of the optic nerve fuses with the periosteum of the sphenoid bone, where it is surrounded by the annulus of Zinn, a structure formed by the origins of the rectus muscles. Within the optic canal the nerve is firmly anchored to the surrounding bone by the connective tissue strands of the pia–arachnoid which, in turn, are firmly attached to the dura/periosteum. Within the optic canal, in company with the optic nerve, lie the ophthalmic artery and a few branches of the tertiary sympathetic neurons connecting the superior cervical ganglion with the eye. Cerebrospinal fluid passes readily through the subarachnoid space of the optic canal.

The optic nerves emerge from the canals to converge towards one another at the optic chiasm. The chiasm lies posterior and superior to the inner aspect of the optic canals, such that the nerves must rise a distance of approximately 10 mm along a 15-mm course to arrive at the chiasm. The optic chiasm, in turn, is approximately 8-mm thick from anterior to posterior and lies at the base of the third ventricle of the brain. A small depression at the most extreme anteroinferior extent of the third ventricle is referred to as the *optic recess*, where intraventricular cerebrospinal fluid bathes the most posterior portions of the chiasm.

VASCULAR SUPPLY OF THE OPTIC NERVE

The vascular supply of the optic nerve is complex and is derived exclusively from the ophthalmic artery. In most individuals the ophthalmic artery is the first major intracranial branch of the internal carotid artery. However, in a small percentage of people the ophthalmic artery arises as a branch of the external carotid tree, usually as a major branch of the middle meningeal artery. The capillary supply of the transmural (prelaminar and laminar) portions of the optic nerve has a dual origin (Fig. 1.12). Some vessels originate in the perineural plexus in the most anterior portions of the subarachnoid space that surrounds the optic nerve. These are fed by small arterioles which

1.12 | Schematic representation of blood supply to anterior optic nerve. Capillaries in laminar region derive from two sources: choroid (via short posterior ciliary arteries), and pial plexus. There are considerable interindividual variations in this pattern.

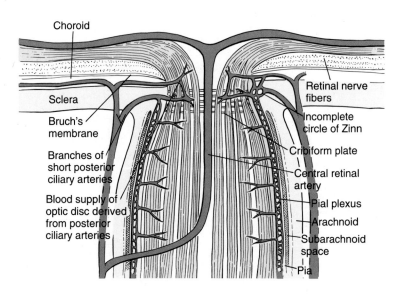

Choroid

Sclera

Bruch's membrane

Branches of short posterior ciliary arteries

Blood supply of optic disc derived from posterior ciliary arteries

Retinal nerve fibers

Incomplete circle of Zinn

Cribiform plate

Central retinal artery

Pial plexus

Arachnoid

Subarachnoid space

Pia

are supplied, in turn, by branches of the ophthalmic artery. They penetrate the substance of the anterior optic nerve in a radial pattern. The second source of blood supply to the anterior nerve consists of peripapillary choroidal branches fed through the choroidal circulation by the short posterior ciliary arteries that penetrate the scleral wall at various distances from the optic nerve. The retrobulbar, intraorbital portions of the optic nerve are perfused by vessels arising from the ophthalmic artery, which enter the nerve from the pial surface in a symmetrical, radially distributed pattern. The central retinal artery first pierces the optic nerve approximately 1.0 to 1.5 cm posterior to the globe. In a few specimens vessels have been seen to arise from the central retinal artery within the core of the nerve, although this is not the rule. The radial distribution of vessels derived from the perineural pial plexus within the nerve, from its prelaminar portions all the way back through the orbital and intracanalicular segments, is undoubtedly related to the segmental pattern of damage to the nerve that frequently occurs with vascular disease. Vascular insults to the optic nerve often cause sectoral damage, producing defects in the visual field that are also sectoral. Thus, altitudinal hemianopias and visual field defects obeying the horizontal meridian and defects that are sectoral in shape with their apices directed towards the center of the visual field are common after interruption of the vascular supply to the optic nerve.

The optic chiasm is formed by the confluence of the two optic nerves. The nerve fibers originating in the nasal retina decussate across the midline within the chiasm. The body of the chiasm itself is approximately 8-mm wide in anteroposterior dimension, approximately 12 mm across in the horizontal plane, and approximately 4-mm thick. The inferior border of the chiasm lies approximately 10 mm superior to the dorsum sella (Fig. 1.13). The

CHIASM

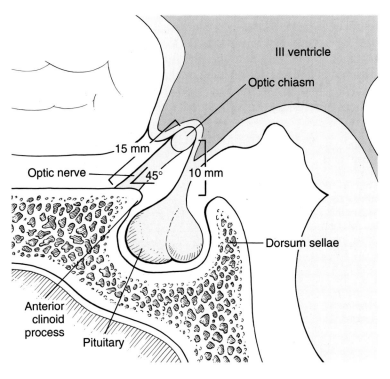

1.13 | Approximate spatial relations between optic nerves, chiasm, and sella turcica. The nerves rise at about a 45 degree angle, reaching the chiasm at about 10 mm above the diaphragma sella. Pituitary macroadenomas must escape the sella and enlarge a distance of about 1 cm before contacting the chiasm.

intracranial portions of the optic nerve and the chiasm are suspended within the suprasellar space and are bathed by cerebrospinal fluid. The intracanalicular and intracranial portions of the optic nerves receive their vascular supply from branches of the internal carotid artery that form a generous plexus of pial vessels.

After decussation of the nasal fibers, the posterolateral margins of the chiasm give rise to the optic tracts. At the site where the optic nerves first make contact with the chiasm, the lower portion of the nasal fibers that make up the decussation pass medially across the most anterior portions of the chiasm to form a small loop or "knee" in the proximal portions of the contralateral optic nerve. This feature, referred to as Wilbrand's knee,[10] accounts for the pattern of visual field defect referred to as "junctional" in diseases that happen to impinge upon the junction of the optic nerve with the chiasm (Fig. 1.14).

The classic example of a junctional lesion is a meningioma pressing on the intracranial portion of the proximal optic nerve on one side, producing a dense ipsilateral central visual field defect, associated with a superotemporal sectoral field defect in the opposite eye (Fig. 1.15). Patients with advanced visual field loss in one eye who are suspected of having intracranial disease should be examined carefully to rule out the presence in the contralateral eye of early temporal defects involving the peripheral or central visual field and obeying the vertical meridian superior to fixation.

Emerging from the posterolateral aspects of the chiasm, the optic tracts diverge from one another and take a somewhat semicircular course to pass around the cerebral peduncles, arriving at the lateral geniculate nuclei. Ganglion cell axons that form the afferent limb of the pupillomotor reflex leave the optic tract to pass through the brachium of the superior colliculus, arriving at the mesencephalic pretectal region.

RETINOTOPIC ORGANIZATION OF THE PREGENICULATE VISUAL SYSTEM

The visual field of the eye is projected directly onto the retina, and there is a direct one-to-one correspondence between retinal location and visual direction in space. This retinotopic organization of the external visual world is preserved throughout the extent of the afferent visual system and is the principal anatomic feature that allows topographic localization of disease on the basis of mapped representations of the visual field. The retinal image of external space is optically inverted, so that the inferior retina represents the superior

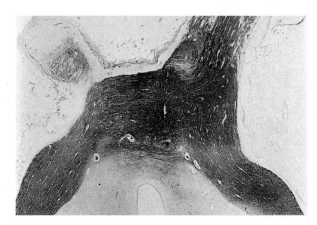

1.14 | Photomicrograph of myelin-stained horizontal section through chiasm, including optic nerves (above) and optic tracts (below) in patient who had lost an eye to trauma years before death. The atrophic optic nerve shows a small nubbin of myelin located just anterior to the chiasm proper, while a corresponding defect in the myelination of the opposite nerve is also visible. This pattern, referred to as "Wilbrand's knee," is formed by inferior nasal fibers of the optic nerve decussating into the proximal regions of the contralateral nerve before passing on through the chiasm and into the optic tract. This feature accounts for the pattern of visual loss found in lesions at the junction of the optic nerve and chiasm. (From Breen LA, et al: Neuroanatomical feature photo. *J Clin Neuro-ophthalmol* 1983;3:283–284.)

visual field, the superior retina represents the inferior visual field, the nasal retina represents the temporal visual field, and the temporal retina represents the nasal visual field. Vertical division of the visual field in eye and brain is mapped relative to the vertical line in space falling across the center of the retina and passing through the foveola. Thus, the optic disc lies nasal to the vertical division of the retina and projects to the temporal side of the visual field. Ganglion cells located to the temporal side of the vertical division of the retina contribute axon processes that remain segregated to the ipsilateral side of the brain. Conversely, ganglion cells lying to the nasal side of the vertical division give rise to axons that decussate in the chiasm, passing their information to the contralateral side of the brain. The temporal half of the visual field is larger than the nasal half, and there is a correspondingly greater number of decussating than nondecussating axons in the chiasm.

Of the approximately 1–1.5 million ganglion cells located in the retina of a single human eye, the majority are located in the macular portions of the retina. Here, the macula can be loosely defined as the central 10 degrees of eccentricity from the foveola. The axon fibers from these cells form the papillomacular bundle, which is the largest and most important central bundle of afferent fibers within the optic nerve. Damage to these fibers results in defects in the central visual field (see Figs. 1.7 and 1.16). Such defects are usually associated with measurable impairment of visual acuity, color discrimination, brightness (luminance) sensation and afferent input to the pupillary light reflex. Because of this predominant representation of the central visual field among the axon fibers comprising the optic nerves and chiasm, the latter structures are commonly thought of as being dominated by input from the macular portion of the visual field. The principal diagnostic feature of disease of the optic nerve and chiasm is damage to visual function in the central portions of the visual field.

Clinical visual field testing can be divided into two very different varieties: kinetic and static. Kinetic perimetry is the nonautomated type of examination commonly associated with the Goldmann instrument, a hemispheric projection device with an ingenious pantographic arm that enables the operator to manipulate the presentation and movement of test objects (Fig. 1.17). The test objects are ovals of light that can be set to various levels of size and

GENERAL PRINCIPLES OF PERIMETRIC TESTING

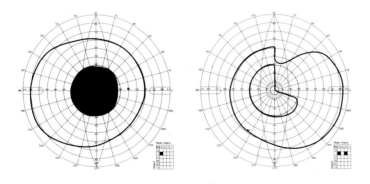

1.15 | So-called junctional lesion (of the proximal optic nerve and anterolateral chiasm) commonly produces ipsilateral central scotoma by compressing intracranial optic nerve, accompanied by superior temporal sector field defect of contralteral eye, caused by damage to Wilbrand's knee. Patients with central scotomas in one eye should have careful examination of visual field in the opposite eye. (From Spalton DJ: Neuro-ophthalmology, in Spalton DJ, Hitchings RA, Hunter PA (eds): *Atlas of Clinical Ophthalmology.* London: Gower Medical Publishing, 1984, 19.20.)

brightness by means of a shutter, various apertures, and a series of neutral density filters. The adapting background of the hemisphere is uniformly illuminated at a standard level of brightness (32.5 apostilb). Projected test objects have a maximal luminance of 1,000 apostilb.

Static perimetry has been developed to its present state of sophistication over the past two decades, a process that has been driven by development of the microprocessor. Static perimetry should now be thought of solely as an automated form of visual field testing. There are fundamentally important differences between static and kinetic perimetry. Whereas kinetic perimetry uses test objects of constant size and brightness that are interactively manipulated in space by a human examiner, static perimetry is controlled by automated algorithms that present test objects at a predetermined

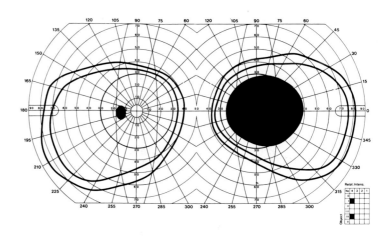

1.16 | Dense central scotoma of one eye, characteristic of compressive and demyelinating lesions of retrobulbar optic nerve. Such a scotoma is invariably associated with an afferent pupillary defect, and loss of acuity, color and brightness sensation. (From Spalton DJ, Sanders MD: The optic disc, in Spalton DJ, Hitchings RA, Hunter PA (eds): *Atlas of Clinical Ophthalmology*. London: Gower Medical Publishing, 1984, 17.15.)

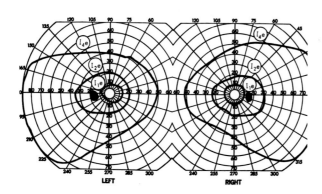

1.17 | Normal visual field, as recorded by manual kinetic perimetry. This type of examination is particularly suited to defining the peripheral visual field (eccentricities of 30 degrees and more from fixation).

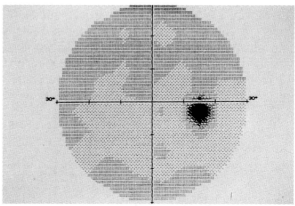

1.18 | Typical result of automated static perimetry of central 30 degrees of visual field in normal right eye. Physiologic blind spot is centered 15 degrees to temporal side of fixation and just below the horizontal meridian. Pseudo-gray-scale representation: higher sensitivity represented by lighter shades of gray, lower sensitivity by darker shades.

series of discrete locations, while varying their brightness from one presentation to the next. Sensitivity for the detection of stimuli at each location is measured by determining the threshold for detection. Threshold is defined as the brightness of the test object at which the subject has a 50% likelihood of responding affirmatively. Static perimetry is chiefly of value for testing the central portions of the visual field, inside the circle of 30 degrees of retinal eccentricity (Fig. 1.18).

Kinetic perimetry is ideally suited to examination of the peripheral visual field. Large areas can be tested quickly and efficiently without unduly fatiguing the subject. In addition, because the peripheral visual field is dominated by mixtures of rod and cone input and by high neural convergence onto ganglion cells of the M-cell variety, it is specialized for the detection of moving stimuli. Kinetic perimetry is of the greatest value at more than 30 degrees of retinal eccentricity away from the point of fixation. The value of kinetic perimetry, however, does not carry over into the central visual field, where small or subtle (but still important) visual field defects are not easily detected by manual testing. Here, where the visual system is specialized for cone-dominated visual functions (spatial acuity and color discrimination), static perimetry has much better sensitivity for detecting the types of clinically important visual field disturbances found in diseases of the anterior visual pathways.

Unfortunately, static perimetry is laborious and time consuming. A patient who is sick or tired is easily exhausted by the experience. There is only a limited period of time during which valuable information can be collected. Therefore, the examination must be limited to exploration of the areas most likely to be diseased and most likely to be well defined by static testing methods. Automated static perimetry is of greatest value in areas within the circle of 30 degrees of eccentricity. Furthermore, when the clinical suspicion is one of macular or papillomacular bundle disease, concentration of static testing within the central 10 degrees of the visual field is warranted.

The selection of a technique for perimetric examination should be directed by the examiner's initial suspicions, based on the patient's complaints and a few simple tests, such as optotype acuity, brightness and color comparisons between the two eyes, confrontation testing of the visual field (e.g., finger counting in the mid-periphery of each quadrant), and pupillary testing. When a peripheral visual field defect is suspected, kinetic perimetry is the preferable form of testing. If, for example, the patient complains of poor dark adaptation or of difficulty in detecting objects in the periphery, but has normal acuity and color discrimination by simple testing, then manual kinetic perimetry stands a very good chance of describing the topography of any significant visual field defect.

When the examiner suspects damage to central visual function, static perimetry is the modality of choice. If the complaint is one of reduced acuity, altered color perception, metamorphopsia, loss of brightness perception, or positive paracentral scotoma, then static perimetry in the central 30 degrees of the visual field is more likely to be of value.

TOPOGRAPHIC LOCALIZATION OF PRECHIASMAL, CHIASMAL, POSTCHIASMAL, AND POSTGENICULATE DISEASE

In evaluating patients with visual loss, a constellation of findings usually allows a clear topographic separation between pre- and postchiasmal and pre- and postgeniculate disease. Visual field defects arising from prechiasmal damage to ganglion cell axons do not respect the vertical meridian, whereas those found in chiasmal and postchiasmal disorders do. A principal feature of pregeniculate disease is the presence of abnormal pupillary function, a feature not found in postgeniculate disorders. This, of course, is due to the parting of pupillary afferent fibers from the visual afferent axons at the level of the optic tracts, just anterior to the lateral geniculate nuclei. The principal pupillary sign of importance is the relative afferent defect, which clearly establishes the presence of asymmetry of optic nerve function. See Chapter 5 for a discussion of pupillary testing.

A relative afferent pupillary defect can be produced by lesions of the optic tract that also produce complete homonymous hemianopias. This is due to the fact that more than half of the fibers in the optic nerve arise from the nasal retina (temporal field) and decussate at the chiasm. Therefore, a homonymous defect from a tract lesion is likely to involve more fibers from the nasal retina of the contralateral eye than from the temporal retina of the ipsilateral eye (a right tract lesion can produce a left relative afferent pupillary defect.)

Reductions in acuity are also characteristic of pregeniculate disease. This is an obvious outcome in diseases of the macula and the optic nerve, but (less intuitively) is also found in most cases of damage to the chiasm and optic tract. This is because most of the processes that damage these structures (e.g., compressive masses, inflammations, demyelination) are not cleanly confined to one side or the other, nor are midline chiasmal processes usually restricted to damage only of decussating fibers. Isolated disease of the optic tract is rare. Most tract lesions are caused by diseases that arise in the suprasellar region, usually involving the posterior chiasm on one side in addition to damaging tract fibers. Therefore, both crossing and uncrossed fibers in the vicinity of the chiasm are commonly damaged by lesions in this region, and unexplained reductions in visual acuity are a prominent presenting feature of pregeniculate disease in the chiasm and/or tract.

For the same reasons that acuity is reduced in pregeniculate disease, color vision is similarly affected. Occasionally the patient's principal complaint is of impaired color perception. A few simple clinical tests can be used to screen

1.19 | Partial superior arcuate nerve fiber bundle visual field defect, as recorded by threshold static perimetry. Pattern corresponds to subtotal damage to bundle of nerve fibers crossing inferotemporal border of optic disc.

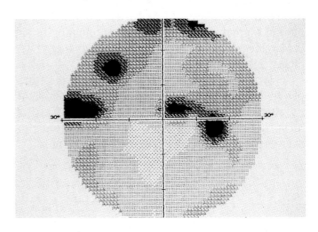

patients for acquired dyschromatopsia. Interocular color comparisons of small, bright-colored objects (e.g., the red cap of a bottle of mydriatic drops), or the plates of a pseudoisochromatic album such as the Ishihara or the Hardy-Rand Rittler (HRR) tests, can be quickly used and are very sensitive for the detection of subtle disease. Similar to the use of color comparisons, testing for relative deficits in brightness perception is a very useful clinical tool. Damage to axons of the papillomacular bundle results in a decrease in subjective brightness perception that exactly parallels the deficits in acuity and color vision.

Monocularity or strong asymmetry is also characteristic of most pregeniculate diseases. Although many diseases are usually bilateral (e.g., macular degeneration, glaucoma, toxic/nutritional optic neuropathies), they are also usually asymmetric. Ophthalmoscopic evidence of disease is common in pregeniculate disease as well. Acute damage to retrobulbar nerve, chiasm, or tract may be initially unapparent but will soon be followed by optic atrophy. In cases of recent onset, the absence of ophthalmoscopic findings is usually not a problem, because the signs of pupillary defect, reduced acuity and color/brightness deficits implicate the anterior visual system.

Given a strong clinical suspicion of pregeniculate disease, the shape and location of visual field defects often allow precise localization of pathology to retina, disc, nerve, chiasm, or tract. Retinal lesions, such as areas of schisis or chorioretinal scars, produce dense, sharply delineated visual field defects (scotomas or peripheral depressions) confined to the areas of the field that are the direct optical projections of the affected areas of retina. Macular degeneration produces central scotomas of variable depth and shape, largely confined to the central 10 degrees of the field. Pigmentary degenerations produce pericentral, ring-shaped depressions outside the central 25 degrees of the field, and with progression can destroy the entire peripheral field while preserving function in most of the central 20 degrees of the field. Macular edema and toxic maculopathies (e.g., chloroquine retinopathy), result in more centrally placed ring-shaped depressions that surround fixation within the central 10 degrees of the field (see Fig. 1.4).

Diseases of the optic disc and the peripapillary retina commonly produce nerve fiber bundle defects in the central 30 degrees of the visual field (see discussion of retinal nerve fiber layer above and Figs. 1.5 through 1.7). These are areas of reduced sensitivity in the central 30 degrees of the field that have generally arcuate shapes conforming to the pattern of the axons in the nerve fiber layer of the retina[8] (Figs. 1.19–1.22). Early or subtle forms of

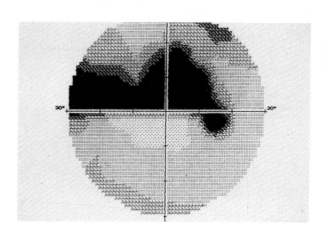

1.20 | Dense superior arcuate nerve fiber bundle visual field defect, as recorded by threshold static perimetry. Pattern is typical of complete destruction of retinal nerve fibers at inferotemporal border of optic disc (right eye).

1.21 | Double arcuate nerve fiber bundle visual field
defect (left eye), as recorded by static perimetry in
patient with advanced glaucoma. Damage to retinal
nerve fibers has occurred chiefly in superior and inferior
temporal quadrants of optic disc, producing a dense,
ring-like depression of the central visual field, relatively
sparing a small island of vision in the central 10 degrees
of field.

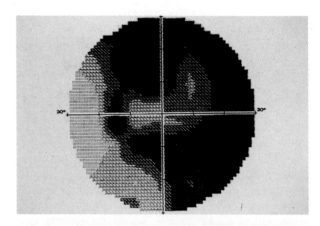

1.22 | Visible retinal nerve fiber bundles. The temporal
vascular arcades of the retina are associated with the
positions of the arcuate nerve fiber bundles that cross
the supero- and inferotemporal sectors of the optic disc
margin. The fundus photograph shows the nerve fiber
bundles, visible as arcuate zones of lighter color, and
the line drawing illustrates the topographic features. The
apparent boundaries of visible nerve fiber bundles are
indicated by the arrows.

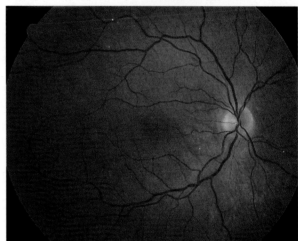

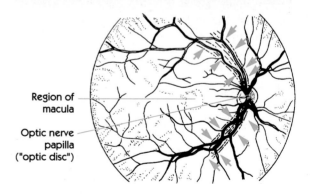

Region of
macula

Optic nerve
papilla
("optic disc")

this pattern consist of ill-defined areas of relative paracentral scotomas which, when coalesced with one another, result in the characteristic arcuate shape with a nasal border respecting the horizontal meridian. Similar defects can be produced, however, by retrobulbar disease of the optic nerves and chiasm.[11] Any focal damage to adjacent bundles of nerve fibers, such as might be caused by discrete areas of infarction or demyelination, can result in a defect indistinguishable from a bundle defect caused by intraocular disease. As a general rule, however, one should ordinarily expect to find some intraocular process as the cause of a clearly defined nerve fiber bundle-like defect (Fig. 1.23).

The hallmark of chiasmal disease is the bitemporal (heteronymous) visual field defect that respects the vertical meridian (Fig. 1.24A). This common pattern may involve predominantly the peripheral visual field (i.e., 30 degrees or more away from fixation), may be confined to small areas of the central visual field, and may be very asymmetric, involving one eye much more than the other. The pattern is present in a series of variations, depending on which portions of the chiasmal structure have been damaged. A particularly important syndrome is that of the anterior or junctional lesion of the chiasm, in which the most proximal (intracranial) portions of an optic nerve are damaged at the site of its connection with the anterolateral border of the chiasm (see Figs. 1.14 and 1.15). The fibers from inferonasal portions of retina pass through the inferonasal quadrant of the nerve and, on reach-

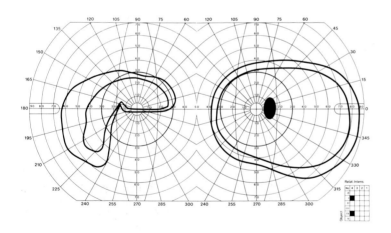

1.23 | Dense inferior nerve fiber bundle visual field defect, as recorded by kinetic perimetry, in left eye of patient with ischemic optic neuropathy. This results from small vessel infarction of prelaminar optic nerve, a common complication in patients with hypertension and/or diabetes mellitus. (From Spalton DJ, Sanders MD: The optic disc, in Spalton DJ, Hitchings RA, Hunter PA (eds): *Atlas of Clinical Ophthalmology*. London: Gower Medical Publishing, 1984, 17.17.)

ing the chiasm, make a detour to form a short loop within the proximal portions of the contralateral nerve (see discussion above of *Wilbrand's knee*). Damage to the nerve at this location results in the usual findings of optic nerve damage in the ipsilateral eye: reduced acuity, reduced brightness sensation, and reduced color perception with a variable central scotoma and an afferent pupillary defect, accompanied by a superotemporal sector defect in the field of the contralateral eye (see Fig. 1.15).

Another common pattern of visual field damage in chiasmal disease is that caused by compression from below by slowly expanding pituitary macroadenomas (Fig. 1.24). Tumors that rise above the diaphragma sella must extend a distance of at least 10 mm before making contact with the body of the chiasm. It is therefore not uncommon to find moderately large pituitary tumors that have not yet caused any significant damage to the afferent visual system. Slowly progressive compression from below, however, tends to damage the fibers located in the inferior portions of the chiasm, those that originated in the inferior halves of the retina (Fig. 1.25). This produces a peripheral, superior, bitemporal hemianopia that tends to respect the vertical meridian. Although this pattern is most obvious by kinetic perimetric testing in the peripheral field, it can also be found extending into the central 30 degrees of the field, when static perimetry is used.

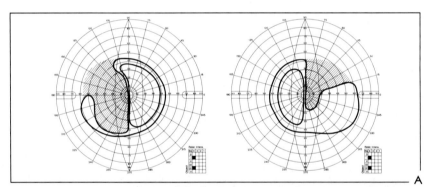

A

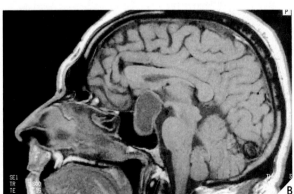

B

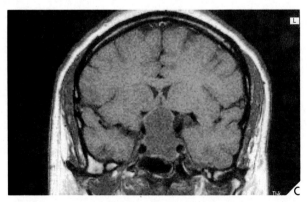

C

1.24 | *A:* Typical visual field defect found in lesions compressing the optic chiasm from below. Manual kinetic perimetry shows bitemporal (heteronymous) hemianopia respecting the vertical meridian, with preponderance of visual loss in superior portions of visual field. Such damage is usually associated with loss of central visual function, including impairments of acuity, color, and brightness. Gradual onset is also commonly associated with visible pallor (atrophy) of the optic disc. *B:* MRI, sagittal view, of pituitary macroadenoma rising more than 1 cm above the diaphragma sella, producing significant chiasmal compression. *C:* Same tumor seen in coronal section. Tumor fills and enlarges the sella, which balloons down into the sphenoid sinus and is flanked on either side by the intracavernous portions of the carotid arteries. (From Spalton DJ: Neuro-ophthalmology, in Spalton DJ, Hitchings RA, Hunter PA (eds): *Atlas of Clinical Ophthalmology.* London: Gower Medical Publishing, 1984, 19.21.)

As noted above, as this type of tumor slowly progresses it commonly affects both crossed and uncrossed fibers, resulting in a reduction in all the specialized modalities of central vision (e.g., acuity, color perception, brightness sense). However, in very slowly progressing disease, and in cases where tumors have been resected, allowing some recovery of central visual function, one may encounter dense, complete, bitemporal hemianopias in the presence of normal acuity. Even here, however, where acuity is 20/20 in each eye, one can usually demonstrate a significant reduction in color perception. A consequence of such a dense, bitemporal defect respecting the vertical meridian is that there are no areas of binocular visual field. Each nasal hemifield is deprived of the temporal field of the opposite eye, containing the projections of corresponding retinal locations. The sensory stimulus for binocular vergence movements is therefore extinguished, often resulting in a curious form of "diplopia" in which the remaining nasal hemifields move independently of one another, sometimes overlapping so as to produce visual confusion, and sometimes diverging, resulting in a vertical central band of absolute blindness bordered on either side by the preserved nasal hemifields of vision.

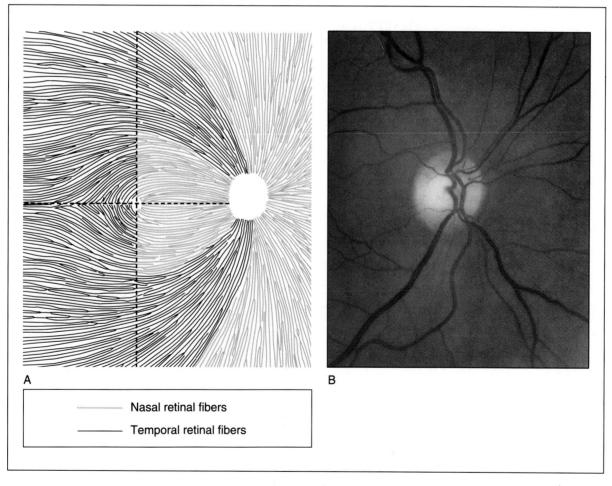

A   B

- Nasal retinal fibers
- Temporal retinal fibers

1.25 | With chiasmal compression for greater than 6 weeks, a pattern of "bowtie" atrophy may occur. The nasal retinal fibers, subserving the temporal hemifield of vision, enter the disc in the pattern shown on the left. Because the nasal retinal fibers are defined by those fibers nasal to the fovea, nasal retinal fibers will include those originating nasal to the disc and those originating temporal to the disc but nasal to the fovea. With long-standing chiasmal compression, the nasal retinal fibers become atrophic and pallor may be seen in a pattern corresponding to the location of these fibers on the disc.

ANATOMY OF THE LATERAL GENICULATE NUCLEUS

The lateral geniculate nuclei constitute the first principal synaptic component of the retrobulbar afferent visual system. The ganglion cell fibers terminate here and make synaptic contact with the cells giving rise to the geniculo-calcarine radiations. The cell bodies of these fibers are arranged in alternating layers that receive input from crossed and uncrossed fibers of the optic tract (Fig. 1.26). The crossed and uncrossed fibers within the tract are apparently randomly mixed, because disease of the optic tract is notorious for producing incongruous visual field defects (see above: incongruity is the phenomenon of asymmetry in which homonymous hemianopic defects of the visual field differ markedly in extent when one eye is compared with the other). In contrast to the mixed arrangement of fibers in the tract, the laminar structure of the lateral geniculate nucleus segregates crossed and uncrossed fibers completely. The laminae of the lateral geniculate body are made up of alternating layers of myelinated fibers and neuron cell bodies. There are six cellular laminae, three for each of the contralateral and ipsilateral optic nerve fibers. The cell layers are numbered 1 through 6 from ventral to dorsal. They are draped over one another to produce a somewhat crescentic shape, thickest at the center and tapered towards the edges. The central sector of the crescent contains all six laminae, but the tapered lateral horn is made up of the edges of layers 1, 2, 3, and 6, while the medial horn contains only layers 4 through 6.

The cell bodies in the two most ventral layers (1 and 2) are large and comprise the so-called magnocellular portion of the lateral geniculate nucleus. Layers 3 through 6, lying dorsally, contain small cell bodies and make up the so-called parvocellular (P-cell) portion of the lateral geniculate nucleus.[9] The parvocellular laminae appear to receive fibers from ganglion cells spread across the retina, concentrated in the central portions but covering the entire visual field, whereas the magnocellular layers appear to receive their principal input from ganglion cells located in the retinal periphery, with only a small proportion of ganglion cells in the perifoveal macula pro-

1.26 | Diagram of laminar structure of lateral geniculate body. Cell bodies are clustered together into six layers, numbered 1–6 from the hilum below to the crest above. Layers are separated from one another by laminae of myelinated fibers. All six layers are found in the central wedge-shaped area (indicated by dashed lines) in which the macular representation of the visual field is contained. Layers 1, 4, and 6 receive input from fibers originating in the contralateral eye, while layers 2, 3, and 5 receive fibers from the ipsilateral eye. Layers 1 and 2 constitute the magnocellular division of the LGN, and layers 3 through 6 make up the parvocellular division.

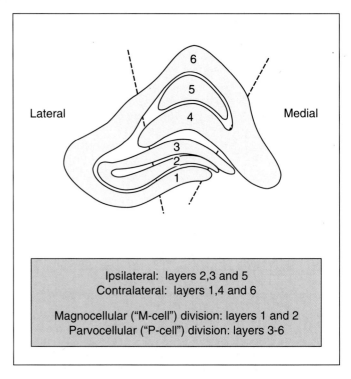

Ipsilateral: layers 2,3 and 5
Contralateral: layers 1,4 and 6

Magnocellular ("M-cell") division: layers 1 and 2
Parvocellular ("P-cell") division: layers 3-6

jecting to the magnocellular layers. The nerve fibers making contact in the magnocellular layer tend to arise from larger ganglion cells having larger axons with faster conduction velocities, whereas nerve fibers arriving in the parvocellular layers arise from smaller ganglion cells having smaller axons with slower conduction velocities.

The optic radiations (the so-called *geniculocalcarine tract*) are formed by the myelinated axons of the cell bodies located in the lateral geniculate nuclei (Fig. 1.27). These axons extend from the lateral geniculate nuclei to the primary visual cortex in the occipital lobe. They leave the lateral geniculate body as the optic peduncle, the extreme posterior end of the posterior limb of the internal capsule. Fibers located in the inferior portions of the optic peduncle spread inferolaterally in a large loop that sweeps around the inferior horn of the lateral ventricle, whereas those lying dorsally take a more direct course posteriorly. The two groups join one another to form the external sagittal striatum, hugging the lateral wall of the lateral ventricle. Disease in the temporal lobe commonly causes selective damage to the inferior half of the geniculocalcarine radiations, producing a visual field defect consisting of a contralateral homonymous superior quadrantanopia. The dorsoventral segregation of fibers in the optic radiations is maintained all the way from the geniculate body back to the occipital cortex. Posteriorly, the external sagittal striatum divides to pass above and below the occipital horn of the lateral ventricle and arrives at the medial aspect of the occipital lobe, deep to the calcarine cortex. Fibers in the dorsal half of the radiations make their synaptic contacts with areas of primary visual cortex located superior to the calcarine fissure, and those in the inferior half of the radiations terminate in cortex located inferior to the calcarine fissure.

RETROGENICULATE PATHWAYS

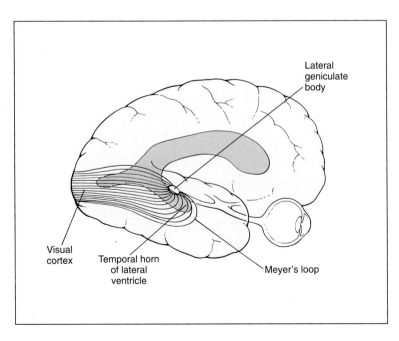

Lateral geniculate body

Visual cortex

Temporal horn of lateral ventricle

Meyer's loop

1.27 | The geniculocalacarine (optic) radiations through temporal, parietal, and occipital lobes of cerebral hemispheres. The inferior fibers arising from the lateral geniculate nucleus form a redundant loop around the anterior horn of the lateral ventricle (Meyer's loop). Damage to these fibers associated with temporal lobe disease results in a contralateral, homonymous, incongruous, superior quadrantanopia.

OCCIPITAL CORTEX

The primary visual cortex or area V_1, also known as the *striate cortex*, the *calcarine cortex*, or *Brodman's area 17*, lies largely within the folds of the calcarine fissure on the medial side of the occipital lobe. The primary visual cortex extends all the way from the posterior tip of the occipital lobe to the splenium of the corpus callosum. To a variable extent, a small portion of the primary visual cortex extends onto the tip of the occipital lobe, where it is visible on the exterior aspect of the brain posteriorly. The cortex is organized into six or more recognizable layers, numbered I to VI starting from the pial surface. The incoming geniculocortical fibers enter the cortex from the white-matter side, extending perpendicularly through the cortical layers, and making most of their synaptic contacts on cells within one of the sublaminae of layer IV. Closely associated groups of cortical cells receive input from geniculocalcarine fibers having closely corresponding retinotopic origins in the ipsi- and contralateral eyes. This mapping of corresponding points is so precise that damage to focal areas of cortex uniformly produces homonymous visual field defects of precisely identical locations, sizes, and shapes when the two eyes are compared. This extraordinary degree of congruence is the hallmark of occipital cortical disease.

RETINOTOPIC ORGANIZATION OF GENICULATE AND RETROGENICULATE STRUCTURES

Nerve fibers originating from the inferior half of the retina tend to maintain an inferior location within the optic nerve, chiasm, and optic tracts; conversely, those arising from the superior retina maintain a superior position within these same structures. This vertical segregation is generally maintained through the geniculocalcarine radiations and at the primary visual cortex. However, at the level of the lateral geniculate nucleus things are somewhat more complex.

The generalization of vertical segregation of superior and inferior ganglion cell fibers into superior and inferior portions of optic nerve and chiasm begins to break down at the level of the optic tract, where the retinotopic organization begins to deviate from the general rule. The structural organization of the geniculate body appears to be rotated approximately 90 degrees out of the plane maintained within the prechiasmal and retrogeniculate visual system. Nerve fibers arising from the superior retina become displaced

1.28 | Manual kinetic perimetry of visual field defect found in isolated damage to the lateral geniculate nucleus. Such lesions are very uncommon, but produce a characteristic pattern: a homonymous, partially congruous, horizontal sector hemianopia that straddles the horizontal meridian.

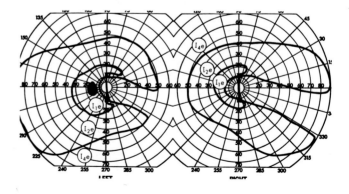

medially, and those arising from the inferior portions of the retina are moved to a more lateral location. Thus, superior retinal fibers subserve medial geniculate nuclear layers, whereas the inferior fibers arrive at the more laterally located portions of the geniculate laminae.

Analogous to the optic nerve and chiasm, the centralmost portion of the geniculate body, comprising approximately three quarters of its cross-sectional area, is a sector-shaped region devoted to the macular representation of the visual field. Straight lines drawn in a dorsoventral direction through the six laminae of the geniculate nucleus intersect groups of cells that receive ganglion cell input from a single retinal locus. This pattern is true for corresponding retinal locations in both eyes subserving a single visual direction in space.

Although primary disease of the lateral geniculate nucleus is rare, when it does occur it is usually the result of vascular or demyelinating lesions. An isolated lesion of the lateral geniculate nucleus produces a characteristic visual field defect. This is seen as a homonymous horizontal sector- or wedge-shaped defect that overlaps the horizontal meridian and extends from the periphery to the center of the field. The tip of the wedge respects the vertical meridian and usually splits the point of fixation (Fig. 1.28).

The retinotopic organization of primary visual cortex maps the superior retina onto the superior half of the primary visual cortex and the inferior retina onto the inferior half of the primary visual cortex. The macular or central representation at the visual field lies at the posterior aspect of calcarine cortex, where it wraps around onto the occipital pole on the exposed posterior surface of the occipital lobe. Proceeding anteriorly along the medial surface of the occipital lobe, one passes through more peripheral locations of the visual field, with the extreme periphery of the visual field located most anteriorly towards the splenium of the corpus callosum. The most peripheral portions of the nasal retina of the contralateral eye subserve the most temporal portions of the visual field, the monocular portion. This monocular temporal crescent of the visual field is represented by the portion of primary visual cortex lying closest to the corpus callosum. The area of cortex devoted to a given area of visual field is highly variable, depending on the visual sensory characteristics of the area in question. This is referred to as a variable cortical "magnification" factor. The macular representation of the field covers a disproportionately large area of cortex, reflecting the complexity of visual function in this highly developed region of the visual field. The cortical map of the central 10 degrees of the field lies most posteriorly, and in some cases extends around the tip of the occipital pole onto the external surface of the cerebral hemisphere (see discussion below and Fig. 1.31).

Temporal lobe disease that damages the optic radiations will produce either a complete or partial homonymous hemianopia.[12] Partial hemianopias may be congruous or incongruous, but the latter is the rule. Partial incongruous hemianopias of temporal lobe disease are most likely to produce superior homonymous quadrantic defects, because the inferior geniculocalcarine fibers of Meyer's loop are preferentially damaged (Fig. 1.29). As in all unilat-

TOPOGRAPHIC LOCALIZATION OF RETROGENICULATE DISEASE

eral retrochiasmal syndromes, acuity is unaffected. The superior quadrant defects may be precisely quadrantic in shape, but are more likely to be incongruous sectors that respect the vertical meridian. The incongruence usually involves the irregular lower borders of the sectors, which may extend further down in one eye than the other. Neither the periphery nor the central portions of the field are spared by these defects, making them detectable by both kinetic and automated static perimetry.

Hemianopias arising from parietal lobe disease are usually complete. Suspicion of parietal lobe involvement therefore depends on the simultaneous presence of nonvisual neurologic deficits. The optic radiations are deep in the parietal lobe and are often spared by diseases that cause extensive cortical damage. Infarcts, demyelination, inflammation and neoplasia producing isolated damage to the optic radiations in this area are quite rare. Parietal cortical disease produces dramatic deficits in the functions of language and/or intellect. Under these circumstances perimetry can be a challenge to the most patient examiner. Individuals with parietal disease often have a profound impersistence of visual attention, making steady fixation impossible. In such cases detection of visual field deficits is sometimes limited to the use of simple confrontation testing. This may be sufficient in those with complete homonymous deficits. In such a situation, the simultaneous presence of an OKN abnormality will confirm the parietal lobe as the locus of disease. (In this context, the principal abnormality of optokinetic nystagmus is a lateralizing asymmetry in which the slow phase of pursuit is defective towards the side ipsilateral to the parietal damage.

Many patients with parietal disease also have a hemi-neglect involving all modalities of sensation, particularly with involvement of the nondominant hemisphere. In such instances it may be difficult to distinguish between sensory hemi-neglect and homonymous hemianopia. Incomplete hemianopias consisting of inferior homonymous quadrantic defects have been

1.29 | Kinetic perimetry of visual field defect commonly associated with temporal lobe disease. Damage has occurred to the portion of the optic radiations called Meyer's loop (see Fig. 1.27). (From Spalton DJ: Neuro-ophthalmology, in Spalton DJ, Hitchings RA, Hunter PA (eds): *Atlas of Clinical Ophthalmology.* London: Gower Medical Publishing, 1984, 19.22.)

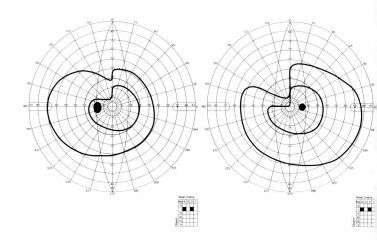

reported in patients with deep, focal parietal lobe disease that has presumably damaged the superior half of the optic radiations. However, such defects are very infrequent. In keeping with the general rule that homonymous defects are increasingly congruous with increasing distance behind the geniculate bodies, incomplete hemianopias of parietal lobe origin are usually more congruous than those arising from temporal lobe disease.

The visual field defects of occipital lobe disease are among the most dramatic and intriguing. They are exquisitely congruous and often have bizarre shapes, suggesting a random pattern of damage to cortical or subcortical structures. Trauma and occlusive vascular disease are the most common causes of occipital damage. A curious phenomenon associated with the hemianopias of occipital lobe disease is that of "macular sparing." This is a tendency for the small area immediately surrounding the point of fixation (the central 3 to 5 degrees) to be spared when the rest of the hemifield may have been completely extinguished. Some have proposed that this is evidence of bilateral hemispheric representation for the macular portions of the visual field. However, no anatomic substrate for this has yet been demonstrated. A more plausible explanation is that since the macular representation of the visual field occupies a relatively large area of cortex, it is more likely to be spared by subtotal disease. In addition, because the macular area of cortex is located at the extreme posterior pole of the occipital lobe, where there is a "watershed" zone of variable overlap between the distributions of the middle and posterior cerebral arteries, this portion of primary visual cortex stands a greater likelihood of escaping damage in occlusive disease of the posterior cerebral arteries.

As mentioned above, another unique feature of disease in the striate cortex is preservation (or extinction) of the monocular temporal crescent in one or both eyes. Primary cortical disease can destroy most of a homonymous hemifield, leaving a small portion of cortex intact at the anterior end

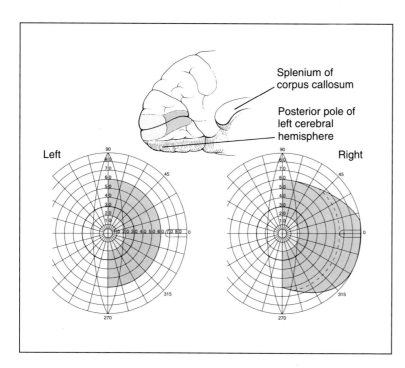

1.30 | Damage to the primary visual cortex produces highly congruous homonymous visual field defects. Sparing of a small central region close to fixation and sparing of the monocular temporal crescent are uniquely characteristic of primary cortical disease.

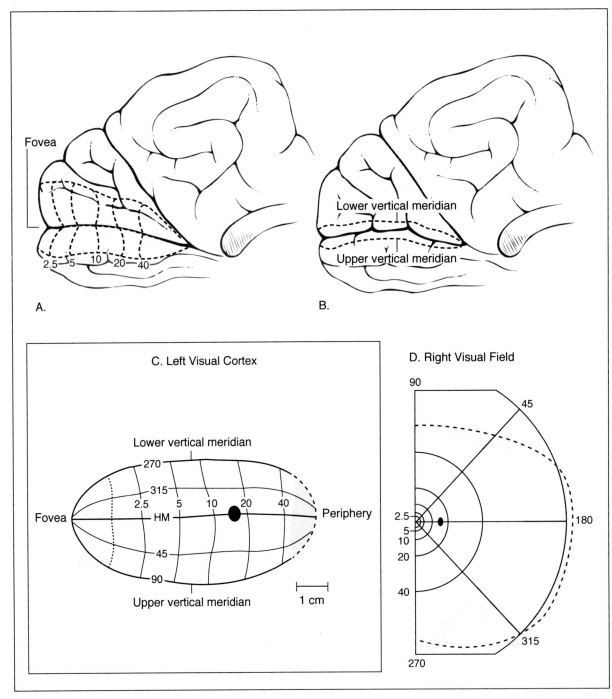

A.

B.

C. Left Visual Cortex

Lower vertical meridian

270

315

2.5   5   10   20   40

Fovea   HM   Periphery

45

90

Upper vertical meridian   1 cm

D. Right Visual Field

90

45

2.5
5
10
20

40

180

315

270

1.31 | Visual field representation in the human striate cortex. *A:* Calcarine fissure spread apart to expose striate cortex. Dashed lines correspond to coordinates of visual field map, bottom left. Vertical dashed lines map to concentric circles of isoeccentricity in visual field (from 2.5–40 degrees). *B:* Vertical meridians of visual field map to boundary separating primary visual cortex (V$_1$) from surrounding extrastriatal cortex (V$_2$). *C:* Exposed and flattened striate cortex has general shape of a horizontal ellipse. Vertical row of dots marks location where striate cortex wraps around occipital pole. Area of cortex from foveal representation to dotted line lies on exposed posterior surface of occipital lobe. "HM" marks horizontal meridian of visual field. Black oval marks location of physiologic blind spot in temporal half of field in contralateral eye. This region of cortex receives only monocular input from ipsilateral eye. Stippled region receives only monocular input from peripheral temporal crescent of field of contralateral eye. *D:* Right hemivisual field represented in left visual cortex. Stippled area is monocular temporal crescent. (Adapted from Horton J, Hoyt WF: The representation of the visual field in human striate cortex. A revision of the classic Holmes map. *Arch Ophthalmol 1991;109:816.* Copyright 1991, American Medical Association.)

of the striate region, where the temporal monocular crescent of the contralateral eye is represented. Preservation of this part of the field in an otherwise total homonymous hemianopia is pathognomonic for disease of the primary visual cortex (Figs. 1.30 and 1.31). Occasionally, occipital disease produces a congruous homonymous quandrantic defect that respects both the vertical and horizontal meridians. Horton and Hoyt have reported cases in which this pattern was found in patients with isolated disease of the extrastriatal occipital cortex.[13] These authors attributed the phenomenon to disease of the associational visual cortex (areas V_2 and V_3 or Brodman's areas 18 and 19), where retinotopic mapping is thought to be folded along the horizontal meridian in annular bands of peristriate cortex that surround the primary visual cortex.

2 | DISTINGUISHING OPTIC NERVE DISEASE FROM RETINAL/MACULAR DISEASE

Alfredo A. Sadun

Optic nerve disease may be mild or severe; the latter leads to profound losses of visual acuity, color vision, and visual field, among other things. However, mild optic neuropathies may have a minimal impact on these parameters of vision and thus may make the diagnosis more difficult. Optic neuropathies and maculopathies often have similar presentations; examples include optic neuritis and central serous retinopathy, both of which can present with acute visual loss. At times the relative absence of fundus findings in patients with acute visual loss will further frustrate the clinician's ability to make the correct diagnosis.[1-4] Impairments of vision caused by optic nerve dysfunction may be harbingers of intracranial pathology,[5] necessitating either pharmacologic or neurosurgical intervention, whereas maculopathies often respond to treatment such as laser photocoagulation or corticosteroids.[6] Therefore, the physician is compelled to make an early and accurate distinction between optic neuropathy and maculopathy. Several elements culled from the history, clinical examination, and special studies are useful in distinguishing between optic nerve and macular disease.

PRESENTATION

Many aspects of the symptomatology will help in the characterization of the visual impairment. It is important to elicit from the patient the tempo of the onset and course of symptoms.[7,8] For example, was the visual loss sudden? Did it continue to get worse or did it begin to improve? Maculopathies can be acute or insidious in onset. Optic neuritis usually develops over hours to days, stabilizes, and then shows improvement over the ensuing weeks.[9] Anterior ischemic optic neuropathy causes a sudden loss of vision with very little progression or resolution thereafter.[10] Pain may be associated with certain optic neuropathies, but not with maculopathies (Fig. 2.1). For example, patients with optic neuritis usually have a few days of retro-orbital pain at about the time of onset of visual loss; this pain may occur with or may be exacerbated by lateral ductions.[9]

Transient obscurations of vision (TOVs) are not usually due to macular disease.[10] Monocular TOVs that last for 2 to 5 seconds often are provoked by changes in posture.[11] These types of TOVs are seen with disc edema (resulting from any cause, including increased intracranial pressure) or other abnormalities of the optic nerve head, such as optic disc drusen.[11] Carotid artery disease also can cause monocular TOVs that usually last about 5 minutes[10]; these patients are usually elderly and often have hypertension or cardiac disease. Diffuse insufficiency of the anterior circulation on one side leads to the symptom of concentric loss from the periphery ("Vision gets dark and closes down like a tunnel"). Local blockage of arterial flow near the optic nerve head leads to the symptoms of a dark shade descending from above or ascending from below.

The character of the visual loss is useful in distinguishing optic neuropathies from maculopathies. Loss in acuity caused by optic nerve disease is often associated with a sense of generalized dimness, patchy dark spots, or black curtains across the visual field.[10] Patients with optic neuropathies also

FIGURE 2.1. History, Examination, and Studies in Patients with Optic Nerve vs. Macular Disease

PRESENTATION

HISTORY	OPTIC NERVE	MACULA
1. Transient obscurations of vision	Present	Absent
2. Course (tempo)	Sudden, progressive or stable	Slow changes
3. Pain	Sometimes	Almost never
4. Description of deficit	Dark areas	Distortions

CLINICAL EXAMINATION

ASSESSMENT	OPTIC NERVE	MACULA
1. Visual acuity	Variable	Reduced
2. Refractive errors	Unchanged	Towards hyperopia
3. Relative afferent pupillary defect	Obvious	Absent or small
4. Brightness-sense	Very reduced	Normal or slightly increased
5. Color vision	Very reduced or slightly reduced	Slightly reduced or normal
6. Visual field	Variable	Normal or central scotoma

SPECIAL TESTS AND STUDIES

TEST	OPTIC NERVE	MACULA
1. Photostress	Normal	Abnormal
2. TAG	Central scotoma	Metamorphopsia/scotoma
3. VER	Large latency delay	Small latency delay
4. CSF	Greatest losses in mid-spatial frequencies	Greatest losses in high spatial freq.

TAG = threshold Amsler grid; VER = visual evoked response; CSF = contrast sensitivity function. (Adapted from Sadun AA: Distinguishing between optic neuropathies and maculopathies. *Metab Pediatr Syst Ophthalmol* 1990;13:79–84.)

describe a darkening or desaturation of colors; objects may appear to have less contrast and may become indistinguishable. Patients with optic neuritis may also describe phosphenes with eye movements.

In contradistinction, patients with maculopathies usually complain of central visual field metamorphopsia[12,13]; edges and lines appear bowed, bent, or otherwise distorted. Micropsia is more common than macropsia. In addition, patients with macular disease may experience slight photophobia and may complain of glare or dazzle. Instead of noting that objects appear dim (as in optic neuropathies), patients with maculopathies may complain that objects appear too bright.

EXAMINATION

Visual acuity remains the cornerstone of the ophthalmic examination. Whereas visual acuity is invariably affected by macular disease, albeit subtly in some instances, it may be totally spared by some diseases of the optic nerve (see Fig. 2.1). Three tests—measurement of the pupillary response,[14,15] color vision,[16,17] and brightness-sense testing,[18–20]—are particularly sensitive to impairment of the optic nerve. The swinging flashlight test compares the afferent signal of one optic nerve to that of the contralateral optic nerve (Fig. 2.2). A consensual pupillary response that is greater than the direct pupillary response is indicative of an afferent pupillary defect (APD). This is usually judged qualitatively, although Fineberg and Thompson[14] advocate a 1 to 4+ quantitation with the use of neutral density filters.

Color vision is most thoroughly assessed with a Farnsworth–Munsell 100-hue test,[16] but this is usually too tedious for both the practitioner and the patient. An option is to perform a shorter, desaturated form of the Farnsworth–Munsell test, the D-15, that requires the alignment of only 15 color caps. In the office, color vision is often tested with pseudo-isochromatic plates of the A-O or Ishihara type.[14] For practical purposes, a relatively sensitive assessment of color saturation can be made by asking the patient to compare a bright red target when viewed with either eye.[21] Disease of the optic nerve invariably produces an ipsilateral, subjective loss of color vividness.[17,22]

Another sign of optic neuropathy is a change in brightness sense, which can be measured quantitatively with special spectacles (Fig. 2.3) consisting of two pairs of cross-polarizing filters.[23] The patient is asked to rotate the filter in front of the eye that sees the target as brighter (i.e., the normal eye); rotation of the polarizing filter produces a diminution of light transmission, thereby neutralizing the brightness disparity produced by the optic neuropathy in the abnormal eye. The angle of rotation can indicate the percentage of brightness-sense loss in the affected eye.[23] A simple, nonquantitative comparison as done in color testing is also effective.

Extensive retinal disease can produce mild abnormalities in color vision, brightness sense, and pupillary response, accompanied by marked visual loss.[23] However, when two or more of these tests show impairment in the presence of minimal loss of visual acuity an optic neuropathy is likely.

Visual fields can be assessed manually or by automated perimetry.[24–26] Despite the great advances in both static and kinetic automated perimetry, these tests are more useful for monitoring the progression of visual field defects (such as in glaucoma) than for the diagnosis of macular or optic nerve disease. Tangent field testing remains a very effective means of assessing the central 20 degrees of visual field and when performed at a distance of 2 meters can make the identification of a small central scotoma much easier. Amsler grid testing provides a very sensitive assessment of the central 10

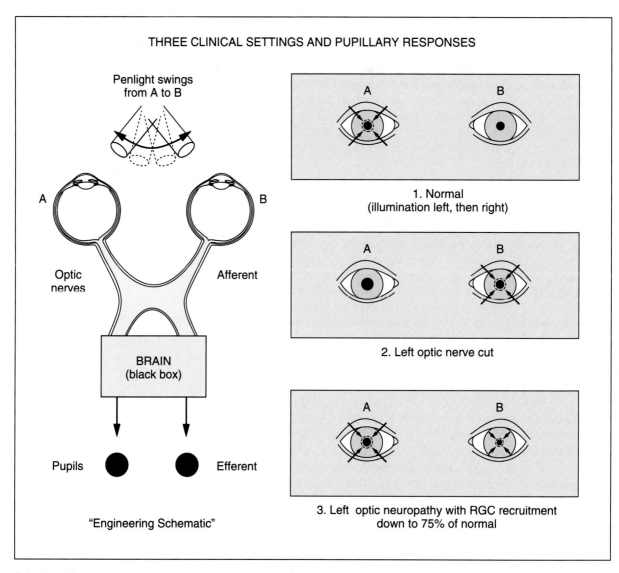

THREE CLINICAL SETTINGS AND PUPILLARY RESPONSES

Penlight swings
from A to B

A

B

Optic
nerves

Afferent

BRAIN
(black box)

Pupils

Efferent

"Engineering Schematic"

A   B

1. Normal
(illumination left, then right)

A   B

2. Left optic nerve cut

A   B

3. Left optic neuropathy with RGC recruitment
down to 75% of normal

2.2 | The afferent pupillary defect (APD) is demonstrated by swinging a flashlight from eye to eye. The direct pupillary response is compared to the consensual in the sec- ond eye (right eye above). Thus, going from left to right produces no change in pupil size in situation 1, constriction in situation 2, and further constriction in situation 3.

degrees of visual field,[27,28] and documents the presence or absence of meta-morphopsia, a strong indicator of macular disease.[29]

In general, macular disease produces a central scotoma, metamorphopsia, or both.[29] Optic nerve diseases can produce a large variety of visual field defects. Optic neuritis is usually associated with paracentral scotomas.[30] Toxic or nutritional amblyopia produces, in most cases, centrocecal field defects.[31] Disease of the optic nerve head often produces an arcuate or an altitudinal field defect.[32,33] Anterior ischemic optic neuropathy, in particular, is often associated with an altitudinal visual field loss, a type of arcuate bundle defect.

The fundus examination can be very helpful in distinguishing between optic nerve and macular disease. Optic disc swelling can result from inflammation or compression of the optic nerve; as such, it can be seen in posterior uveitis or in the face of increased intracranial pressure.[34,35] Disc elevation per se does not produce significant impairment of visual function.[36] However, optic atrophy may occur with chronic disc edema; it usually takes at least 1 month for optic atrophy to develop clinically after acute injury to the nerve. Longstanding injury to the optic nerve will eventually produce optic atrophy. More recent and more subtle injuries to the optic nerve can be detected by looking at the nerve fiber layer. Optic neuropathies may produce diffuse dropout or segmental losses in the nerve fiber layer, and certain lesions can produce slits or rake defects[37] in the nerve fiber layer that may be seen as early as 1 week after injury to the optic nerve. Specific and characteristic changes to the optic nerve, such as sectoral disc edema with flame-shaped hemorrhages (anterior ischemic optic neuropathy), lumps and bumps (optic disc drusen), pathologic cupping (glaucoma), sectoral optic atrophy, secondary optic atrophy, or butterfly optic atrophy, are patterns of disc change that indicate nerve damage of specific types.

2.3 | Brightness sense glasses. *A:* The observer wears the glasses while viewing white paper. After alternate occlusion, the subject identifies the eye that sees the brighter image. *B:* The glasses contain cross-polarizers that can reduce light transmittance to the normal eye so as to neutralize the brightness sense disparity.

Serous detachments, retinal pigment epithelial window defects, vascular abnormalities, and exudates can all be seen by direct or indirect ophthalmoscopy (for the latter, a low-power 14 diopter lens is recommended). Alternatively, a hand-held 78 or 90 diopter lens, used in conjunction with slit lamp biomicroscopy, gives an excellent high-magnification, stereoscopic view of the macula, although stereopsis is best obtained with a posterior pole contact lens. Subtle lesions, such as cellophane maculopathy, central serous retinopathy, lamellar holes, or cysts, are most easily appreciated with the use of such lenses.

STUDIES

A number of specialized tests are very useful in distinguishing between optic neuropathies and maculopathies (see Fig. 2.1). Several of these tests are very simple, inexpensive, and easy to perform in the office.

Visual field assessment is particularly useful in making the distinction between optic nerve and macular disease, and can be performed utilizing automated perimetry. Emphasis should be on the central 30 degrees (such as Humphrey strategy 30-1 or 30-2 or Octopus strategy 31 or 32), which is the area of greatest concern in evaluating either macular or optic nerve lesions. Despite the usefulness of automated static and Goldmann kinetic perimetry, the central field can often be better evaluated by the use of a tangent screen. A large screen at 2 meters is especially advantageous, since it magnifies by 6x the scotoma identified by bowl perimetry. Similarly, Amsler grid testing is extremely useful despite the fact that information is limited to the central 10 degrees.[27]

One disadvantage of the standard Amsler grid is that the 90% to 100% contrast between the black lines and the white background (or vice versa) is very easily distinguishable and represents a suprathreshold test. Therefore, this test is useful in looking for absolute scotomas in the central field. A rela-

2.4 | The visual island. Standard Amsler grid (SA) testing uses a suprathreshold stimulus. It thus "cuts" across the island at lower retinal sensitivities. The threshold Amsler grid (TA) test is near threshold and "cuts" nearer the top of retinal sensitivity. Thus, TA testing reveals shallow relative scotomas missed by SA. The scotoma may also appear bigger on TA testing. Areas of mild retinal distrubance (e.g., macular edema) may appear as zones of metamorphopsia on SA and as scotomas on TA.

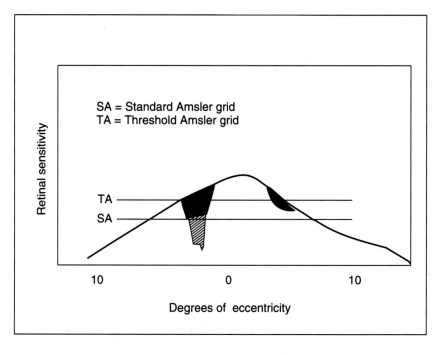

tive scotoma would be missed, since there still exists enough retinal sensitivity to pick up the high-contrast target. However, a method for making the Amsler grid far more sensitive has been developed[28] and is termed threshold Amsler grid testing (TAG). In TAG, the patient wears specialized glasses that have cross-polarizers in front of both oculars. Testing one eye at a time, the patient looks at an Amsler grid while the cross-polarizers are rotated until the patient can barely perceive the grid. Thus, the apparent contrast is reduced; the cut through the visual island (Fig. 2.4) is made much closer to the apex (area of greatest retinal sensitivity). Patients with a variety of optic neuropathies and maculopathies were tested with TAG and paracentral scotomas were found that had been missed on standard Amsler grid testing of the central 10 degrees.[28]

Regardless of the method of visual field assessment, disease at the level of the optic disc usually produces arcuate scotomas or altitudinal field defects.[38,39] The blind spot may be enlarged, but only rarely is there nonspecific generalized constriction.[39] Toxic optic neuropathies, as well as compressive optic neuropathies, can produce central or centrocecal visual field defects. Optic neuritis usually produces central or paracentral scotomas. Disease near the optic chiasm is manifested by specific visual field patterns, such as bitemporal field defects, junctional scotomas and, rarely, by binasal visual field defects.[40,41] In contradistinction, the visual field defect of a maculopathy is almost invariably a central scotoma.[29] Interestingly, surrounding the central scotoma there is often a zone of metamorphopsia. In most maculopathies the central scotoma is only a relative defect (not an absolute defect), and the slope at the edge of the central scotoma is usually gradual. Amsler grid testing of a patient with maculopathy often reveals a region of metamorphopsia without a scotoma in the central field. When this same patient is tested with TAG, however, the area in which what was described as metamorphopsia on Amsler grid often is described as a complete scotoma (see Fig. 2.4).

Photostress testing can be very helpful in distinguishing between maculopathies and optic nerve disorders.[42] In macular disease there is usually a delay in the recovery of visual pigments that are bleached by a bright light, but bright light has no effect on optic nerve conduction. Glaser and colleagues[43] have described the test as follows. Establish the patient's best corrected visual acuity with each eye. A bright light (usually from a penlight) is directed into the normal eye for a 15-second period, with the other eye covered. The patient is then asked to read the line above what was previously the smallest line the patient was able to see on the Snellen chart. The recovery time is recorded as the interval between removal of the bright light and the time the patient is able to read the "next largest" Snellen chart line. The procedure is then repeated for the defective eye, and the recovery period (to read one line larger than before) is compared. In macular disease the recovery time is markedly prolonged to about three times normal (typically 120 seconds vs. 40 seconds for the normal eye). Patients with optic neuropathies show little or no prolongation of this recovery time. This test is most helpful when visual acuity is not worse than 20/80. Fundus fluorescein angiography can be very useful in characterizing retinal diseases. The pattern of chorioretinal pigment, flow, and a leakage through choroidal or retinal vessels, and the presence of edema or other retinal lesions, can often be assessed by fluorescein angiography. Macular lesions, such as central serous retinopathy, are particularly well studied by this technique.

The visual evoked response (VER) can also be used to document optic nerve dysfunction.[44,45] However, increased latency in the VER can be due to a variety of other diseases, including refractive error, a maculopathy,[46] or even feigned visual loss.[47] Nevertheless, the test can be very useful when there is a question of subclinical and/or bilateral disease of the optic nerve. It can be invaluable when documentation is desired for medicolegal purposes; however, the usefulness of the test is limited by the fact that it is possible to feign a poor response.[47]

The Pulfrich phenomenon is sometimes called "the poor man's VER." It can usually be elicited in a patient with unilateral optic nerve conduction block in whom a latency delay could be noted with VER.[48] In this test the patient is asked to observe a swinging pendulum with both eyes open. Normally, the pendulum is seen to swing in only one plane. However, the presence of a unilateral conduction delay due to an optic neuropathy produces for the patient the impression that the pendulum is swinging through an elliptical arc. If the optic nerve conduction defect is in the left eye, the patient will describe the illusion of a pendulum moving away from the left eye and towards the right eye as it completes the ellipse.

Contrast sensitivity testing is one of the newest methods for both screening and characterization of visual function.[49-51] Patients are asked to view a series of sinusoidal gratings of different spatial frequencies, such as those described by Arden and Jacobson.[52] Alternatively, the Vistech plates can be used, which have the advantage of eliciting a forced-choice response that is easy and reproducible.[53,54] The patient looks across the chart, and identifies the stripes perceived, and also describes their orientation. In this way, a two-dimensional graph can be generated, associating contrast sensitivity with spatial frequency (Fig. 2.5). Patients with optic neuropathies may have deficiencies in the middle to high spatial frequencies; patients with maculopathies usually have deficiencies in the highest spatial frequencies (see Fig. 2.1).

2.5 | Contrast sensitivity functions (CSF) can be measured by a two-dimensional chart. Different spatial frequencies are represented on rows A–E (A = 1.5 cycles/degree; E = 18 cycles/degree). Progressively less contrast (closer shades of gray) is presented in columns 1–9. The patient attempts to identify the bar orientations for each patch. This generates a two-dimensional graph of CSF as a function of spatial frequency. (Photograph courtesy of Vistech Consultants, Inc.)

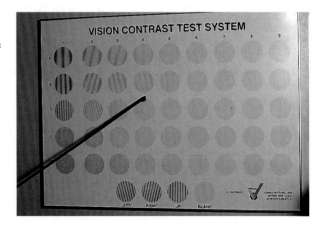

Subtle optic neuropathies or maculopathies are often very difficult to diagnose, because patients with these conditions often present with ambiguous complaints and the examination may not disclose any obvious abnormality. There is an old adage that, in patients with optic neuritis, "the patient sees nothing and the doctor sees nothing." Much the same could also be said for central serous retinopathy. Several key aspects in patient assessment can be used not only to distinguish between optic neuropathies and maculopathies but often to characterize these lesions as well. Figure 2.1 presents the most common differences in history, signs, and the results of special tests.

In summary, specific aspects of history, examination, and psychophysical testing are particularly likely to reveal the presence of optic neuropathies and maculopathies. Visual dysfunctions caused by optic nerve lesions are often described in terms of a dimness or grayness, and these lesions can usually be diagnosed by the tempo of onset. Macular lesions often reduce visual acuity profoundly and almost always produce metamorphopsia or micropsia. Amsler grid testing or TAG testing can be very useful in revealing metamorphopsia or central scotomas caused by macular disease. Optic nerve lesions produce impairments in the triad of optic nerve function tests that are out of proportion to losses in visual acuity. The assessment of visual fields can be extremely useful. The greatest attention should be paid to the central visual field area; tangent screen field testing and Amsler grid testing are often much more helpful than is Goldmann or automated perimetry. Finally, specialized in-office techniques, such as TAG, photostress testing, and the Pulfrich phenomenon, can be quite useful in differentiating between optic neuropathies and macular disease.

OVERVIEW

3

THE OPTIC NEUROPATHIES

Barrett Katz
Michael Wall

HEREDITARY OPTIC NEUROPATHIES

The hereditary optic neuropathies are a heterogeneous group of diseases whose primary clinical signature is optic nerve dysfunction. They share hereditary characteristics, although their specific causes remain unknown. The categorization of an optic neuropathy as hereditary does not preclude its being primarily metabolic, ischemic, or inflammatory in cause. Such processes may be primarily retinal in cause or may be a declaration of an inborn error of metabolism primarily affecting neural tissue. Our classification is one that is always changing, and is only as current as our understanding of underlying pathophysiologic mechanisms.

An inherited optic neuropathy should be a bilateral process and symmetric between eyes. It can be expected to culminate in loss of central vision, dyschromatopsia, and clinically recognizable alterations in the anatomy of the optic nerve head. There are usually alterations of visual field and electrophysiologic function. Occasionally, there are associated neurologic findings. Our usual classification of the inherited optic neuropathies takes into account the genetics of transmission (be it Mendelian or mitochondrial), the age of presentation of the clinical illness, and the association (or lack thereof) of neurologic or systemic signs.

OPTIC NEUROPATHIES WITH MENDELIAN INHERITANCE PATTERNS

DOMINANT OPTIC ATROPHY

Clinicians have long recognized an autosomally dominant optic atrophy (DOA) whose transmission appears to follow classic Mendelian laws. DOA is an abiotrophy of neural tissue that usually presents in the first decade of life.[1-3] It has not been recognized congenitally nor in infancy.[4-6] Most patients report onset of symptoms before the age of 10. The onset is insidious, with mild visual dysfunction occurring without nyctalopia or rapid progression. As a rule there is symmetric involvement. Vision ranges from 20/30 through 20/200; almost 40% of patients have vision of 20/60 or better.[3,6]

DOA declares itself in a recognizable matrix of optic atrophy characterized by pallor of the temporal aspect of each optic nerve head, with associated temporal excavation of the optic disc (Fig. 3.1). The optic atrophy may be subtle or dramatic. There is bilateral loss of the nerve fiber layer within the papillomacular bundle and loss of superficial capillarity of the temporal aspect of the disc. Visual field changes include central, centrocecal, or paracentral scotomas, often associated with mid-peripheral temporal depression. The moderate depression of temporal isopters can on occasion superficially resemble a bitemporal hemianopic defect. Peripheral fields are expected to be normal in DOA, however. There is an associated acquired blue/yellow dyschromatopsia which, when present, may be pathognomonic.[7,8] This dyschromatopsia can be recognized on tangent screen by demonstrating a more constricted field plotted with a blue test object in comparison to a field plotted with the same size red test object, an inversion of the usual circumstance.

Although the dominant pedigree of DOA is characteristic, it is not uncommon for patients to be ignorant of the familial nature of their disease. The diagnosis is often made in an asymptomatic, affected patient consequent to screening examination of all family members of a more severely affected proband, attesting to significant intrafamilial variation of its clinical manifestations and often minimal disturbances of visual function.

Visual evoked potentials in affected individuals are characterized by both diminished amplitudes and prolonged latencies. Patients with DOA are expected to be neurologically normal, although 10% of Kjer's early cases were said to show "mental abnormalities."[3] Concomitant hearing loss, mutism, and deuteronomalous color deficits have been reported.[9] Whether such instances of "dominant optic atrophy plus" are separate nosologic entities or the extreme declaration of a single genetic disorder is not yet known.

The pathologic findings in DOA include diffuse atrophy of the retinal ganglion cell layer, atrophy and loss of myelin within the optic nerves, thinning of the papillomacular bundle itself, and wedge-shaped loss of temporal disc substance, all seen in the setting of normal inner and outer nuclear layers.[10,11]

3.1 | Dominant optic atrophy (DOA). Typical appearance of optic nerve head in a dominantly inherited optic neuropathy, illustrating pallor and excavation most prominent in the temporal quadrant.

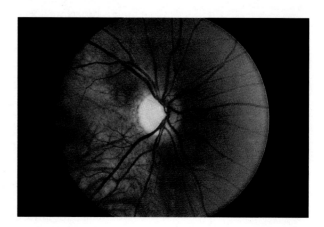

Juvenile-onset dominant optic atrophy is the most common of the heredofamilial optic abiotrophies. Most patients can be expected to maintain reading vision throughout their school years and to lead productive and relatively normal lives. There is evidence that the disease is not static, however. Kjer noted that none of his patients below the age of 15 had acuities as severe as 20/200, whereas 20% of his patients 45 years and older lost vision to these levels.[3] The diagnosis remains a clinical one; examination of other family members often allows confirmation. When the clinical course shows dramatic or rapid progression, further neurologic investigation is imperative. The underlying pathophysiologic mechanisms and the specific genetic markers remain to be discovered.

RECESSIVE OPTIC ATROPHIES
CONGENITAL (SIMPLE) OPTIC ATROPHY

The autosomal recessive form of optic atrophy seen in isolation is rare. Clinical manifestations are more severe than in DOA and occur earlier. Marked visual disability is evident before the child reaches the age of 4 years, and a searching, pendular "sensory" nystagmus can be present. Visual fields are severely disturbed, and optic discs more completely atrophic (possibly more deeply excavated), than in dominant optic atrophy. Although peripapillary attenuation of the retinal arteriolar tree may initially suggest a tapetoretinal degeneration, electroretinography is normal. The disability is severe, stable, and predictably unassociated with other systemic or neurologic declarations.[12,13] On occasion there may be consanguinity between parents.

COMPLICATED (INFANTILE) HEREDITARY OPTIC ATROPHY

In this variant of recessively inherited optic atrophy accompanied by neurologic dysfunction, disc pallor can be recognized in early childhood and is associated with ataxia, mental retardation, pyramidal tract dysfunction, increased tonicity, urinary incontinence, and pes cavus.[14] Although initially recognized only in males, subsequent reports indicate its occurrence in both sexes. Optic atrophy is severe and is especially marked in the temporal aspect. It is usually accompanied by severe visual loss, nystagmus, and dyschromatopsia. This nosologic entity may be a part of a continuum, encompassing optic atrophy seen as a manifestation of the hereditary ataxias.[15,16]

AUTOSOMAL RECESSIVE OPTIC ATROPHY ASSOCIATED WITH JUVENILE DIABETES

The association of juvenile-onset diabetes mellitus and progressive visual loss with optic atrophy has been reported.[17] Its clinical spectrum has expanded from a limited association of glucose intolerance and optic pallor, known as Wolfram's syndrome, to include the development of neurosensory hearing loss, neurogenic bladder, and diabetes insipidus. When it occurs as diabetes insipidus (DI), diabetes mellitus (DM), optic atrophy (OA), and deafness (D), it has been called the DIDMOAD syndrome.[18] Glucose intolerance usually presents before visual dysfunction. Visual acuity may remain normal in the early stage, despite mild dyschromatopsia and recognized optic atrophy. As the optic neuropathy progresses, visual loss can become severe. Dyschromatopsia is an invariate feature; visual fields eventually show central scotomas with progressive generalized constriction. Optic atrophy is often dramatic and may be associated with mild to moderate excavation of the disc itself. Optic nerve changes appear to be unrelated to the presence or development of underlying diabetic retinopathy.

The incidence of neurosensory hearing loss and diabetes insipidus is variable. A reported frequency of 32% for DI is probably an underestimate, since polyuria is often mistakenly attributed to poor control of diabetes mellitus. Both or either may begin in the first or second decade of life. Deafness is not universal, and may be detected only as a high frequency (>4,000 Hz) hearing loss at audiometry. Other anomalies have been recorded in these patients, especially dilatation of the lower urinary tract. Additional abnormalities reported include ptosis, ataxia, seizure diathesis, mental retardation, nystagmus, abnormal electroretinography, elevated cerebrospinal fluid protein, and short stature.[19]

It is the slowly progressive nature of this inherited optic neuropathy and its association with underlying insulin-dependent, ketosis-prone glucose intolerance that makes it distinctive.

OPTIC NEUROPATHY NOT INHERITED ACCORDING TO MENDELIAN PATTERNS
LEBER'S HEREDITARY OPTIC NEUROPATHY

Mitochondria are unique among cell organelles in that they contain their own genetic material which is transmitted exclusively by the mother, contains very few noncoding sequences, and has a slightly different genetic code.[20] Defects within this small segment of the human genome are associated with specific disease entities of disparate clinical presentations. A recent addition to this list of alterations of mitochondrial DNA with clinical import is Leber's hereditary optic neuropathy (LHON). Leber described a disease of young males characterized by abrupt loss of central vision occurring in the second and third decades of life. Its genetic pattern seemed to imply an absence of transmission through men, with transmission occurring through only the female line.[21] The age of onset is now known to vary widely. In the United States LHON occurs primarily in males (at a male-to-female ratio of approximately 4 to 1)[22]; in Japan, the ratio of male-to-female involvement approaches 6 to 4.

Although initial involvement is unilateral, the second eye can be expected to become involved, usually within days or weeks. Intervals of involvement between eyes have extended to many years; therefore, LHON seems almost always to be a sequential, bilateral optic neuropathy. All levels of visual loss have been recognized. Commonly, vision is lost to levels of 20/200; on occasion it is reduced to hand motions, light perception, or even no light perception. Accompanying visual field deficits are usually central or centrocecal in nature. Whereas these scotomas are relative during the early stages of the disease, as visual loss progresses they become absolute.

The classic ophthalmoscopic findings of acute LHON encompass rather specific signatures of altered anatomy. Disc hyperemia and fullness are frequently observed (Fig. 3.2). There is a circumpapillary telangectatic microangiopathy and swelling of the nerve fiber layer around the disc (a pseudo-edema, one without leakage from the disc, when studied by fluorescein angiography).[23] Prominent vascular tortuosity of surface disc vessels and fine arteriovenous shunt-like vessels can be seen on fluorescein angiography. Retinal striations may extend from the disc margin; there may be associated macular edema, and retinal hemorrhages can occur on and adjacent to the nerve head. This microangiopathy occurs not only in the presymptomatic phase of involved eyes but also in a high proportion of asymptomatic offspring of the female line. Increased shunting and disc hyperemia presage the acute phase of visual loss; the telangectatic microangiopathy can be thought of as an inherited marker of the disease, implying some risk of future optic nerve insult.

During the acute phase of visual loss, patients are otherwise well. Rarely, headaches and vertigo may be reported; some observers have interpreted these as signs of meningeal inflammation and arachnoid involvement. After several weeks the telangectatic vessels disappear, and the pseudo-edema of the disc resolves, with ensuing optic atrophy and loss of nerve fiber layer. Although nerve fiber loss is most prominent in the papillomacular bundle, the entire nerve fiber layer commonly disappears, leaving the disc diffusely pale. There is a spectrum of presentations; some patients exhibit relative preservation of the superior and inferior arcuate bundles, although some loss of extramacular nerve fiber layers is expected to occur in all cases.

Abnormalities of color perception have been documented. Changed visual evoked responses have been recorded after loss of central acuity. The results of the Farnsworth–Munsell 100-hue test may be abnormal before central acuity falls.[24] Relative stability of visual function after the acute episode is anticipated; a gradual decline (perhaps a third of patients) or surprising improvement after many years of stationary vision (rarely) has been

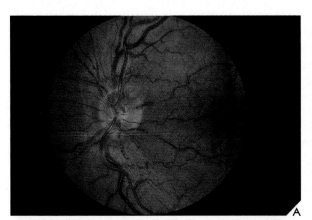

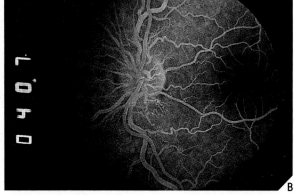

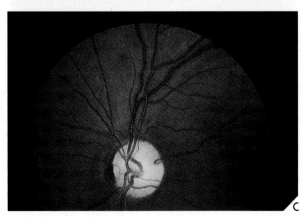

3.2 | Leber's hereditary optic neuropathy. *A:* Typical appearance of optic nerve head during acute phase of Leber's optic neuropathy. Disc is edematous and hyperemic, with circumpapillary telangiectatic microangiopathy characterized by prominent vascular tortuosity of vessels on and just off the disc's surface. *B:* Fluorescein angiogram of same patient during acute phase, demonstrating fine arteriovenous shunt-like vessels within peripapillary retina and absence of leakage from the disc itself despite the presence of disc edema. *C:* Late atrophic phase of nerve head demonstrating loss of many of the previously visible telangiectatic vessels, and diffuse pallor with nerve fiber layer loss. (Photos courtesy of Dr. Eeva Nikoskelainen.)

observed.[25,26] When vision returns, recovery is in one eye only.[27] Should such visual recovery occur, further recurrence of visual failure is not expected.[28] Observations of occasional spontaneous recovery have made the assessment of possible treatment modalities difficult. Reports of improvement after hydroxycobalamine administration and after craniotomy (for lysis of presumed optochiasmatic arachnoidal adhesion) have appeared,[29,30] although the latter surgery was never widely advocated for LHON, and the natural history of the process makes reports of the former suspect.

Visual loss is usually the primary characteristic of this disease. Disparate neurologic signs have been recognized, most commonly pyramidal, cerebellar, or peripheral. These include spastic paraparesis, hyperactive deep tendon reflexes, muscle wasting, changes in primary sensory modalities, ataxia, and pyramidal tract dysfunction.[31-33] As is true for many of the heredofamilial neurologic syndromes, associated defects in cardiac conduction are also recognized.[34] Neuroradiologic investigation and cerebrospinal fluid studies are expected to be normal in these patients during the presymptomatic and acute stages.[35] After the acute phase, imaging of the optic nerve with MRI or CT is reported to show increased optic nerve signal intensities.[36]

The analysis of mitochondrial DNA from patients with Leber's hereditary optic neuropathy and their relatives has shown, in 40% to 60% of cases, a single mutation at one select base pair.[37] This mutation presumably leads to an amino acid alteration of the gene that encodes for a subunit of NADH dehydrogenase. This relatively conservative alteration (both amino acids are basic) culminates in some degradation of the enzyme complexes involved in Complex I of the electron transport chain, resulting in dysfunction within the mitochondrial energy-producing pathways of oxidative phosphorylation. Although a specific abnormal protein has not yet been identified, reduced activity of an enzyme of this system (NADH-coenzyme Q oxidoreductase) has been demonstrated within platelets of four men with a Leber's-like hereditary optic neuropathy.[38]

It is difficult to explain how a widespread mitochondrial DNA defect interfering with respiratory chain function leads to the eventual development of subacute loss of vision in young male adults. Such metabolic pathways are concerned with the generation of ATP; decreased catalytic activities of Complex I, therefore, may result in insufficient availability of energy for basic cellular metabolic requirements. Cellular pumps may be adequate for normal physiologic function for some finite time, yet not able to withstand additional stress or further metabolic demands. The optic nerve may therefore function normally for many years, with ensuing visual loss as some additional factor or factors concur.

Not all families with clinical Leber's disease have this specific mutation; the disease has been known to occur in the absence of such a mutation.[39,40] Indeed, LHON is a genetically heterogeneous disorder, with up to half of cases due to some mutation other than the 11778. Genetic analysis of some cases of LHON (the minority) have demonstrated mixtures of both mutant and normal (wild-type) mitochondrial DNA molecules, speaking for a spectrum of genetic heteroplasmy.[22] This point mutation therefore appears to be neither a necessary nor a sufficient criterion for the clinical disease. Presumably, additional factors are involved in the expression of the mutant phenotype.[39-41] We must learn much more about the genetics of the mitochondrial DNA and its segregation before we will be able to use molecular genotypes to make strict clinical correlations with the clinical disease as we know it.[40] In addition, we must await a final explanation of how this genetic defect of respiratory enzyme function causes such specific pathognomonic change (the characteristic ophthalmoscopic findings of Leber's) at a characteristic location (the intraocular segment of optic nerve) after a latency period characteristically measured in decades.

The exposure to or the deficiency of many substances may damage the optic nerves, resulting in loss of central vision, color vision, and visual field and, eventually, diffuse pallor of the nerve head. Because a toxic or nutritional optic neuropathy is part of a larger systemic insult, the process usually affects each nerve equally, with symmetric loss of vision and symmetrically changed optic nerve head anatomy. Vision may be affected minimally or dramatically; patients can reach levels of acuity to hand motion. Dyschromatopsia is an invariate feature. Visual field changes include both central and centrocecal scotomas, often associated with concentric constriction of all isopters. The pupillary response may also be affected, yielding pupils poorly reactive to direct and consensual stimulation; a relative afferent pupillary defect is commonly absent, as both nerves suffer symmetric injury. Some toxic optic neuropathies are reversible; when the insulting agent is withdrawn there may be a gradual return of visual function. However, recovery of dead axons cannot be expected; once optic atrophy occurs, the nerves remain pale forever.

> The current edition of *Grant's Toxicology of the Eye* lists many substances that have been reported to produce toxic optic neuropathy, either by affecting anterior structures or retrobulbar anatomy. The reader should be cautioned, however, in that many associations are based on single case reports; such associations may be serendipitous. Figure 3.3 lists the agents most frequently involved in toxic optic neuropathy.

NUTRITIONAL AND TOXIC OPTIC NEUROPATHIES

FIGURE 3.3. Most Common Offending Agents in Toxic Optic Neuropathy

Amiodarone	DDT (dichlorodiphenyl-trichloroethane)	Iodoform
Amoproxan	Emetine	Isoniazid
Aniline dyes	Ethambutol	Lead
Barbiturates	Ethchlorvynol	Methyl alcohol
BCNU [1,3-bis (2-chloroethyl)-1-nitrosourea]	Ethylene glycol	Organophosphates
Cafergot® (ergotamine tartrate and caffeine)	5-Fluorouracil	Penicillamine
Carbromal	Heavy metals	Sulfonamides
Cephaloridine	Hexachlorophene	Thioglycolate
Chloroamphenicol	Hydroxyquinolines	Toluene
		Trichloroethylene

The antitubercular medications have notoriously been associated with acquired, dose-dependent subacute optic neuropathy, most convincing of which is ethambutol; data on other such medications are equivocal.[42–44] Clinical manifestations of ethambutol-induced optic neuropathy are usually seen after several months of treatment with the usual dosage used in anti-tuberculin therapy; toxicity with dosages of less than 15 mg/kg/day is uncommon unless concomitant renal disease is present. However, effects may not become evident until 12 months after the onset of therapy. Both axial and periaxial presentations have been recorded, the former with central field loss and the latter with peripheral field change. Field defects are typically centrocecal; occasionally a bitemporal depression reminiscent of chiasmal dysfunction is observed. Acuities can be depressed to moderate levels, with associated changed parameters of color vision and contrast sensitivity.[45] Ethambutol-induced optic neuropathy is usually but not invariably reversible. Indeed, there may be progression of visual loss soon after recognition of the drug's toxic effects on the optic nerves, despite discontinuation of the medication. A persistent visual evoked response abnormality may even be a permanent signature of the subclinical effects of ethambutol toxicity.[46]

Isoniazid has been reported to cause an acquired optic neuropathy that can be distinguished from that provoked by ethambutol, which is often administered concurrently. However, definitive evidence of this agent's neurotoxicity is not available. The toxicity of INH is said to be associated with swelling of the disc, and to occur earlier than toxicity from ethambutol.[47] Changed visual parameters are expected, with depression of central vision, color vision, and anterior visual pathways field deficits. Precisely how these antituberculous medications precipitate insult to the nerve is unknown.[42] There may be a depletion of copper and zinc, with decreased activity of cytochrome C oxidase activity.

Other commonly employed agents that have been implicated in neurotoxicity directed to the anterior visual pathways are legion. These include chloroamphenicol,[48] 5-fluorouracil,[49] carmustine,[50] penicillamine,[51] amiodarone,[52] the halogenated hydroxyquinolines,[53] and ethchlorvynols.[54] As new chemotherapeutic agents become available, we can expect to see additional drugs toxic to the optic nerves. Toxic optic neuropathy should always be a diagnosis of exclusion, with an exhaustive search for a treatable underlying structural lesion affecting the anterior visual pathways.

TOBACCO, ALCOHOL, AND AMBLYOPIA

In many areas of ophthalmology, controversy exists about the cause or best therapy of a disease. For tobacco/alcohol-induced amblyopia, there appears to be controversy about its very existence. Patients who drink and smoke heavily can develop bilateral painless progressive loss of vision accompanied by dyschromatopsia and either cecocentral or central scotomas. Although their optic nerves may look perfectly normal (especially early in the course of their disease), a dramatic optic neuropathy may ensue, leaving them visually disabled, with anatomy forever changed. The specific pathogenesis of this disorder, and the number of unique processes that may contribute to its clinical picture, are yet to be ascertained. No consensus exists concerning the ability of tobacco to injure the anterior visual pathways. Many observers deny the existence of tobacco-induced amblyopia,[55] while others remain convinced of its existence.[56]

There do seem to be several points of clinical agreement. Tobacco and alcohol do not seem to act synergistically to insult the anterior visual pathways. Visual loss that ensues is probably due to malnutrition rather than to a direct toxic effect of the alcohol or tobacco itself. The nutritional deficiency aspects of tobacco/alcohol amblyopia are derived from clinical studies that document its existence in malnutritional states that occurred without concomitant tobacco or alcohol abuse,[57] its clinical response to vitamin therapy,[58] and its serological profile.[59]

Given the number of people who abuse alcohol, the prevalence of such a nutritionally related amblyopia is distinctly uncommon. Also unusual is the fact that dyschromatopsia plays such a dramatic role in the patient's observations. These are the patients who complain bitterly that their color vision is disturbed. They often do not appear malnourished, although they usually are not obese; many work productively within society. Tobacco/alcohol amblyopia is noteworthy for its dramatic symmetry of involvement, both in visual parameters and in optic nerve anatomy, be it normal or atrophic. It is characterized by a gradual onset of symptomatology. Although vision can reach levels of counting fingers or even hand motion, it is not expected to progress to total blindness.

The fundus may be normal early in the course of disease, but progresses to symmetric papillomacular nerve fiber loss, with temporal pallor. Patients usually have centrocecal or central scotomas. Many patients exhibit signs of an associated distal polyneuropathy and have megaloblastic changes on their peripheral blood smear even when there is no demonstrable vitamin deficiency (as determined by serum vitamin B12 analysis). Specific indicators of nutritional optic neuropathy may be observable when a patient presents during the acute phase.[60] Evanescent dilatation and tortuosity of the smaller retinal vessels within the arcade, occasionally associated with fine hemorrhages at the posterior pole, can occur. This vascular dilatation is short-lived and can be seen during the pre-atrophic stages of this optic neuropathy.

The pathology of tobacco/alcohol amblyopia is nonspecific and is characterized by selective loss of the papillomacular bundle, associated with a sectoral (temporal) pattern of ganglion cell loss. Interestingly, this distribution may correspond to a subpopulation of smaller ganglion cells and their nerve fibers.[61] Such a pathologic pattern may therefore suggest that the smaller ganglion cells are the most susceptible to malnutrition and vitamin deprivation.[62] Therapy is warranted, consisting of multivitamins and thiamine (25 mg P.O. thrice daily). Although there is no strong objection to adding intramuscular hydroxycobalamine, there seems to be no compelling reason to require it. Patients should be advised to decrease their intake of alcohol and tobacco and to improve their dietary habits. Although the literature suggests that many patients recover vision, many do not.

An entirely different alcoholic insult is that seen with acute methanol ingestion. This produces a rapid onset of visual signs and symptoms after ingestion of even small amounts. Loss of vision may ensue within several hours; the discs may appear normal or edematous.[63] Dyschromatopsia and central scotomas accompany the visual loss, which can be transient. With ingestion of larger amounts, recovery may be partial, although residual loss of axons and associated disc pallor are expected; whether or not the ultimate outcome depends on the success of treating the associated metabolic acidosis is yet to be determined. Cases studied histopathologically demonstrate axonal preservation, albeit with damage to myelin which is presumably secondary to anoxia at an area known to be a watershed for vascular flow.

TRAUMATIC OPTIC NEUROPATHY

DIRECT INJURY OF THE OPTIC NERVE

Perhaps the most frequent direct traumatic optic neuropathy is that due to nerve damage following a penetrating injury of the orbit. If the nerve is injured immediately behind the globe, obvious funduscopic changes should be apparent, associated with interference of both the retinal and choroidal circulations, concomitant loss of visual acuity (usually immediate), and eventual optic atrophy (weeks later). History and examination usually suggest the inciting wounds. The management of direct optic nerve injuries is mostly reparative and cosmetic.

INDIRECT INJURY OF THE OPTIC NERVE

Trauma to the eye, orbital adnexa, or head that results in visual loss not accounted for by direct injury to the globe or nerve itself, yet followed by optic atrophy, can be presumed to represent indirect optic neuropathy.[64,65] The optic nerve is tethered at the anterior aspect of the optic canal, within the canal, and at the intracranial window of the canal's entrance. Because the nerve is therefore fixed within the canal, it is affected by shearing forces as brain and orbital content move freely, meeting resistance at the orbital and intracranial canalicular windows. This suggests that the major stress points for traumatic injuries are at nerve segments within the apex of the orbit and at the intracranial entrance to the optic canal. The mechanisms of such axonal insult remain speculative. A list of postulated incriminating pathophysiologies includes contusion of the retrobulbar axons and secondary necrosis, hemorrhage within the sheath of the nerve, central retinal artery or vein occlusion, acute glaucoma, posterior ischemic optic neuropathy, reflex vasospasm or compression of the retinal and ciliary vasculature, and secondary metabolic ischemia.

The nerve itself may on rare occasion be avulsed as a result of indirect injury pursuant to orbital trauma. Examination would be expected to show significant intraocular hemorrhage and tissue destruction, obscuring changes that occur at the scleral canal and the intraocular segment of optic nerve. Whether the nerve can be dislocated from the globe as a result of a blow to the anterior surface of the eye remains controversial. Holographic interferometry suggests that a force applied to anterior structures is transmitted to the posterior aspects of the orbital apex. An indirect traumatic injury to the nerve is therefore most likely to occur posteriorly within the orbit and may spare the central retinal artery and vein, thus giving the retina a remarkably normal appearance in the face of depressed optic nerve function.

A common example of a traumatic (and treatable) optic neuropathy is that which occurs with orbital hemorrhage, as a result of trauma itself or pursuant to orbital surgery. Visual loss can be dramatically depressed, to levels of no light perception. Orbital hemorrhage is usually accompanied by periorbital pain and swelling, with a tense, tight orbit and some element of proptosis. Optic neuropathy from such orbital trauma is related to the anatomy of the orbital cavity. The orbit is a poorly expandable space in comparison with the cranial cavity; it is bounded posteriorly and on its sides by rigid bony structures. Anteriorly, the orbital space is limited by the globe and orbital septum. Any demand for expansion of this orbital space can be met only by anterior displacement of the globe and septum. Although there is some limited capacity for such forward displacement (by stretching of the septum), once a minimal amount of proptosis is generated the globe acts as a plug in a fully distended palpebral fissure. The orbit is then "sealed" by its "anterior wall." That the orbit is sealed posteriorly is demonstrated by the fact that orbital hemorrhages do not spontaneously decompress themselves by dissecting intracranially. When trauma and orbital hemorrhage ensue, the globe moves forward until it reaches the orbit's anatomic boundary. As further bleeding and edema occur within the orbital space, there can be little increase in volume to accommodate an increase in tissue pressures, which then become distributed equally throughout the entire orbital contents. This increased orbital pressure acting on the vascular supply of the nerve accounts for that element of a traumatic optic neuropathy that may be reversible. Axons that are rendered necrotic by the initial trauma are lost forever. Axons that are ischemic and/or compressed (although not yet infarcted) may be saved by timely intervention.

Three separate vascular beds can be affected in optic neuropathy associated with orbital hemorrhage: the retinal circulation, the choroidal circulation, and the blood supply to the nerve itself. However, the primary circulation of import in such traumatic optic neuropathies appears to be the vascular supply to the intraorbital optic nerve. Evidence includes the usually normal appearance of retinal blood flow (as observed on ophthalmoscopy), a normal-appearing fluoroscein angiogram, a lack of immediate return of vision on anterior chamber paracentesis, and the observation of an abnormal VER when the ERG is normal.[64,66]

Neurosurgical procedures performed as the patient lies in a face-down position may also result in loss of visual function but are most probably related to inadvertent tamponade of the globe with ensuing decreased retinal blood flow, and are not a result of optic neuropathy.[67]

Fracture of the optic canal itself is rare; nevertheless, compression of the optic nerve within the canal may be a reversible cause of traumatic optic neuropathy. As ischemic compression of the nerve within the canal seems a logical cause of injury, one would expect surgical decompression of the canalicular segment of nerve to be a frequent and successful operation; whether this is so remains controversial.[64] The safety of transcranial decompression has been demonstrated[68]; indeed, the availability of both transethmoidal and transsphenoidal decompression would be expected to strengthen the argument for surgical intervention in presumed compromise to the nerve caused by canalicular embarrassment. No consensus yet exists on the management of such indirect injury to the optic nerve. Anderson has advocated the use of intravenous dexamethasone sodium phosphate in doses greater than 1 mg/kg/day.[69] He reserves canalicular decompression for patients who demonstrate a delayed loss of vision unresponsive to 12 hours of megadose IV steroids, or for those who initially experience return of vision with high-dose steroids but who subsequently lose vision again as doses are decreased. A recent report describes 14 patients with a posterior traumatic optic neuropathy who underwent optic nerve decompression by a single surgeon, employing the standard ethmoidectomy approach, and steroid therapy during the perioperative period.[70] Visual results were impressive. Although these patients were not consecutive, not comatose, not randomized, and were not subjected to the same steroid regimen, a substantial percentage, even those with profound visual loss, experienced some recovery. The authors recommend a combination of steroid intervention and surgery for posterior orbital trauma until a larger, randomized clinical trial addresses the contributions of steroids, surgery, and changes in the natural history of untreated optic nerve trauma. (See Fukado[71] for additional surgical arguments.)

The management of indirect optic nerve injuries is controversial and is changing. Recovery has been recorded with no intervention, after administration of steroids, and after a variety of neurosurgical and ophthalmologic decompressions. Whether it requires very high doses of intravenous steroids is still debated.[72,73] Interpreting the effects of the various forms of therapy is difficult because patients improve under all treatment regimens. The relevant variable for the clinician must be to decide where the insult is and what its underlying pathophysiology might be. When a hemorrhage occurs within the sheaths of the intraorbital or intracranial segment of optic nerve, a decompression of that segment of nerve is warranted. When orbital hemorrhage occurs, with compromise of the vascular supply to the posterior optic nerve, orbital decompression (often lateral canthotomy alone), done in a timely fashion, may afford dramatic relief. Faced with multiple bone injuries in an unconscious patient with an afferent pupillary defect, one cannot be dogmatic about any therapy. A reasoned approach would be to eschew surgery in any comatose patient when it is done solely for an afferent pupillary defect, to argue strongly for surgery when loss of vision follows a window of time during which some element of vision was preserved (choosing the operation based on where in its extracranial segment the optic nerve is most likely to be damaged), and to treat all patients with visual loss following trauma with high-dose steroids.

ANTERIOR ISCHEMIC OPTIC NEUROPATHY

Anterior ischemic optic neuropathy (AION) is a syndrome consisting of precipitous loss of peripheral or central vision associated with optic disc swelling and, commonly, peripapillary nerve fiber layer hemorrhage. Patients experience sudden loss of vision that may be progressive over days but is usually stable thereafter; on rare occasions a progressive loss of acuity is noted. Vision may improve, albeit incompletely; recurrences in the same eye are unusual. AION is, after glaucoma, the most prevalent optic neuropathy of adults. It is the most frequent cause of disc edema in adults over the age of 50. It can be categorized as idiopathic (perhaps in association with hypertension or diabetes), arteritic (most commonly as a manifestation of temporal arteritis), associated with recognizable systemic disease (e.g., lupus arteriopathy, radiation-induced necrosis, hypercoaguable state), or related to systemic hypoperfusion (as seen in acute blood loss or surgery).

IDIOPATHIC AION (NONARTERITIC, ARTERIOSCLEROTIC)

The most frequent variant of AION is that which occurs with an almost monotonous funduscopic appearance of disc edema, peripapillary retinal hemorrhage, loss of central vision, dyschromatopsia, and anterior visual pathway field loss. The presence of disc edema confirms the diagnosis; in theory, a posterior ischemic optic neuropathy can occur but must be exceedingly uncommon.

AION is a disease of mid and later life, with peak incidence in the 50s and 60s. There is a bell-shaped curve of age at onset, which extends to the 40s and through the 70s.[74] There is involvement of central vision and a visual field deficit consistent with insult to the anterior visual pathways. Classically, altitudinal field loss is the most common visual field defect with AION.[75] However, any visual field defect consistent with optic nerve dysfunction anterior to the chiasm has been recognized in AION. Interestingly, the inferior hemifield is more commonly affected than the superior hemiretinal field; fixation is usually involved. Visual deficits are usually maximal at onset, although occasionally a stuttering course presages the nadir of functioning. One generally expects insignificant recovery of vision; however, this rule is not inviolate, and occasional patients do show improved visual function. Visual acuity may be only mildly affected, or dramatically lost.[76] All patients with AION are expected to show a relative afferent pupillary defect on the involved side (unless a previous insult had occurred to the contralateral optic nerve), and associated dyschromatopsia. The amount of dyschromatopsia usually parallels the amount of loss of central vision.

AION, expectedly, involves the prelaminar region of the anterior optic nerve. Much of what we know about AION emanates from the most dramatic cases in which vision is severely disturbed and the entire disc is edematous. More commonly, it occurs as a sectoral ischemic insult to the optic disc, and so may have only minimal associated change in visual parameters. Nevertheless, some element of disc edema can be observed during the acute event. This edema may be minimal and may involve only a few clock hours of the optic disc. It may be associated with small flame hemorrhages, with fullness to the superficial nerve fiber layer extending but a short distance past the margin of the disc margin (Fig. 3.4). The disc edema is short-lived and resolves rapidly, over several weeks, with ensuing optic atrophy corresponding to sectors of previous edema. Such atrophy is not expected to be associated with significant (acquired) excavation of the nerve head. It is associated with attenuation of the superficial arteriolar tree, both on the disc and immediately surrounding it. This clinical sign (a narrowing of the appearance of blood flow in an arteriole on the disc itself, which widens perhaps one disc diameter away from the disc) often permits recognition of the

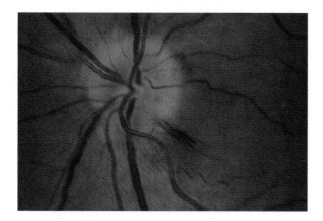

3.4 | Anterior ischemic optic neuropathy. Typical appearance of acute AION, with diffuse disc edema, superficial nerve fiber layer hemorrhage, and glutting of the peripapillary axons.

ischemic nature of a patient's optic atrophy when that patient is first seen after the acute event. This change seems relatively specific for an anterior ischemic optic neuropathy and previous edema to the intraocular segment of the optic nerve (Fig. 3.5).

Experimental work suggests that AION is a stroke syndrome of the distal optic nerve, caused by vascular insufficiency in the posterior ciliary bed.[77,78] Branches of the peripapillary choroidal bed form a watershed area at the laminar and prelaminar region of the nerve. When they suffer insufficient blood flow from decreased perfusion pressure of whatever cause, consequent ischemia and infarction of the nerve fiber layer and disc substance just anterior to the laminar cribrosa occur. It is important to recognize that pathologic specimens of idiopathic AION are exceedingly rare, and much of what we presume to be its underlying anatomic correlates and pathophysiology are derived from pathologic specimens of the arteritic variant of AION (see below).

Factors that predispose certain eyes to develop ischemic optic neuropathy have been recognized.[79-83] An eye with a congenitally crowded and small optic disc (one with a small cup-to-disc ratio) appears to be anatomically predisposed to suffer AION. Acquired processes too seem to influence the eventual development of AION. Diabetes and hypertension are commonly associated (though not invariably so).[77,78] It may be that some precipitating factor (such as transiently elevated intraocular pressure or acute posterior vitreous detachment), occurring in an eye with an anatomically susceptible nerve (one that shows crowding of axons through a smaller scleral canal) and mild arteriopathy (due to diabetes or hypertension), may combine to effect focal edema at a watershed zone between the retinal and choroidal circulations (the laminar region of the optic nerve).

If AION is purely an ischemic disease, the more common circumstance should be transient ischemia to the nerve, rather than infarction. Such patients seem few and far between; perhaps much of what we presume to be embolic disease to the retina (amaurosis fugax) is, in fact, transient ischemia to the nerve itself. Patients who suffer AION do not appear to be at special risk for cerebrovascular disease, although this remains controversial; AION may not be a harbinger for future vascular events in other vascular beds.[8]

Although many therapies have been tried for AION, none have been proven efficacious in restoring visual function. In theory, corticosteroid usage might decrease local edema which, in an acute setting, might be adding to focal ischemia at the prelaminar region of the optic nerve. Recently, optic nerve sheath decompression in cases of idiopathic AION that seemed progressive (the overwhelming minority) was reported to afford some element of improvement, although this observation is untested, unconfirmed, and controversial.[84] Other reports have suggested lowering the intraocular pressure in the other eye to afford some protection for that eye's involvement,[82,83] although this, too, is untested and controversial. AION is commonly a sequential, bilateral optic neuropathy that involves the second eye in more than half of all cases.[85]

Although some workers have produced a clinical picture reminiscent of AION in monkeys by occlusion of their posterior ciliary arteries,[77,78,86] experimentally manipulated flow to the posterior ciliary vascular bed does not produce permanent or even transient damage in all primates so studied.[87] Histologic examination of human cadavers has demonstrated minimal but diffuse intimal thickening in the posterior ciliary arteries and in the walls of the arterioles within the pia and nerve itself.[88] That this vascular bed is critical in at least some cases of AION seems well documented by other histopathology, as embolic multifocal small vessel occlusions have been described in infarction of the laminar region of the optic nerve.[89] It may be that any element of AION requires diffuse small-vessel disease; the full pathophysiologic description of this entity awaits further study.

An arteritic variant of AION occurs. It is seen much less frequently than the idiopathic variety, but is important to recognize because its recognition dictates treatment. In idiopathic AION, we know of nothing that can be done to protect the second eye; in arteritic AION, steroid therapy is presumed to decrease the frequency of the second eye's involvement, if initiated in a timely fashion.

Arteritic AION occurs in an older age group than idiopathic AION, commonly in the 70s and 80s. The visual loss is more severe, and the episode itself may be stuttering and associated with systemic signs and symptoms such as jaw claudication, temporal headache, weight loss, and fatigue. When arteritic AION is present, it is part of a larger underlying arteritis and the specific nature of that vasculopathy must be searched for. Giant-cell arteritis (temporal arteritis) is the likely arteritis to eventuate in this clinical syndrome, yet it can be seen in lupus erythematosus, polyarteritis nodosa, syphilis, and radiation necrosis.

The disc edema generated in the arteritic variant of AION is somewhat different; it is usually more severe, more pallid in appearance, and extends somewhat further from the margins of the disc itself. Whereas idiopathic AION is almost always an acute unilateral process, simultaneous AION suggests the arteritic variety.[85] The second eye is said to be involved more frequently in the arteritic variant of AION and, when it happens, usually does so within weeks or months of the first eye's declaration. Clinicians agree that the most dangerous risk period for the second eye is in the months after the first eye's involvement. It is imperative for the clinician to recognize the arteritic varieties of AION, since prompt steroid therapy may afford real protection for the second eye.

It is necessary for the clinician to have a high level of suspicion for the arteritic variant of AION. It requires immediate high-dose steroid therapy

ARTERITIC AION (GIANT-CELL ARTERITIS, TEMPORAL ARTERITIS)

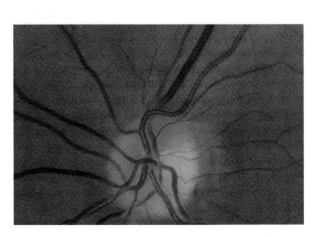

3.5 | Anterior ischemic optic neuropathy. Typical appearance of a resolved sectoral AION (from 8 o'clock through the 2 o'clock position). Note peripapillary attenuation of the retinal arteriole (and the venule immediately inferior to it), leaving the optic nerve head at the 8:30–9:00 o'clock position, whose blood flow columns widen as they leave the immediate peripapillary region.

while the results of ESR are being awaited and as the discussion of whether to do a temporal artery biopsy begins. How does one recognize arteritic AION? The diagnosis of arteritic AION is a clinical one, based on the patient's signs and symptoms, and is supported by an elevated ESR and positive temporal artery biopsy. The gold standard for deciding which patients to biopsy has been the combination of the elevated ESR (although this is a very nonspecific test), a suggestive clinical history of headache or jaw claudication, or pallid disc edema on presentation. Occasional cases of cranial arteritis and associated AION are seen when the ESR is normal (10%) or the biopsy negative (5%). The clinician must therefore not view laboratory data as gospel. When the clinical history is overwhelming in an elderly patient (with temporal head pain, a beaded temporal artery on palpation, jaw claudication, and an elevated ESR), the diagnosis is inescapable. Immediate high-dose steroid therapy must be initiated (at least 60 mg prednisone p.o. daily). It is dangerous to wait for biopsy results if the disease is suspected on clinical grounds. Indeed, a negative biopsy does not rule out the diagnosis of temporal arteritis, since areas of "skip lesions" have been reported in detailed pathologic examinations of temporal arteries from patients with giant-cell arteritis.[91] This problem can be prevented by obtaining a 1-inch segment of artery and sectioning it 1 mm at a time.

How long to treat for the arteritic variant of AION is an arbitrary decision without a definitive answer. Conservative therapy dictates that a patient be treated with daily prednisone for a minimum of 3 months; many consultants treat for 9 to 12 months. Cranial arteritis seems to be a disease primarily of a non-black population. Cranial arteritis itself may be part of the systemic disease, polymyalgia rheumatica, from which it cannot be definitively differentiated either clinically or histopathologically. Treatment for patients with polymyalgia rheumatica (PMR) or temporal arteritis without ocular manifestations is not yet known. Such patients are not usually placed on daily high-dose steroids, since we do not know if treating them would prevent ocular involvement. We know only that once ocular involvement has occurred in one eye, we afford some protection for the second eye by instituting therapy; although PMR itself responds symptomatically to steroids administered every other day, daily steroids are needed to suppress the inflammatory response adequately.

UNCOMMON ASSOCIATIONS

An occasional patient with adult onset diabetes mellitus will have an acquired optic neuropathy that looks very much like a chronic, persisting AION; this has been called diabetic papillopathy.[92] Diabetic papillopathy was reported initially in teenage patients with longstanding juvenile diabetes. Over the years its clinical spectrum has expanded to include an adult population with insulin-dependent diabetes and chronic disc edema. Diabetic papillopathy is usually bilateral, usually affords good prognosis for both central vision and field, and is characterized by a disc edema that shows prominent surface telangectatic change without neovascularization. It is not expected to be followed by dramatic optic atrophy, and does not appear to be related to the presence or absence of other diabetic retinopathic changes.

AION has been recognized after cataract extraction, with visual loss appearing immediately or soon after operative intervention.[93] It is presumed to be due to a transient elevation of intraocular pressure in an eye with a disc that was anatomically predisposed to ischemia.[94] This variant of AION lends credence to the hypothesis that some cases of idiopathic AION are influenced by intraocular pressure. Because it has a high incidence of bilaterality, lowering of intraocular tension (perioperatively) before surgery of the second eye is warranted.

Other associations are occasionally reported with AION. This list is long and is ever expanding; it includes migraine, acute blood loss and hypotension, uremia, embolization following cardiac catheterization or cardiac surgery; and occasionally it is seen as a declaration of underlying hematologic anomaly (e.g., antiphospholipid antibody syndrome). Carotid artery disease itself, or ensuing emboli thereof, does not seem to be a significant factor in the etiology or pathogenesis of most AION, although this, too, is controversial.[95,96]

IDIOPATHIC INTRA-CRANIAL HYPERTENSION AND PAPILLEDEMA

Idiopathic intracranial hypertension (IIH), also called *pseudotumor cerebri*, is a syndrome characterized by increased intracranial pressure with its associated symptoms and signs in an alert and oriented patient, but without localizing neurologic findings. Its major morbidity, present in most patients, is visual loss that often is reversible. Diagnostic criteria are found in Figure 3.6.

EPIDEMIOLOGY

The annual incidence of IIH is 1/100,000 persons.[97] More than 90% of IIH patients are obese and over 90% are women.[98] Although symptoms and signs may be recurrent in about 10%, asymptomatic elevated intracranial pressure may persist for years.[99] The average age at the time of diagnosis is 30 years.

PATHOPHYSIOLOGY

A popular hypothesis is that IIH is a syndrome of decreased CSF absorption. Reduced conductance (the inverse of resistance) to CSF re-uptake may be due to dysfunction of the absorptive mechanism of the arachnoid granulations. Intracranial pressure then must rise for CSF absorption to occur. Increased brain water may accompany this change, resulting in a reduction in brain compliance and prevention of ventricular dilatation.

FIGURE 3.6. Diagnostic Criteria for IIH

Signs and symptoms of increased intracranial pressure
Absence of localizing findings on neurologic examination
Absence of deformity, displacement or obstruction of the
    ventricular system, and otherwise normal neurodiagnostic
    studies, except for increased CSF pressure
Patient awake and alert
No other cause of increased intracranial pressure present

SYMPTOMS

The symptoms of IIH are those of generalized increased intracranial pressure (Fig. 3.7).[100] Interestingly, these symptoms also occur in a normal population, but in the latter they seldom occur daily. The most prominent symptom of IIH is headache. The headache profile is that of severe daily headaches described as pulsatile. They are different from any previous headache, may awaken the patient, and usually last for hours. Nausea is common and vomiting less so.

3.7 | Frequency in percentage of symptoms in IIH and a control group. ICN = Pulsatile intracranial noises. TVO = Transient visual obscurations.

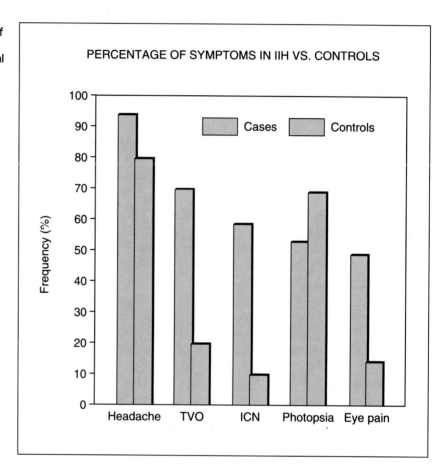

The signs of IIH are a consequence of increased intracranial pressure: papilledema with its resultant visual loss and VI nerve palsies (present in 10% to 20%) (Fig. 3.8).[98] Papilledema (optic disc edema due to increased intracranial pressure) is the major mechanism of the visual loss of IIH. Papilledema is due to stasis of axoplasmic flow (Fig. 3.9). Although there is a significant correlation between high grade papilledema and atrophic papilledema and visual loss,[101] in the individual patient the severity of visual loss cannot be predicted from the severity of the papilledema.

A common problem is the failure to recognize early papilledema. Papilledema progresses and regresses in five characteristic stages and can be graded.[102] The earliest sign of papilledema is disc elevation. Unfortunately, this sign may also be present from birth as a normal variant. The earliest signs of the edema definitely being acquired are: (a) edema in the peripapillary region, obscuring the details of the adjacent nerve fiber layer (often in a

SIGNS

FIGURE 3.8. Frequency of Visual Signs in 50 Patients at the Initial and Final Visits

	INITIAL (PERCENT INVOLVED OR ABNORMAL)	FINAL (PERCENT INVOLVED OR ABNORMAL)
Papilledema	100	64
Papilledema grade >=2*	64	38
Goldmann perimetry	96	60
Goldmann grade >=2	62	44
Automated perimetry	92	84
Automated grade >=2	84	64
Contrast sensitivity	50	26
Color comparison	40	24
Confrontation field	32	22
Choroidal folds	24	18
Snellen acuity	22	18
Color plate score	16	10
Relative pupil defect	14	18
VI nerve palsy	12	0
Optic atrophy	4	6

* >=2 = Greater than or equal to grade 2.
(From Wall M, George D: Idiopathic intracranial hypertension (pseudotumor cerebri): A prospective study of 50 patients. *Brain* 1991;114:155, with permission.)

C-shaped halo) (Fig. 3.10A); (b) coarsening and irregularity of this nerve fiber layer (Fig. 3.10B); (c) loss of spontaneous venous pulsations after previous documentation of their presence; and (d) associated choroidal folds (Fig. 3.10B). With increased severity of the papilledema, the C-shaped halo fills in (grade 2) (Fig. 3.10C).

Early disc elevation is difficult to appreciate by direct ophthalmoscopy; stereoscopic fundus photography or indirect ophthalmoscopy (especially

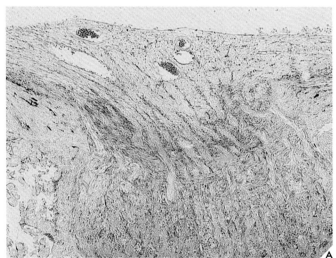

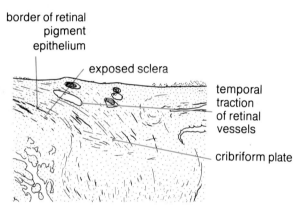

3.9 | *A:* Histology of normal optic nerve shows that retinal aperture is larger than the scleral aperture of the optic disc, with a deficiency of retina and choroid on the temporal side revealing the bare sclera. *B:* Histology of papilledema. Note the swollen axons resulting from block of axoplasmic transport. Vascular engorgement and edema are also present. (From Spalton DJ, Sanders MD: The optic disc, in Spalton DJ, Hitchings RA, Hunter PA (eds): *Atlas of Clinical Ophthalmology.* London: Gower Medical Publishing, 1984, 17.9.)

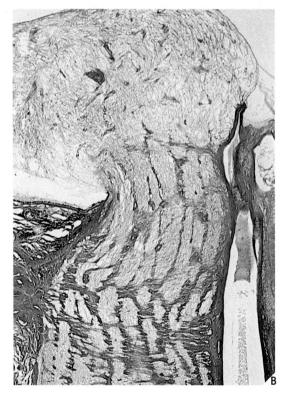

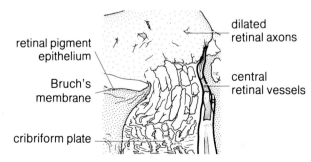

with a high-magnification lens) is usually necessary. When the presence of papilledema is difficult to determine, repeated examinations or serial stereoscopic optic disc photographs will usually give a definitive answer. Papilledema can be graded according to Frisén's scheme when photographs are not available.[102]

Visual acuity remains normal in patients with papilledema until the chronic condition leads to an associated axon death. Relative afferent pupillary defects occur in about 25% of patients. Contrast sensitivity testing reveals deficits in 50% to 75% of eyes tested.[103,104] In addition, contrast sensitivity and perimetry are the only measures shown to be sensitive to change.[101]

PERIMETRY

In a prospective study of patients with IIH, visual loss in at least one eye (other than enlargement of the physiologic blind spot) was found in 96% of patients with Goldmann perimetry and in 92% with threshold automated perimetry.[98] About one quarter of this visual loss is mild and is unlikely to be noticed by the patient; it serves as a marker for intervention. Patients particularly at risk for visual loss are those with marked recent weight gain[98] and black males.[105]

The visual field defects found in IIH are the same types as those reported to occur in papilledema resulting from other causes. These "disc-related" defects are similar to those found in glaucoma. The loss of visual

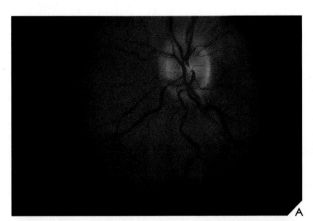

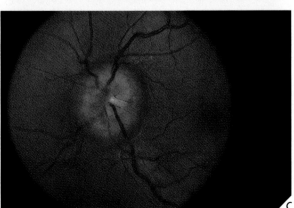

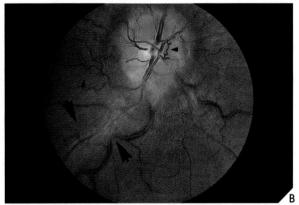

3.10 | Signs of early papilledema. *A:* Characteristic C-shaped halo with a temporal gap surrounding the disc of early papilledema (grade 1 papilledema).[102] *B:* Choroidal folds (large arrow) in a case of IIH. Disc edema obscures the peripapillary nerve fiber layer and some vessels as they leave the disc characteristic of grade 3 papilledema. An optociliary collateral vessel is present, signifying chronic papilledema (arrowhead). Also note the coarse peripapillary nerve fiber layer (between open arrows). *C:* The complete halo of edema surrounding the disc of grade 2 papilledema.

field may be progressive and severe, leading to blindness in about 10% of patients. Although the temporal profile of visual loss is usually gradual, acute and severe visual loss of the type seen in ischemic optic neuropathy can occur. The frequencies of the various defects are shown in Figure 3.11. A typical nasal step defect with Goldmann perimetry and corresponding automated visual field is shown in Figure 3.12.

Blind spot enlargement is ubiquitous in IIH. Because refraction often eliminates this defect, it should not be used to follow the course of therapy. Automated perimetry thresholds show generalized loss, most pronounced on the nasal side of the visual field on the initial examination. With improvement in papilledema there is generalized improvement, which is least in the central and inferior paracentral areas.[101] This reversibility of visual field loss in IIH is not widely appreciated.

3.11 | Goldmann perimetry compared with automated perimetry at the initial and final examinations. Sup Arc = Superior arcuate scotoma. Inf Arc = Inferior arcuate scotoma. Cecocentral = Cecocentral scotoma. Inf Nasal = Inferior nasal defect. Constrict = Visual field constriction.

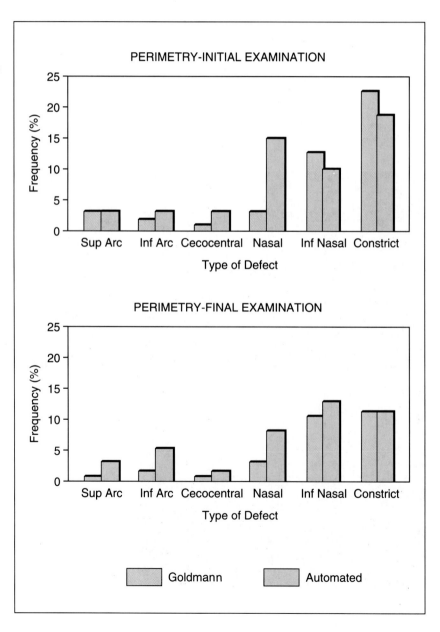

Figure 3.13 provides recommendations for evaluation of IIH patients. Corbett and Thompson correctly point out that IIH patients are often followed with the wrong tests.[106] Snellen acuity and the visual evoked response are insensitive tests to the visual loss of IIH. Measurement of cerebrospinal fluid pressure can be misleading, because CSF pressure fluctuates throughout the day and does not correlate well with the clinical state. Patients with IIH should be followed with perimetry utilizing a specified, reproducible, and sensitive strategy[98] and serial stereoscopic fundus photos or indirect ophthalmoscopy. Automated perimetry is used for attentive and motivated subjects; in others, manual (kinetic) perimetry should be used.

RECOMMENDATIONS FOR EVALUATION

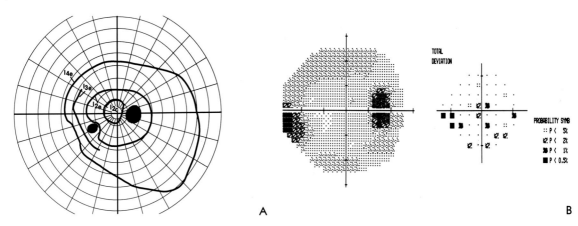

A   B

3.12 | *A:* A typical inferonasal step defect found on Goldmann perimetry.
B: Automated perimetry on the same day also shows this defect.

FIGURE 3.13. Evaluation of IIH

For diagnosis, be sure patient adheres to Dandy criteria
Rule out secondary causes
Blood tests: ESR, ANA, VDRL, FTA-Abs, T4,* TSH,* serum calcium and
   phosphorus, serum cortisol* and electrolytes, BUN and creatinine
Lumbar puncture: opening pressure, cell count, glucose, protein, VDRL
Neuroimaging: CT or MRI (cerebral angiography when venous sinus
   thrombosis is considered)
Manual perimetry with a disease-specific strategy or automated
   perimetry of the central 30°
Contrast sensitivity testing*
Stereoscopic fundus photography

*Optional

DIFFERENTIAL DIAGNOSIS

The differential diagnosis of patients with signs and symptoms of increased intracranial pressure that fulfil the criteria shown in Figure 3.6 is shown in Figure 3.14.[107] Many unlisted conditions are delineated by abnormalities of neuroimaging and CSF constituents. A number of associations such as pregnancy, irregular menses, oral contraceptive use, and use of many drugs have been found to occur with the same frequency in IIH patients as in the general population (chance associations) and are not included.[100,108,109]

FIGURE 3.14. Differential Diagnosis of IIH
(Cases Must Meet the Modified Dandy Criteria of IIH Except That a Cause Is Found)

HIGHLY LIKELY
Decreased flow through arachnoid granulations
    Scarring from previous inflammation, e.g.,
       meningitis, sequel to subarachnoid
       hemorrhage
Obstruction to venous drainage
    Venous sinus thrombosis
    Hypercoaguable states
    Contiguous infection (e.g., middle ear or
       mastoid, otitic hydrocephalus)
    Bilateral radical neck dissections
    Superior vena cava syndrome
Increased right heart pressure
Endocrine disorders
    Addison's disease
    Hypoparathyroidism
    Obesity
    Steroid withdrawal
Nutritional disorders
    Hypervitaminosis A (vitamin, liver, or
      isotretinoin intake)
    Hyperalimentation in deprivation dwarfism
Arteriovenous malformations

PROBABLE CAUSES
Anabolic steroids (may cause venous sinus
    thrombosis)
Kepone® (chlordecone)
Ketoprofen or indomethacin in Bartter's syndrome
Systemic lupus erythematosus
Thyroid replacement therapy in hypothyroid
    children
Uremia

POSSIBLE CAUSES
Amiodarone
Diphenylhydantoin
Iron-deficiency anemia
Lithium carbonate
Nalidixic acid
Sarcoidosis
Sulfa antibiotics

CAUSES FREQUENTLY CITED BUT UNPROVEN
Corticosteroid intake
Hyperthyroidism
Hypovitaminosis A
Menarche
Menstrual irregularities
Multivitamin intake
Oral contraceptive use
Pregnancy
Tetracycline use

(From Wall M: Idiopathic intercranial hypertension, in Breen L (ed): *Neurology Clinics of North America.* Vol 9. Philadelphia: WB Saunders, 1991.)

TREATMENT

Treatment strategies are listed in Figure 3.15 and are applicable to visual loss due to increased intracranial pressure regardless of the cause. Patient education about IIH, with an emphasis on blindness as a potential outcome, may provide the incentive to lose weight. Because in individual patients the symptoms and the degree of papilledema may not correlate with loss of visual function, treatment decisions must be made primarily on the basis of perimetric findings using a sensitive, disease-specific strategy (not a routine screening protocol).[98] The following case is illustrative:

A 22-year-old woman with headaches was found to have bilateral disc edema and was referred for further evaluation. On examination, visual acuity was 20/20 OU. A 0.6 log unit, left relative afferent pupillary defect was present. Motility examination was normal, as were contrast sensitivity and color testing. Visual field examination by automated perimetry showed some mild

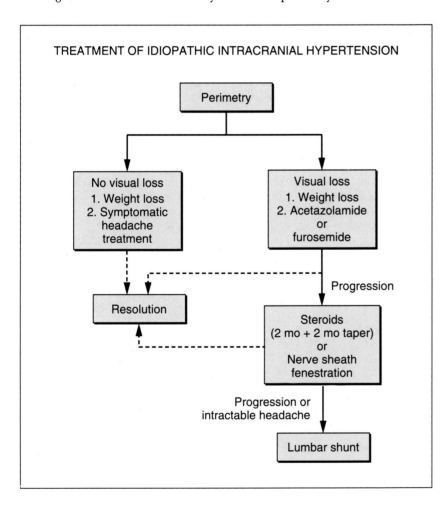

3.15 | Treatment algorithm for IIH. To determine the presence of visual loss, contrast sensitivity (if available) is added to perimetry. Visual loss does not include enlargement of the blind spot unless it is compromising vision. Optic nerve sheath fenestration is preferred over steroids. (Adapted from Wall M: Idiopathic intracranial hypertension, in Breen L (ed): *Neurology Clinics in North America.* Vol 9. Philadelphia: WB Saunders, 1991.)

diffuse loss in the left eye (Fig. 3.16A) as compared with the normal right eye (not shown). Her evaluation was otherwise normal except for an elevated opening pressure on lumbar puncture.

In spite of treatment with Diamox® 3 g/day, her vision gradually worsened in the left eye (Fig. 3.16B). Note the filled triangles on the far right plot marking loci of statistically significant worsening. A recommendation was made for an optic nerve sheath fenestration after the patient was repeatedly urged to lose weight. She refused surgery, lost 15 pounds, and had coincident improvement in her visual field which remained stable, as did her weight. Although she did not notice progressive visual loss, it was apparent on perimetry. As in glaucoma, the visual loss of IIH usually spares fixation and is often unnoticed by the patient. This underscores the need for serial perimetry with a sensitive strategy.

When a patient with IIH is losing vision despite maximal medical treatment, an optic nerve sheath fenestration is recommended.[110,111] Digre et al have reviewed treatment for the pregnant patient.[109]

OPTIC NEURITIS

Optic neuritis is a clinical syndrome of visual loss resulting from immunologically mediated inflammation of optic nerve myelin.[112] It is usually accompanied by pain, especially on eye movement, and may be associated with multiple sclerosis. Because it is a clinical diagnosis, it is a common source of diagnostic error.

EPIDEMIOLOGY

The age of onset is usually 20 to 50 years, with a mean of 30 years. About 60% of cases are women.[113]

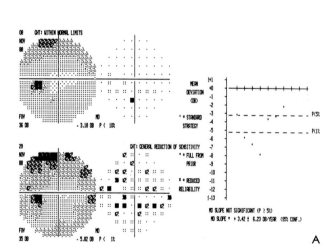

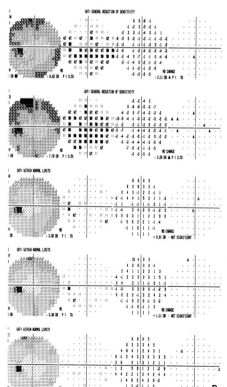

3.16 | A: Baseline fields for the Humphrey Statpac 2 glaucoma change analysis. B: Follow-up visual fields. Note the gradual worsening of the gray scale and related increase in number of abnormal test points on the total deviation probability plots (top two fields). This apparent change is found to be statistically significant in the change probability found on the far right. Although the patient did not notice progressive visual loss, it was present on perimetry and served as a marker for guiding therapy.

The acute pathologic response is inflammatory, with perivascular cuffing and infiltration of plasma cells and T-cells. This leads to formation of plaques in the pregeniculate sensory visual system.

PATHOLOGY

Patients usually present with unilateral visual loss that can be gradually progressive over about 2 weeks.[113,114] The visual loss is minimal to severe; it is often preceded or accompanied by sharp pain, especially with eye movement. The pain, which occurs in about 90% of patients, is probably due to stretching of the inflamed optic nerve sheath. Patients may complain of phosphenes (flashes of light that occur with eye movement or lid closure). Patients sometimes report worsening of their symptoms with elevated body temperature (Uhthoff's symptom).

SYMPTOMS

The optic disc may initially appear normal in about 65% of patients and is termed retrobulbar optic neuritis, or may be swollen in the remainder (termed papillitis). Snellen acuity is usually affected. If loss is greater than 20/200, the differential should include autoimmune optic neuritis.[115]

SIGNS

Perivenous sheathing is present in about 10% of cases of optic neuritis; it appears to be more common in cases associated with multiple sclerosis.[116] Arnold and associates have described histopathologic changes in eyes of patients with optic neuritis resulting from multiple sclerosis.[117] Four of 47 patients examined had lymphocytic or granulomatous retinal periphlebitis; focal lymphocytic or granulomatous retinitis was noted in three cases. Graham and colleagues have reported nine patients with multiple sclerosis with concomitant uveitis.[118] Iris nodules have also been associated with the uveitis associated with multiple sclerosis.[119] Because lupus and syphilis can mimic multiple sclerosis, these causes of uveitis should be ruled out in such patients.

In acute optic neuritis, the most common visual field defects detected by kinetic perimetry are multiple cecocentral and central scotomas and arcuate defects. Visual field defects are often not detectable with kinetic perimetry 6 months after onset. In contrast, with threshold static perimetry, loss in the mid-peripheral area (between 15 and 30 degrees of eccentricity), altitudinal defects and patchy generalized loss are present. The "uninvolved" eye may be mildly involved.[120]

Color and contrast sensitivity loss are ubiquitous and, unlike Snellen acuity, seldom return to normal. Relative afferent pupillary defects are the rule, and although they improve over time, they usually do not resolve. To look for a second lesion disseminated in time and space (to make a clinical diagnosis of multiple sclerosis), visual function tests are often performed on patients with resolved optic neuritis; these abnormalities are summarized in Figure 3.17.

Patients may complain of abnormalities of depth perception. This can be documented with the elliptical perception of a linearly swinging pendulum (Pulfrich pendulum test). This is caused by a relative delay in conduction through one optic nerve.

DIFFERENTIAL
DIAGNOSIS

Patients should have a characteristic clinical course and should fall into the appropriate age group. Unilateral disc edema in a patient over the age of 50 is usually caused by ischemic optic neuropathy; in most cases, there is not much improvement as the disc edema resolves. Expanding masses cause gradually progressive visual loss (Fig. 3.18). The presence of a macular star (neuroretinitis) is usually seen in children, and a history of an antecedent viral illness is often obtained; this disorder is not associated with multiple sclerosis.[121] Optic neuritis can occur with systemic infectious or inflammatory processes such as lupus or syphilis.

Although optic neuritis may be idiopathic, it is usually associated with multiple sclerosis. On the basis of a life table analysis, Rizzo and Lessell calculated that 74% of women and 34% of men with optic neuritis will develop multiple sclerosis within 15 years.[122] Others have reported a lower incidence of multiple sclerosis after isolated optic neuritis.[123–125] Less commonly, other infectious and inflammatory diseases such as lupus,[126] syphilis, Lyme borreliosis, and sarcoidosis can present as optic neuritis. Ethmoid and sphenoid sinus mucoceles, chromophobe adenomas, and other tumors can masquerade as optic neuritis.

Occasionally the clinical differentiation between optic neuritis and AION is difficult or impossible. Age under 50 years, pain with eye movements, lack of disk edema, gradually progressive course followed by significant improvement, are all suggestive of optic neuritis.

LABORATORY
FINDINGS

The cerebrospinal fluid may show findings of multiple sclerosis (low grade mononuclear pleocytosis, oligoclonal banding, and presence of myelin basic protein). The major positive peak of the visual evoked potential is characteristically prolonged, but this test is seldom necessary. MRI scans of the orbit performed with surface coils and special sequencing sometimes may show evidence of plaques in the optic nerve. Brain MRI may show high signal intensity lesions on the T_2-weighted images throughout the cerebral white matter. Unfortunately, this pattern is nonspecific. The diagnosis of multiple sclerosis is made by documenting two typical clinical central nervous system lesions that follow a characteristic course. The diagnosis is *not* based on spinal fluid or MRI results.

FIGURE 3.17. Prevalence of Persisting Abnormalities in *Resolved* Optic Neuritis with Normal or Near Normal Acuity

Perimetry 75%
Contrast sensitivity 75%
Optic disk changes 75%
F-M 100 hue 63%
VER >90%
Ishihara plates 34%
Relative afferent pupillary defect 92%

If the patient has an atypical presentation, a complete blood count, ESR, VDRL, FTA-Abs, and ANA are usually performed to screen for other inflammatory disorders. Neuroimaging may be done if there is no improvement after 3 weeks, to rule out a compressive etiology.

EVALUATION

The definitive study on which treatment is based was a national collaborative study, the Optic Neuritis Treatment Trial.[127] To be eligible for this study, the patient had to be between the ages of 18 and 46, have a history compatible with acute optic neuritis, and have visual symptoms lasting 8 days or less. In addition, patients were required to have a relative afferent pupillary defect and a visual field defect in the affected eye. The 497 patients were randomized to three groups: (a) oral prednisone, 1 mg/kg/day for 14 days; (b) intravenous methylprednisolone, 1 g/day in divided doses for 3 days followed by oral prednisone for 11 days; (c) placebo. There were no serious side effects in any of the groups.

TREATMENT

It was found that vision recovered faster in the intravenous methylprednisolone group and, in addition, this group had a slightly better visual outcome at 6 months. By one-year followup, no difference in visual outcome could be recognized. The visual outcome in the oral prednisone group did not differ from the placebo group, but the oral prednisone group had a significantly higher rate of new episodes of optic neuritis. Therefore, we do not recommend oral steroids for optic neuritis. Although the success of the methylprednisolone was mild, it was greatest in those with the poorest vision at time of onset, and can be considered for patients with vision of 20/200 or worse who require a rapid recovery.[127]

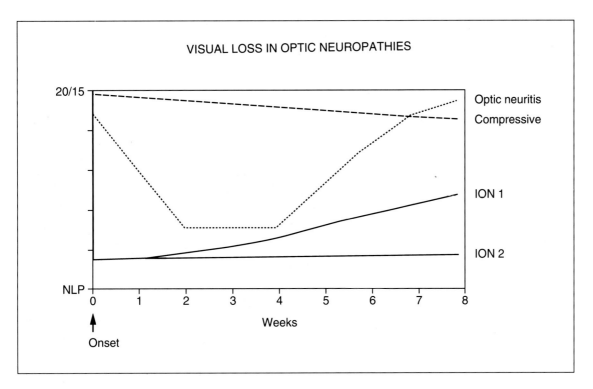

3.18 | Characteristic patterns of visual loss in optic neuropathies. (From Lessel S: Optic neuropathies. *N Engl J Med 1978;299:533–536.*) ION=ischemic optic neuropathy; ION 1=with some recovery; ION 2=without recovery.

Patients should be told that overheating may temporarily degrade and cooling may improve visual function and other demyelinating symptoms. Patients with distortion of moving objects can be fitted with a neutral-density contact lens to balance the luminance difference and the associated conduction delay. Finally, an occasional patient will see better in dim light than bright light. Tinted lenses may improve the quality of such patients' vision.

AUTOIMMUNE OPTIC NEURITIS

A minority of patients with optic neuritis have been categorized as having autoimmune optic neuritis.[115] The age range is 20 to 60 years. The disorder is so named because patients exhibit laboratory abnormalities typical of autoimmune diseases, such as positive antinuclear antibodies. Anticardiolipin antibodies may be present, and skin biopsies of non-sun-exposed skin processed with direct immunofluorescent staining may show immune complex deposition.[127]

In addition to the laboratory abnormalities, such patients may have visual acuity of worse than 20/200. Dramatic improvement after steroid therapy can occur with either intravenous or high dose oral corticosteroids. The disease tends to recrudesce when immunosuppressive therapy is withdrawn too soon.[128]

ANOMALIES OF THE OPTIC DISC
OPTIC DISC HYPOPLASIA

This anomaly has been reported to occur more commonly in males with a bilateral/unilateral ratio of about 1.5:1.[129] The optic disc is small and is usually surrounded by a yellow halo, the "double-ring sign" (Fig. 3.19); this sign is produced by retina and retinal pigment epithelium crossing the lamina cribrosa.[130] On histopathologic examination, there is loss of axons with normal glial tissue and collagen, suggesting a failure of differentiation of glial cells. However, it may also be the result of lesions at any level of the developing sensory nervous system.[131]

Vision may be normal or depressed. There is mild to moderate depression of the visual field; focal hypoplasia may be associated with various nerve fiber bundle defects.

Optic disc hypoplasia can be associated with septo-optic hypoplasia and cranial and intracranial midline anomalies (deMorsier's syndrome);

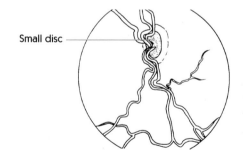

Small disc

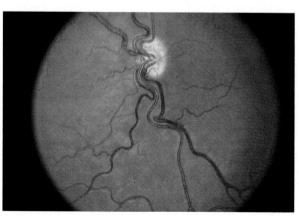

3.19 | Optic disc hypoplasia.

there may be associated neuroendocrine deficiencies that can be life threatening. Optic nerve hypoplasia is also commonly associated with the fetal alcohol syndrome,[132,133] and may occur in association with maternal diabetes mellitus.[134] Patients with optic nerve hypoplasia should undergo an endocrine evaluation and head neuroimaging studies (preferably MRI) to document associated anomalies so that these do not create diagnostic confusion at a later time.

MYELINATED NERVE FIBERS

Myelination of the optic nerve begins in the fetus near the chiasm at about the seventh month. Myelination ceases (usually at the lamina cribrosa) at about 1 month of age; myelination of the optic nerve is complete by about the tenth day after birth.[135] In about 0.5% of the population, myelination continues past the optic disc and into the nerve fiber layer of the retina, and appears as a congenital anomaly. It is more common in males than in females and is unilateral in about 75% of them. The opaque white fibers cover the underlying retinal layers (Fig. 3.20) and may produce a corresponding visual field defect. Myopia is present in about half the cases.[136]

COLOBOMAS, TILTED DISCS AND PITS

A coloboma is a congenital or acquired tissue defect of ocular development.[136] A variety of colobomatous disc anomalies occur subsequent to

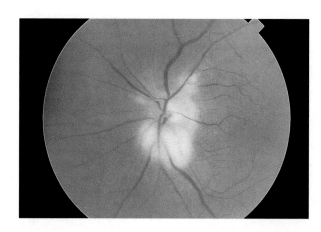

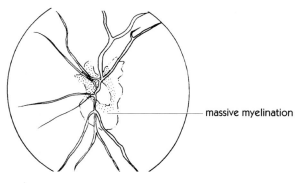

massive myelination

3.20 | Myelinated nerve fibers.

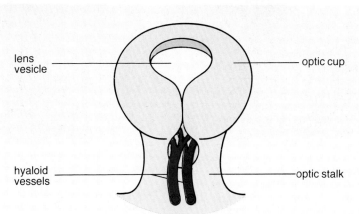

lens vesicle

optic cup

hyaloid vessels

optic stalk

3.21 | The fetal fissure of the optic cup closes inferiorly at about 6 weeks of gestation. The defects that occur produce a coloboma that lies inferiorly at the point where the fetal fissure usually closes. (From Spalton DJ, Sanders MD: The optic disc, in Spalton DJ, Hitchings RA, Hunter PA (eds): *Atlas of Clinical Ophthalmology.* London: Gower Medical Publishing, 1984, 17.3.)

abnormalities of invagination of the optic vesicle with incomplete closure of the embryonic ocular fissure (Fig. 3.21). Closure takes place inferiorly on the disc and neighboring retina so that these defects appear inferiorly. Figure 3.22 shows an optic nerve coloboma. Isolated optic nerve colobomas are rare. They are usually deeply excavated nerve head changes with blood vessels exiting from the margins.

A Fuchs coloboma is more common (1% to 2% of the population). This anomaly is classified as part of the tilted disc anomaly (nasal fundus ectasia syndrome) (Fig. 3.23): (a) tilted disc—the inferior pole of the disc is rotated temporally and the superior portion of the nerve may be elevated; (b) inferior conus or crescent (coloboma); (c) vessels exit temporally instead of nasally (situs inversus of the disc); and (d) posterior inferonasal staphyloma. Myopia with vertical astigmatism is commonly present. Associated visual loss is uncommon but may take the form of a relative bitemporal hemianopia that does not respect the vertical meridian.

Morning glory disc anomaly is another defect of closure of the embryonic optic fissure; it consists of a large coloboma of the optic nerve associated with anomalies of the retinal vessels, peripapillary retinal pigment epithelium changes, and glial proliferation (Fig. 3.24).[137] The optic nerve has a funnel-shaped excavation with a white center that obscures the central retinal vessels; a gray chorioretinal pigment disturbance surrounds the disc. It is usually unilateral, and associated Snellen acuity is worse than 20/200 in over 90% of patients. In addition, about one third of cases develop retinal detach-

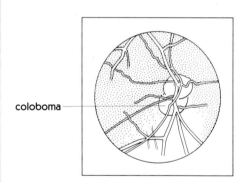

coloboma

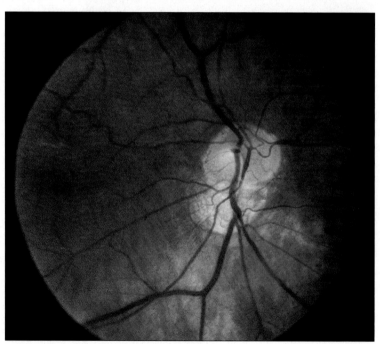

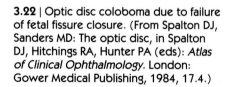

3.22 | Optic disc coloboma due to failure of fetal fissure closure. (From Spalton DJ, Sanders MD: The optic disc, in Spalton DJ, Hitchings RA, Hunter PA (eds): *Atlas of Clinical Ophthalmology.* London: Gower Medical Publishing, 1984, 17.4.)

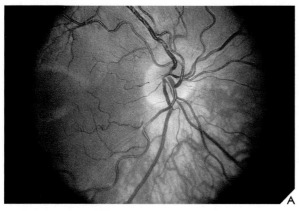

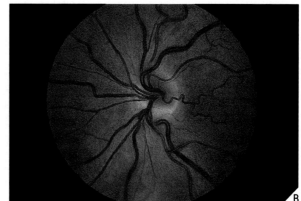

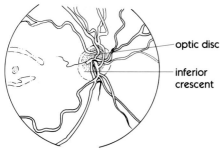

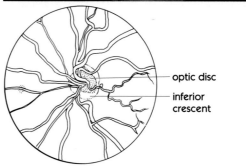

3.23 | *A,B:* Tilted disc anomaly (Fuchs coloboma). Note the disc tilt, inferior crescent (coloboma) and vessels emerging from the temporal rather than the nasal side of the disc. An associated staphyloma is present inferiorly.

In some cases, bitemporal visual field defects that do not respect the vertical midline may accompany this disc anomaly and cause diagnostic confusion.

3.24 | Morning glory disc anomaly. Note the white center and the peripapillary retinal pigment epithelial changes. (Photograph courtesy of Dr. Barrett Haik.)

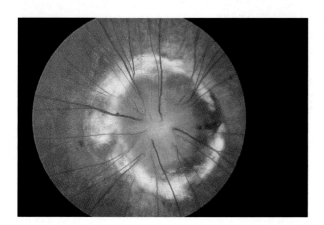

ments.[137] It is important to note the association of basal encephalocele with morning glory disc anomaly (and other colobomas), because failure to detect this anomaly can lead to inappropriate biopsy of brain and meninges.

Optic pits are small yellow or grayish excavations usually found on the inferior and temporal portion of the disc (Fig. 3.25). Some investigators believe that they are colobomas; this may be the case for inferiorly located pits. Retinal pigment epithelial changes and peripapillary chorioretinal atrophy are usually associated with non-centrally located pits. They are usually unilateral and rare. Many are associated with non-rhegmatogenous serous retinal detachment or cystic macular changes; these changes are usually found in association with large, temporally located pits. The longterm visual prognosis for untreated detachments is poor.[138]

ELEVATED CONGENITAL DISC ANOMALY (PSEUDOPAPILLEDEMA)

A congenitally elevated disc is commonly confused with acquired optic disc edema.[139] The disc is typically small and elevated, with a small or absent optic cup (Fig. 3.26). Vessels course through the center of the disc rather than taking the usual exit route nasally; they may be anomalous with frequent and early branching, yet they are easily seen as they climb over the edge of the disc's margin, and are not obscured, as they may be in true disc edema (see signs of papilledema, above). The appearance of this anomaly

3.25 | Optic pit. *A:* Pits are usually present on the inferior temporal portion of the disc. *B:* They may have an associated serous detachment of the macula. (From Spalton DJ, Sanders MD: The optic disc, in Spalton DJ, Hitchings RA, Hunter PA (eds): *Atlas of Clinical Ophthalmology.* London: Gower Medical Publishing, 1984, 17.5.)

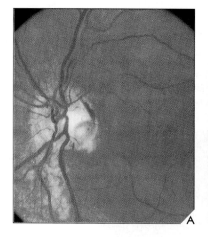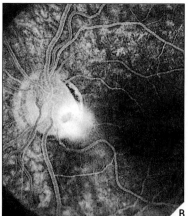

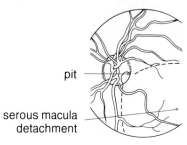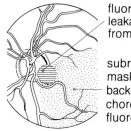

pit

serous macula detachment

fluorescein leakage from pit

subretinal fluid masking background choroidal fluorescence

may also be due to buried drusen; however, unlike the case with drusen, nerve fiber bundle defects do not occur.[140]

Another anomaly characterized by optic disc elevation is buried or extruded drusen.[141] Multiple crystalloid acellular refractile bodies may be embedded in the optic nerve (Fig. 3.27). The incidence in Denmark is 0.34%,[141] and in the post-mortem series of Friedman et al is 2%.[142] The anomaly is usually found in Caucasians. There may be associated visual loss with nerve fiber bundle defects that often spare the central 10 degrees. However, loss of visual acuity is uncommon.[143] As with any disc with a small or absent optic cup, there is an increased risk of ischemic optic neuropathy. Peripapillary subretinal or subpigment epithelial hemorrhage can occur, as can splinter hemorrhages into the substance of the disc.[144] Drusen can be confirmed by autofluorescence with fundus photography or characteristic findings on ultrasonogra-

OPTIC NERVE DRUSEN

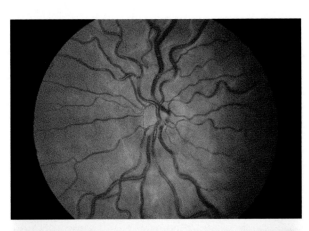

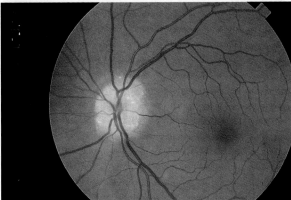

3.26 | Elevated congenital disc anomaly (pseudopapilledema). Note how the vessels pass through the center rather than at the nasal third of the disc and "climb" onto the disc. The small to absent optic cup is characteristic.

3.27 | Optic disc drusen. These refractile crystalloid bodies usually cause an irregularly bumpy, elevated appearance of the surface of the disc.

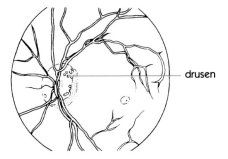

drusen

phy or computerized tomography, but these tests are usually not necessary. Optic disc drusen can result from longstanding disc edema or papilledema; in this case they are probably the result of chronically disturbed axoplasmic flow.

OPTIC DISC TUMORS

Tumors of the optic disc are rare.[145] The *melanocytoma* is a benign pigmented tumor (Fig. 3.28), although malignant conversion has been reported.[146] It is believed to be a specific type of nevus. About half of these tumors occur in blacks, and often a choroidal nevus is associated with the tumor. The tumor is usually asymptomatic and does not cause significant visual loss. Unlike the case with melanomas, fluorescein angiography shows hypofluorescence. Malignant degeneration is rare.

Astrocytic hamartomas of the optic disc usually occur in the setting of tuberous sclerosis (Fig. 3.29) or neurofibromatosis. About half of tuberous sclerosis cases exhibit these lesions. Although they usually occur on the optic disc, they can be present in the peripheral retina. They usually occur as an incidental finding and seldom grow to cause significant visual loss.

Hemangiomas may occur on the optic disc.[145] Capillary hemangiomas of the disc may be associated with cerebellar hemangioblastomas (von Hippel–Lindau disease). Because this disease is transmitted as an autosomal dom-

3.28 | Melanocytoma of the optic disc. (Photograph courtesy of Dr. Barrett Haik.)

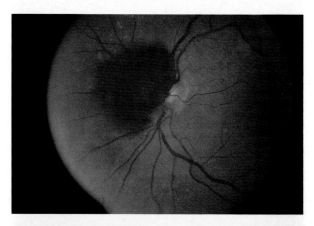

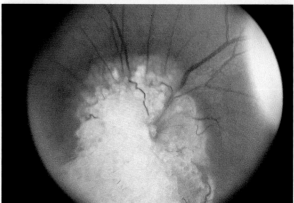

3.29 | Astrocytic hamartoma of the optic disc in a case of tuberous sclerosis. (Photograph courtesy of Dr. Barrett Haik.)

inant trait, family members should be examined. The rare cavernous hemangioma is a grape-like cluster of aneurysmal dilations. Progression or hemorrhage is uncommon. Racemose hemangiomas (more appropriately called arteriovenous malformations) of the disc are rare. In this lesion the involved retinal vessels enter and leave the globe through the optic disc. Their rapid flow with fluorescein angiography distinguishes the arteriovenous malformation from other hemangiomas. Wyburn and Mason reported their association with arteriovenous malformations of midbrain.[147]

Common tumors of the optic nerve are sheath meningioma and astrocytoma. Astrocytomas are of two types: juvenile pilocytic (optic nerve glioma) and malignant astrocytoma, usually of adulthood. Less common tumors include hemangioma, medulloepithelioma, and oligodendroglioma.

Optic nerve tumors are notoriously difficult to diagnose in their early growth phases. Knight and colleagues have described the syndrome of incipient prechiasmal optic nerve compression to elucidate this frequently missed presentation.[148] It consists of slowly progressive dimming of vision with normal or near-normal Snellen acuity. There is usually contrast sensitivity loss and dyschromatopsia. A relative afferent pupillary defect is usually present, and the optic nerve head often appears normal. Perimetry may disclose subtle and nondescript visual field defects which are also progressive. Adequate quality neuroimaging is the key to diagnosis.

OPTIC NERVE TUMORS

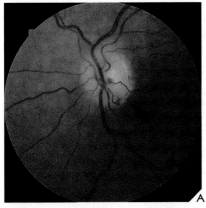
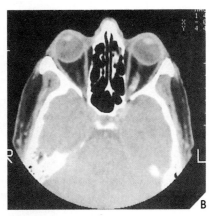
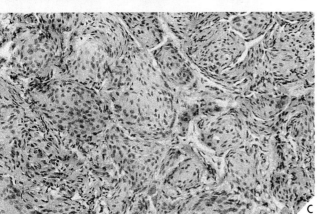

3.30 | Optic nerve sheath meningioma. *A:* The optic disc, as in this case, is characteristically pale, elevated, and has an optociliary collateral vessel (arrow). *B:* CT scan of the same patient shows the "tram track" sign of calcification of the optic nerve sheath. *C:* A biopsy of another case shows a proliferation of meningothelial cells. As is often the case, no psammoma bodies are present. (*C,* from Yanoff M, Fine BS: *Ocular Pathology: A Color Atlas,* ed. 2. New York: Gower Medical Publishing, 1992, 13.8.)

PRIMARY OPTIC NERVE SHEATH MENINGIOMA

One of the most common tumors that presents with the syndrome of incipient prechiasmal optic nerve compression is the optic nerve sheath meningioma.[149] These tumors are more common in women, and their growth rate may accelerate during pregnancy (progesterone and estrogen receptors have been found in cerebral meningiomas).[150] Early in the course, the optic disc may appear normal or mildly elevated. Later, the disc may be swollen, pale, and may have optociliary collateral vessels (Fig. 3.30A). The triad of optic atrophy, visual loss, and optociliary collateral vessels is most often due to a primary optic nerve sheath meningioma.

When primary optic nerve sheath meningioma is suspected, computerized tomography will usually demonstrate the tumor. Calcification within the sheath gives the characteristic "tram track" appearance on computerized tomography (Fig. 3.30B). Hyperostosis of adjacent bone may be present. To evaluate the optic nerve within the optic canal, however, MRI scanning with gadolinium is the procedure of choice.[151] Tumors in the optic canal that are not apparent on CT scan can be demonstrated with MRI. Tumor growth into the canal is important, as it signals potential intracranial spread. Tumors that

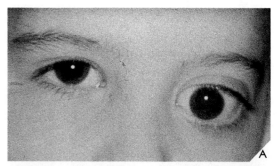

3.31 | Optic nerve glioma. *A:* The patient has proptosis of the left eye caused by a glioma of the optic nerve. Most of the time the proptosis is in a downward and outward direction. *B:* The CT scan of this case shows the glioma enlarging the retrobulbar nerve. *C:* Increased magnification shows enlarged neural bundles between the spread-out pial septa. The neural bundles contain expanded, disordered glial cells and a few axons. (From Yanoff M, Fine BS: *Ocular Pathology: A Color Atlas,* ed. 2. New York: Gower Medical Publishing, 1992, 13.7, 13.8.)

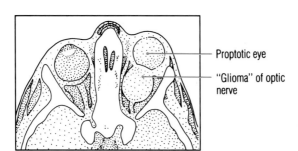

— Proptotic eye

— "Glioma" of optic nerve

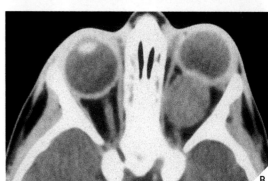

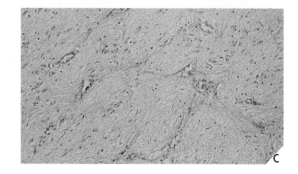

exhibit aggressive growth patterns should be biopsied to be certain of the diagnosis.

The treatment for primary optic nerve sheath meningiomas is controversial. Because the tumor usually is so highly integrated with the blood supply to the optic nerve, surgical removal is usually accompanied by a profound visual loss. Radiotherapy may be beneficial in some cases. In most cases, the patient should be followed at 6-month intervals and should be made aware of the possibility of radiation therapy as progressive visual loss ensues. Surgery is reserved for disfiguring proptosis in an eye with poor vision, or to prevent intracranial extension.[152]

Secondary optic nerve sheath meningiomas arise intracranially and extend into the optic canal. In addition to optic nerve compression, there may be involvement of I, III, IV, V_1, and VI cranial nerves.

OPTIC NERVE GLIOMAS

Optic nerve gliomas comprise a heterogeneous group, and are more benign in children than in adults. With the childhood form, about one quarter of patients have associated neurofibromatosis. Patients usually present with progressive proptosis and visual loss (Fig. 3.31). Children may present with monocular nystagmus and may be misdiagnosed as having spasmus nutans.[153] The tumor may be bilateral and may also involve the optic chiasm. MRI shows double-intensity tubular thickening characteristic of perineural gliomatosis, elongation of the nerves, and downward kinking of the optic nerve in the orbit. Optic nerve gliomas may be found incidentally. There is evidence that many of these tumors in children behave in a benign, self-limited fashion[154,155]; however, death from hypothalamic involvement, surgery on the tumor, or other related problems in the neurofibromatosis patient is not uncommon.[156] Alvord and Lofton reviewed 623 reported cases in adults and children with a life table analysis and concluded that there is a continuous broad spectrum of growth rates from rapid to slow.[157] Like Hoyt and Baghdassarian,[154] they found that tumors confined to the orbit and optic nerve have a good prognosis in patients under age 20.

As with optic nerve sheath meningiomas, treatment is controversial.[158] Although most childhood tumors follow a benign course, more aggressive behavior has been reported. Therefore, treatment must be individualized on the basis of serial clinical examinations, perimetry, and neuroimaging until the growth pattern of the individual patient is established. The patient is then followed until there is no useful vision present in the eye or until neuroimaging demonstrates tumor beginning to grow intracranially.[159] Surgical removal is then considered. Chemotherapy appears to be useful initially for aggressive hypothalamic gliomas[160]; radiation therapy should be delayed, if possible, because of adverse long-term effects such as lowering of the IQ.

The optic pathway glioma of adults acts more like a glioblastoma.[161] It occurs in patients of middle age or older, and usually affects the chiasm. Patients present with a rapid onset of visual loss, occasionally with disc edema; this may lead to an erroneous diagnosis of optic neuritis, especially when steroids are used and result in mild initial improvement. The visual loss progresses over weeks to blindness, and the tumor may be fatal within months. Neuroimaging shows a suprasellar mass with edema or enhancement along the optic tract. Radiation therapy may be helpful.[162]

DYSTHYROID OPTIC NEUROPATHY

The optic neuropathy of Graves' disease is caused by compression of the optic nerve in the posterior orbit; in a series from an orbital clinic, of 675 patients with Graves' orbitopathy, 8.6% had optic neuropathy.[161] Although uncommon, the optic neuropathy of Graves' disease causes disabling visual loss and is both preventable and treatable. Feldon et al have determined that the amount of limitation of lateral gaze is an important risk factor for visual loss.[162] This finding indicates a posterior orbit with little space for the optic nerve (Fig. 3.32).

Graves' ophthalmopathy is the most common cause of unilateral or bilateral proptosis. The enlarged extraocular muscles are inflamed and infiltrated with mucopolysaccharides that results in edema and fibrosis. Symptoms usually progress over about 1 year and seldom for more than 2 years.

It is commonly taught that Graves' patients can be followed with only visual acuity testing. In our experience, this is an insensitive way to follow these patients, because there may be generalized depression of the visual field and various nerve fiber bundle defects in the face of normal acuity. Color and contrast sensitivity testing may aid in early diagnosis of visual loss.[163] In addition to the deficits on visual function testing, some patients exhibit bilateral disc edema from the compressive optic neuropathy, which also can be followed over time.

Patients with optic neuropathy are usually treated initially with a 2-week course of high-dose corticosteroids. If no improvement occurs, surgical decompression by various routes is recommended. Orbital irradiation is also a therapeutic option in some cases.

3.32 | CT scan of the orbit of a patient with Graves' disease shows markedly enlarged extraocular muscles with compression of the optic nerve.

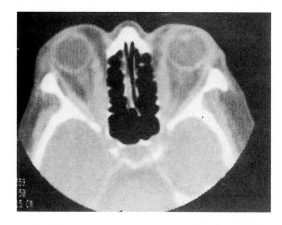

4 | Chiasm, Parachiasmal Syndromes, Retrochiasm, and Disorders of Higher Visual Function

Nancy J. Newman

The clinical practice of neurology and neuro-ophthalmology has been described as "applied neuroanatomy." Nowhere is that more apparent than in patients with chiasmal and retrochiasmal disorders of visual function. Symptoms and signs, in particular those related to visual fields, can exquisitely localize a lesion within the brain. The location, in turn, helps to determine the underlying disease process. Modern neuroimaging routinely confirms previous clinicopathologic correlation but occasionally challenges long-held tenets of neuroanatomic and neurophysiologic design.

CHIASMAL AND PARACHIASMAL ABNORMALITIES
SYMPTOMS AND SIGNS

Lesions of the chiasm or the parachiasmal region may cause symptoms and signs by involvement of the chiasm itself or of its blood supply, by disruption of the function of the many neighboring structures, or by production of a hormonal imbalance. This is a direct reflection of the local anatomy (Fig. 4.1). Symptoms and signs can be divided into those related to loss of vision and visual field (from chiasm and optic nerve dysfunction), disorders of ocular motility, pupillary function, and facial sensation (from involvement of cranial nerves III, IV, VI, the oculosympathetics, and the first two divisions of V), abnormalities of cerebrospinal fluid drainage (from local blockage of normal CSF outflow), and abnormalities of endocrine function (from inappropriate secretion or disruption of the hypothalmus–pituitary axis) (Fig. 4.2).

As long as central acuity remains spared in at least one eye, a patient with a lesion of the chiasm may not be aware of any deficit. The first symptom of a chiasmal field defect in such a case might be a problem with an activity of daily living reflecting the unrecognized deficit, such as negotiating the curb when parking. Other patients may recognize peripheral or central visual loss, either unilateral or bilateral. If a complete bitemporal hemianopia is present, a patient may complain of difficulties with depth perception, especially during reading or performance of other near tasks. This is a reflection of the blind field of vision beyond the object of focus that will necessarily exist in this setting[1,2] (Fig. 4.3). Similarly, with a complete bitemporal hemianopia there are no corresponding retinal points to visually link the two remaining hemifields of the two eyes. If the eyes have a tendency to become misaligned, the nasal fields may separate verti-

4.1 | *A*: Anatomy of the ocular motor pathways. The medial section of the cavernous sinus is shown. *B*: Anatomy of the chiasm, sagittal view. Note the relationship of the chiasm to the pituitary gland. (From Spalton DJ: Neuro-ophthalmology, in Spalton DJ, Hitchings RA, Hunter PA: *Atlas of Clinical Ophthalmology*. London: Gower Medical Publishing, 1984, 19.6, 19.19.)

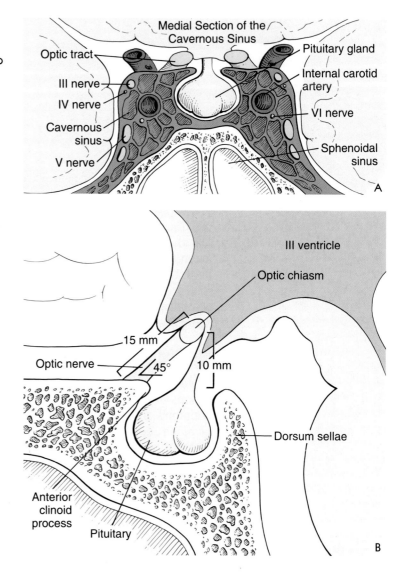

FIGURE 4.2. Symptoms and Signs of Lesions of the Chiasm and Parachiasmal Region

Chiasm, Optic Nerves or Tracts
  Visual acuity loss
  Visual field abnormalities

Cavernous Sinus Structures
  Ocular motor nerves
    Diplopia
    Ptosis
    Anisocoria
    Accommodative insufficiency
    Ocular malalignment
  Trigeminal nerve
    Numbness
    Pain
  Oculosympathetics
    Horner syndrome

Ventricular Obstruction
  Headache
  Somnolence
  Urinary incontinence
  Gait disturbance
  Vertical gaze disturbance
  Pupillary light–near
    dissociation
  Papilledema

Hypothalmus-Pituitary Axis
  Behavior/mentation changes
  Lethargy
  Urinary frequency
  Diabetes insipidus
  Amenorrhea
  Galactorrhea
  Heat or cold intolerance
  Precocious or delayed puberty
  Decreased libido
  Acromegaly
  Abnormal growth

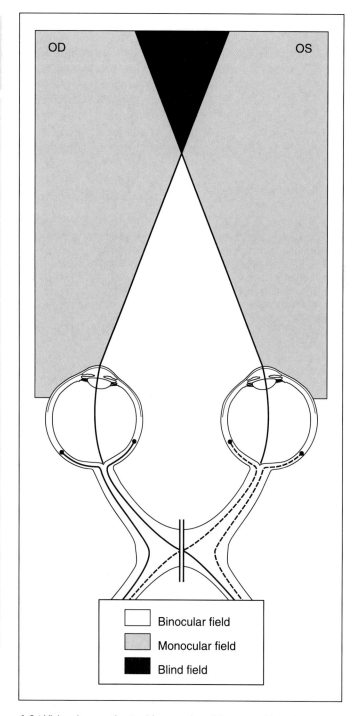

OD   OS

☐ Binocular field
▨ Monocular field
■ Blind field

4.3 | Vision in a patient with complete bitemporal hemianopia. There is a triangular area of blind field beyond the point of fixation. These patients have binocular vision in a triangular area in front of fixation and monocular vision in the remainder of each eye's nasal hemifield.

cally, horizontally, or may overlap (Fig. 4.4). The patient may report this phenomenon as "double vision" and it has been termed "hemifield slide."[1,2]

Involvement of the cavernous sinus or the superior orbital fissure may lead to complaints of diplopia, ptosis, unequally sized pupils, accommodative difficulty, facial pain or numbness, or eye pain. Lesions in the parachiasmal region that cause local compression and blockage of normal cerebrospinal fluid circulation may result in headache, gait difficulties, somnolence, and eventually urinary incontinence. Involvement of the adjacent hypothalamus can cause behavioral changes, lethargy, and urinary frequency. Symptoms of endocrine excess or insufficiency include amenorrhea, galactorrhea, heat or cold intolerance, precocious or delayed puberty, changes in shoe, glove, or ring size, decreased libido, and fatigue.

4.4 | Diagram of the "hemifield slide" phenomenon that can occur in patients with bitemporal hemianopia. If the patients have a preexisting exophoria, hyperphoria, or esophoria, the intact nasal fields may overlap, vertically separate, or horizontally separate, respectively. This may be reported as "double vision." (Adapted from Miller NR: Topical diagnosis of lesions in the visual sensory pathway, in *Walsh and Hoyt's Clinical Neuro-Opthalmology*, ed 4, Vol. 1. Baltimore: Williams & Wilkins, 1982, 124.)

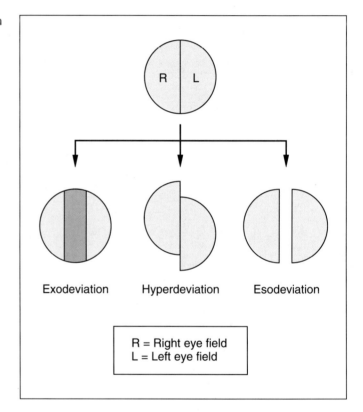

Exodeviation   Hyperdeviation   Esodeviation

R = Right eye field
L = Left eye field

FIGURE 4.5. Chiasmal Lesions

DETERMINANTS OF VISUAL FIELD LOSS PATTERN

Location of chiasm in relation to parachiasmal structures
Arrangement of fibers within anterior visual pathways
Nature of pathologic process

Subsequent findings on examination should also point to the part of the regional anatomy that is affected. Visual fields provide the most sensitive indication of direct chiasmal involvement. The location of the chiasm in relation to the other parachiasmal structures, the arrangement of the fibers within the anterior visual pathways, and the nature of the pathologic process responsible for the chiasmal damage all determine the specific pattern of field loss (Fig. 4.5). The chiasm usually lies directly above the pituitary fossa, but anatomic variants termed "prefixed" and "postfixed" consist of a more anteriorly or posteriorly located decussation of fibers, respectively.[3,4] Involvement of the anterior angle of the chiasm and an optic nerve may result in central defects ipsilaterally and a so-called "junctional scotoma" contralaterally, secondary to damage to Wilbrand's knee[4] (Fig. 4.6). If the body of the chiasm is involved, relative or absolute bitemporal defects may be demonstrated (Fig.

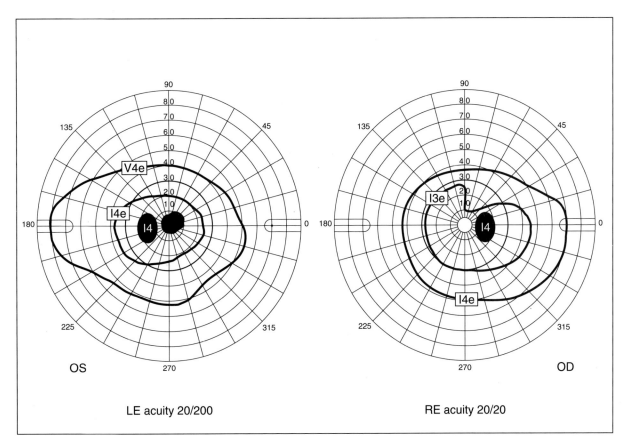

4.6 | Goldmann visual fields of a patient with multiple sclerosis and a "junctional scotoma." Note the central involvement in the left eye resulting in poor visual acuity and the superior temporal defect in the right eye corresponding to damage to the inferonasal fibers in Wilbrand's knee. This visual field defect localizes to the left optic nerve posteriorly at the anterior angle of the chiasm.

4.7). Since the majority of axons within the chiasm are projections from the macular region, early central involvement of visual fields, i.e., hemianopic scotomas, is quite common.[6-11] This may assume the pattern of bitemporal hemianopic scotomas, especially if the crossing macular fibers are initially affected (Fig. 4.8). Because the fibers in the chiasm are the axons of retinal

4.7 | Automated visual fields of a patient with pituitary tumor and bitemporal hemianopia from chiasm involvement. Note superior field loss (greater than inferior) bilaterally.

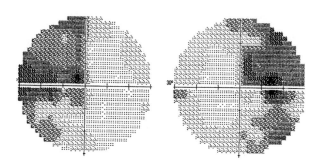

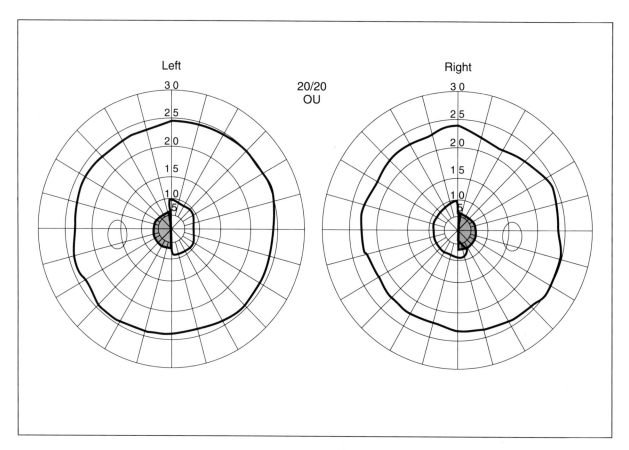

4.8 | Tangent screen visual fields of a patient with bitemporal hemianopic scotomas. This reflects early involvement of the crossing macular fibers in the chiasm.

(Adapted from Glaser JS: Topical diagnosis: The optic chiasm, in Tasman W, Jaeger EA (eds): *Duane's Clinical Ophthalmology,* Vol 2. Philadelphia: JB Lippincott, 1991, 4.)

ganglion cells, another sign of prolonged direct chiasmal involvement is optic atrophy. There may be defects in the nerve fiber layer, temporal pallor of the nerve head, or, if there is a complete bitemporal hemianopia, "band" or "bowtie" atrophy.[12] The classic pattern of bowtie atrophy results from dropout of nasal retinal fibers, both those nasal to the disc and those temporal to the disc that subserve the nasal macula (Fig. 4.9). Its presence should suggest chiasmal damage that has been present for at least 6 weeks and which will probably be permanent. The rare phenomenon of congenital seesaw nystagmus is manifested by each eye alternately rising and intorting and depressing and extorting. The acquired form of seesaw nystagmus is associated with parachiasmal lesions and does not have a torsional component.[13–15]

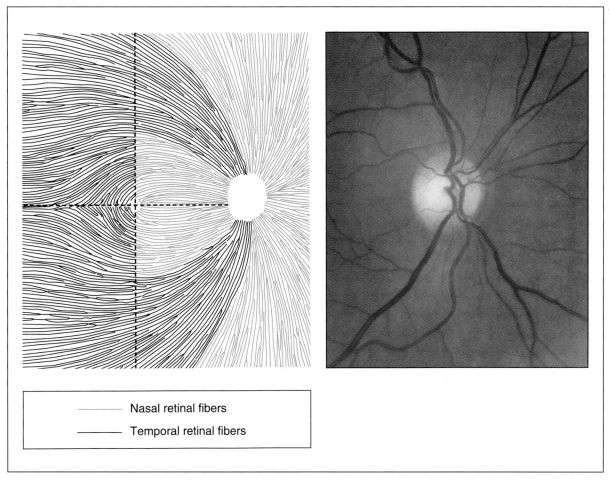

Nasal retinal fibers

Temporal retinal fibers

4.9 | With chiasmal compression for greater than 6 weeks, a pattern of "bowtie" atrophy may occur. The nasal retinal fibers, subserving the temporal hemifield of vision, enter the disc in the pattern shown on the left. Because the nasal retinal fibers are defined by those fibers nasal to the fovea, nasal retinal fibers will include those originating nasal to the disc and those originating temporal to the disc but nasal to the fovea. With long-standing chiasmal compression, the nasal retinal fibers become atrophic and pallor may be seen in a pattern corresponding to the location of these fibers on the disc.

Signs reflecting involvement of parachiasmal structures include palsies of the ocular motor nerves, decreased sensation in the areas innervated by the first or second divisions of the trigeminal nerve, and oculosympathetic paresis (Horner syndrome). When CFS obstruction is present, there may be findings associated with hydrocephalus, such as disturbances of vertical gaze, pupillary light–near dissociation, papilledema, or disorders of gait. Hypothalamic involvement may result in diabetes insipidus or abnormal body habitus. Signs of endocrine dysfunction include acromegaly, abnormal patterns of growth or sexual maturation, galactorrhea, amenorrhea, loss of libido, and infertility.

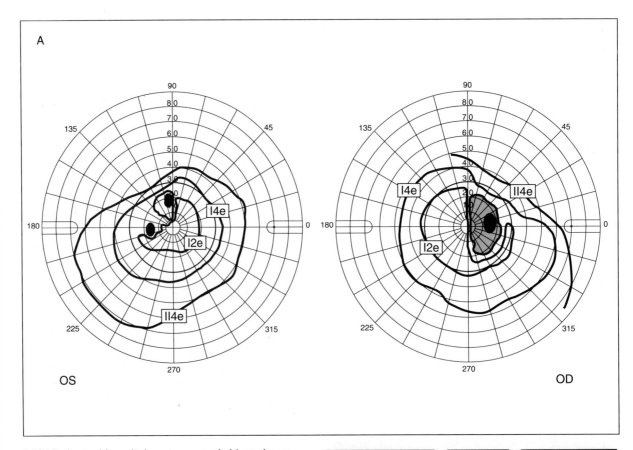

4.10 | Patient with a pituitary tumor and chiasmal compression. *A*: Goldmann visual fields demonstrate superobitemporal defects suggestive of compression from below. *B*: Coronal T1-weighted MRI after the administration of gadolinium shows a large enhancing pituitary tumor compressing the chiasm.

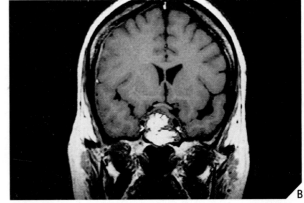

A variety of pathologic processes can occur in this region and can result in a chiasmal syndrome. The most common cause of chiasmal dysfunction is the pituitary adenoma.[16] Because these tumors are characteristically histologically benign, their growth is slow and the progression of their compressive visual defects is also slow. With the possible exception of acromegaly, endocrinologically active tumors will probably present with systemic signs and symptoms before they achieve a size that can cause compressive visual field defects. Nevertheless, in the largest reported series of pituitary tumors, 70% of the patients had visual field defects on initial evaluation which could be ascribed to compression by tumor.[17,18] Because the tumor expands from below the chiasm, the majority of field defects are superobitemporal in configuration (Fig. 4.10). Less frequently, lateral extension of the adenoma into the cavernous sinus occurs, with consequent involvement of cranial nerves III, IV, V, or VI. This may occur with pituitary apoplexy, in which there is a sudden expansion of an adenoma, usually as a result of tumor hemorrhage or infarction[19-23] (Fig. 4.11). Multiple cranial nerve involvement should suggest more invasive malignant tumors.[24]

A prominent cause of chiasmal visual loss in children and young adults is the craniopharyngioma.[25,26] This histologically benign tumor is believed to arise from embryonic tissue remnants of Rathke's pouch between the anterior and posterior lobes of the pituitary. Craniopharyngiomas are frequently cystic. They are difficult to completely remove surgically, and attempts at removing adhering tissue from the visual structures can lead to permanent visual loss, presumably by compromising the blood supply. Cystic reaccumulation of fluid commonly results in recurrent chiasmal compression and con-

CAUSES OF CHIASMAL SYNDROME

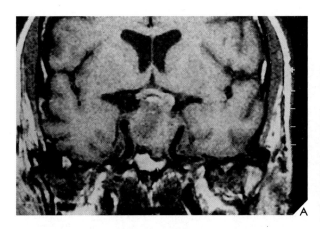

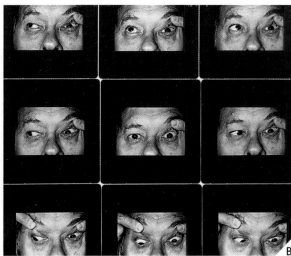

4.11 | Patient with pituitary apoplexy. *A:* T1-weighted coronal MRI reveals a large pituitary tumor with hypointense areas suggestive of previous hemorrhage. The tumor is extending into the left cavernous sinus. *B:* Photographs of the patient looking in the nine cardinal positions of gaze. He has complete left ptosis and limitation of eye movement on the left in all fields of gaze, consistent with damage to the left III, IV, and VI cranial nerves.

sequent visual loss (Fig. 4.12). Meningiomas of the tuberculum sellae or planum sphenoidale can also cause significant visual loss secondary to chiasmal damage.[27] Intrinsic gliomas of the optic chiasm in children tend to be histologically benign and slow-growing, often causing remarkably minimal amounts of visual field loss[28,29] (Fig. 4.13). In adults, these tumors are more malignant.[30,31]

Other compressive causes of the chiasmal syndrome include metastatic disease,[32] nasopharyngeal carcinoma,[33] chordomas,[34] dysgerminomas,[34] aneurysms,[35] dolichoectatic vessels,[36] arteriovenous malformations,[37] hemangiomas,[38] arachnoid cysts,[33-39] abscesses[40-41] and sphenoid sinus mucoceles.[42,43] Inflammatory causes include sarcoid,[44,45] syphilis,[33] other granulomatous diseases, and arachnoiditis.[46,47] Although rare, infarction of the chiasm may occur and has been linked to systemic arteritis.[48] Other causes of the chiasmal syndrome include trauma,[49] demyelinating disease,[50-52] toxins,[53] and delayed radiation necrosis.[54] The chiasm may "prolapse" into an empty sella[55,56] or may be compressed by a dilated third ventricle in the setting of hydrocephalus.[57] Rarely, congenital anomalies occur in the chiasmal region.[58]

EVALUATION AND MANAGEMENT

The patient with symptoms or signs referrable to the region of the optic chiasm needs prompt neuroimaging. Although high-resolution computed tomography can provide direct axial and coronal views and important information regarding the presence of calcification or adjacent bone abnormalities, magnetic resonance imaging is usually a better modality if available. With the use of an intravenous contrast agent, even lesions isointense with normal structures will be demonstrated (Fig. 4.14). Cerebral arteriography may be necessary to further characterize or delineate mass lesions and their blood supply. Referral for complete endocrinologic evaluation is also indicated.

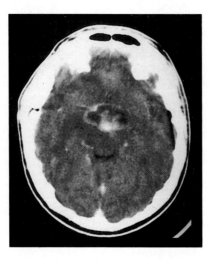

4.12 | Craniopharyngioma. Axial CT scan with contrast shows an enhancing suprasellar mass lesion with a cystic component.

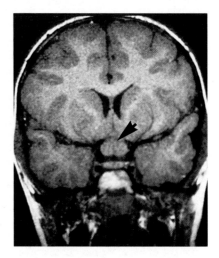

4.13 | Chiasmal glioma. T1-weighted coronal MRI reveals enlargement of the chiasm (arrow).

Obviously, appropriate management depends on the causes of the chiasmal syndrome. When a pituitary adenoma is causing symptoms or signs by involvement of adjacent structures or by abnormal secretory function, surgical removal is usually indicated, frequently by the transsphenoidal approach.[59,60] Exceptions include tumors that secrete prolactin and are therefore potentially responsive to bromocriptine and other dopamine agonists. Oral bromocriptine has been used to treat pituitary macro- and microadenomas with good results.[61-66] Other types of tumors can be surgically removed or radiated. The amount of visual field recovery to be expected after treatment depends on the extent of pretreatment involvement and its chronicity. As a general rule, the anterior visual pathways are quite resilient. If little or no optic atrophy has developed, the prognosis for recovery of visual field is excellent.

If a tumor is partially removed or the patient is to be treated with bromocriptine, vigorous attention to subsequent visual function, particularly visual fields, must be maintained. Suggested intervals for serial examinations vary among authors and should be determined by the individual patient's clinical setting and the concerns about recurrence.

When the retrochiasmal visual pathway is completely interrupted anywhere along its course, the result is a complete homonymous hemianopia. In and of itself this is of little localizing value. Typical patterns of visual field loss and accompanying neurologic abnormalities, however, help to determine whether a lesion has occurred in the optic tract, lateral geniculate body, optic radiations, or striate cortex.

The proximity of the optic tract to the chiasm and optic nerves makes mixed syndromes common. Therefore, symptoms and signs of optic tract disease may be overshadowed by concurrent ipsilateral optic nerve involvement with central visual loss.[67,68] When the lesion is clearly affecting only the retrochiasmal tract, visual acuity should be normal and incongruity of

RETROCHIASMAL LESIONS AND DISORDERS OF HIGHER VISUAL FUNCTION
SYMPTOMS AND SIGNS

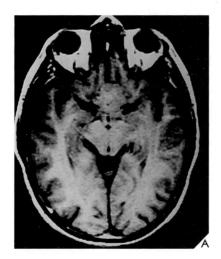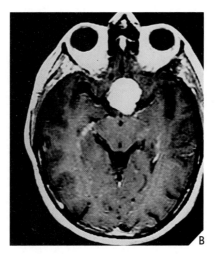

4.14 | Suprasellar meningioma. T1-weighted axial MRIs show a suprasellar mass that is isointense with brain (*A*), but which enhances brightly (*B*) after the administration of gadolinium.

the visual fields is likely[69] (Fig. 4.15). Pupillary findings may help localize a lesion to the optic tract. When the lesion occurs anterior to the exit of afferent pupillary fibers in the brachium of the superior colliculus, a relative afferent pupillary defect will be measurable contralateral to the involved tract.[70–72] This is a direct reflection of the normal anatomy in which the tract contains more crossed than uncrossed fibers (the nasal hemiretina is larger than the temporal hemiretina). Therefore, in an optic tract lesion the contralateral eye has suffered relatively more axonal damage. If the tract abnormality has been present for at least 6 weeks, optic atrophy and/or loss of nerve fiber layer should be discernible. The pattern of atrophy will reflect temporal hemiretinal loss ipsilaterally and nasal hemiretinal loss contralaterally, i.e., temporal pallor and bowtie atrophy, respectively[12] (see Fig. 4.9). Other symptoms and signs encountered with optic tract lesions reflect involvement of neighboring neural structures and include headache, abnormalities of mentation, hypothalamic dysfunction, and contralateral hemiparesis.

Lesions that involve the lateral geniculate body can also produce highly incongruous visual fields and a hemianopic or sectorial pattern of optic atrophy.[73,74] Some very congruous fields have also been reported,

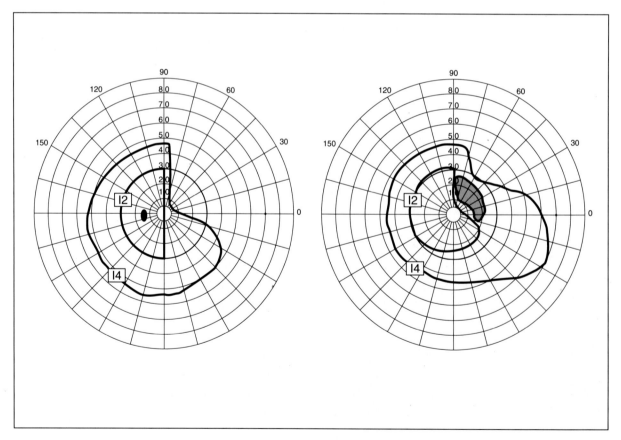

4.15 | Goldmann visual fields demonstrate incongruous, right homonymous field defects consistent with damage to the left optic tract. (Adapted from Lesell S, Lesell IM, Glaser JS: Topical diagnosis: Retrochiasmal visual pathways and higher cortical function, in Tasman W, Jaeger EA (eds): *Duane's Clinical Ophthalmology*, Vol 2, 1991, 3.)

specifically after vascular occlusion in this region.[75,76] Because geniculate lesions do not involve the afferent pupillary fibers, the pupillary abnormalities so notable in tract disorders are not demonstrable. Contralateral hemiparesis and contralateral hemisensory loss or pain reflect involvement of the adjacent pyramidal tract and thalamus, respectively.

An incongruous homonymous superior wedge defect localizes a lesion to the optic radiations in the contralateral temporal lobe. The extent of the defects and the degree of congruity varies, but superior field loss and greater congruity than that seen with tract lesions is the rule[77-80] (Fig. 4.16). Associated symptoms and signs in this region include convulsions, complex partial seizures, and disorders of language.

The more posterior the involvement of the optic radiations, the more congruous the visual field defects. Parietal lobe lesions can produce complete macular splitting homonymous hemianopias, or there may be a predilection

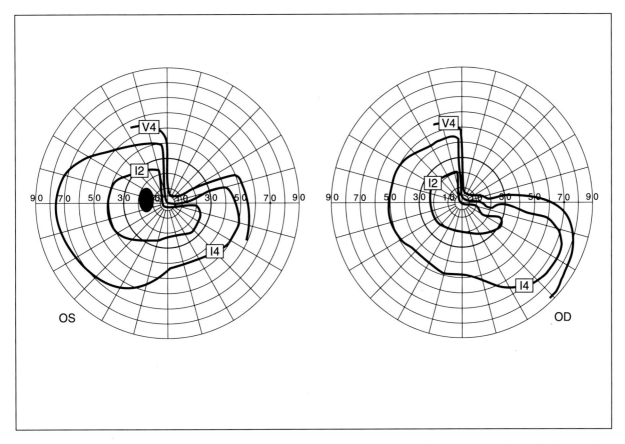

4.16 | Goldmann visual fields reveal a right homonymous superior wedge defect, localizing the lesion to the optic radiations in the left temporal lobe. Note that there is some incongruity, but not as great as that seen with optic tract lesions. (Adapted from Miller NR: Topical diagnosis of lesions in the visual sensory pathway, in *Walsh and Hoyt's Clinical Neuro-Ophthalmology*, ed 4, Vol 1. Baltimore: Williams & Wilkins, 1982, 136.)

for inferior greater than superior field loss (Fig. 4.17). Patients are often unaware of their field defect, especially when caused by an otherwise isolated lesion in the nondominant parietal lobe. Dominance is reflected to some degree by handedness: almost all right-handed individuals, and probably the majority of left-handed individuals, have left cerebral dominance.[81-83] Other patients may report functional difficulties resulting from their hemianopia but are unable to recognize the field defect. With right parietal lesions, for example, there may be problems with reading because the left hemianopia precludes finding the beginning of the next line of text. If a deficit is recognized, the patient often erroneously ascribes the problem to the eye ipsilateral to the temporal field defect.

Because the optic radiations originate from neuronal cell bodies in the lateral geniculate, the ganglion cells that comprise the optic nerve and tract are not affected by acquired retrogeniculate lesions. Optic atrophy should not be present on examination. The exceptions are congenital abnormalities or lesions acquired early in life in which transsynaptic degeneration has

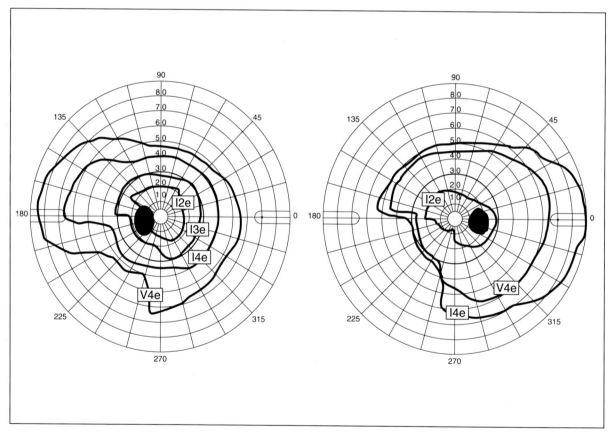

4.17 | Goldmann visual fields demonstrate a left inferior homonymous field defect. This patient had a right parietal lobe tumor.

occurred.[12] Examination of eye movement can also provide evidence of parietal lobe involvement. Conjugate pursuit movements may not be as smooth in the direction of the parietal lesion.[84,85] Optokinetic stimuli may elicit asymmetric responses, with slower slow phases and fewer quick phases demonstrated when the stimulus is rotated in the direction of the involved parietal lobe.[84,86,87] Other symptoms and signs of parietal lobe dysfunction reflect cortical sensory abnormalities. The patient may complain of numbness or tingling, but more often there are more complex problems of sensory integration, such as difficulties with tactile discrimination, position sense, stereognosis, and visual–spatial coordination. Gerstmann syndrome[88] may

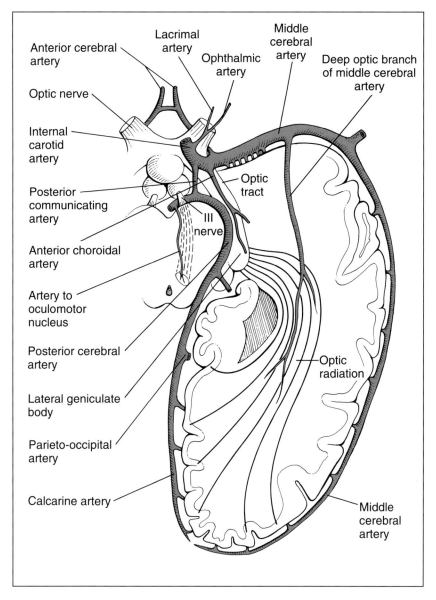

4.18 | Vascular supply to the visual pathways.

accompany a right homonymous hemianopia if the lesion extends to involve the angular gyrus in the dominant left hemisphere. The complete syndrome includes agraphia (inability to write), acalculia (inability to perform simple calculations), finger agnosia (inability to name fingers), and right–left confusion.

The visual field defects from occipital lobe lesions are typically exquisitely congruous. Macular sparing and isolated homonymous hemimacular involvement are phenomena that reflect the anatomy of the striate cortex and its blood supply. Although in some cases bilateral macular representation is responsible for preserved central vision on the side of a homonymous hemianopia,[89–96] macular sparing usually results from a vascular insult that spares the most posterior aspect of the calcarine cortex[97] (Fig. 4.18). Homonymous hemianopic scotomas also reflect the frequent dual blood supply of this region, from the posterior cerebral artery anteriorly and

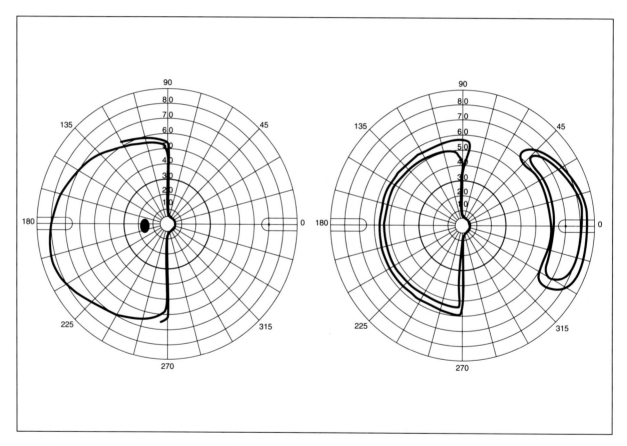

4.19 | Goldmann visual fields of a patient with left occipital lobe infarction from posterior cerebral artery occlusion. Note the macular sparing, the extreme congruity, and the retained temporal crescent of vision in the right eye, all characteristic of an occipital lobe lesion.

(Adapted from Spalton DJ: Neuro-ophthalmology, in Spalton DJ, Hitchings RA, Hunter PA: *Atlas of Clinical Ophthalmology.* London: Gower Medical Publishing, 1984, 19.24.)

medially and the middle cerebral artery posteriorly and laterally (see Fig. 4.18). Another strictly occipital phenomenon is the "temporal crescent." The most anterior portion of the calcarine cortex contains monocular projections that subserve the most peripheral temporal field (60–90°) of the contralateral eye. Occipital lesions may spare this region or may cause only its selective involvement[98,99] (Fig. 4.19).

Lesions in the occipital lobe are frequently isolated with regard to other neurologic signs and symptoms. Occasionally there is transient ipsilateral head, brow, or eye pain, reflecting the dual trigeminal innervation of the posterior dural structures and the periorbital region. The patient may be unaware of this defect, especially when there is macular sparing. Even bilateral field defects may go unrecognized if central vision is spared. Driving and other activities of daily living become hazardous. On examination, visual field abnormalities may be the only sign of disease. Optokinetic nystagmus, a reflection of intact parietal lobe function, remains normal as long as sufficient visual acuity is spared.[100]

When retrochiasmal lesions are bilateral and complete there is cerebral blindness. This is most often caused by bilateral occipital lesions in which there is no macular sparing. Commonly, a previously silent hemianopia contributes to complete cortical blindness when a contralateral lesion occurs.[101] As long as the lesions are retrogeniculate, ocular examination and pupillary function will remain normal and visual acuity will be identical in each eye. Other symptoms or signs of cerebral involvement, such as various degrees of memory loss or dementia, may be apparent, or the cortical blindness may be truly isolated. Some patients with cortical blindness deny their blindness and confabulate, a condition termed Anton syndrome.[102,103]

An isolated homonymous hemianopia may result from damage to the retrochiasmal visual pathways anywhere from tract to striate cortex. In Smith's review of 100 cases of homonymous hemianopia, 39 had proven or presumed disease in the occipital lobes, 33 had lesions attributed to parietal lobe damage, and 24 had temporal lobe disease.[104] Only four patients had lesions localized to the optic tracts or geniculate bodies. Fifty-one percent of cases had assumed locations on clinical evidence alone. The more recent report of 140 cases by Fujino and colleagues confirms the relative localization of lesions causing homonymous hemianopia with more modern techniques of neuro-imaging.[105] Fifty-one percent of cases had occipital lobe pathology, 29% had involvement of the optic radiations, and 21% had lesions in the region of the optic tract and lateral geniculate (Fig. 4.20).

CAUSES

Congenital abnormalities of the retrochiasmal visual pathways may result from intrauterine insults, such as ischemia or hemorrhage, brain maldevelopment, or trauma. Probably all congenital hemianopias have bilateral optic atrophy, classically in a bowtie pattern contralateral to the hemispheric lesion, and temporal pallor ipsilaterally.[12] This may reflect direct damage to the optic tract or transsynaptic degeneration from damage to the visual radiations or striate cortex.

The most common cause of damage to the retrochiasmal visual pathways in adults is vascular disease, and the most common location for vascular involvement is the occipital lobe[104–106] (Fig. 4.21). This is especially notable in patients over the age of 50 and in those with isolated hemianopias. Symptoms, when recognized, are typically of abrupt onset. Embolic or thrombotic involvement of the posterior cerebral artery or its calcarine branches represents the most likely pathogenesis.[97,107,108] If the terminal branches of the middle cerebral artery provide the blood supply to the occip-

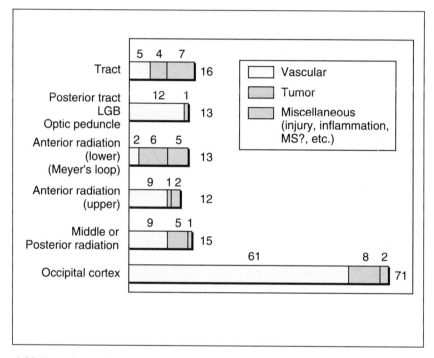

4.20 | Location and cause of homonymous hemianopia in 140 patients. (Adapted from Fujino T, Kigazawa K, Yamada R: Homonymous hemianopia. A retrospective study of 140 cases. *Neuro-Ophthalmology 1986;6:17.*)

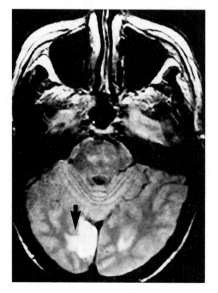

4.21 | T-2 weighted axial MRI indicates an abnormal bright signal in the right medial occipital lobe (arrow), which is consistent with an embolic infarction.

ital pole, macular sparing may be evident. Sources of embolism to this region include the heart and aortic arch, as well as more distal vessels such as the vertebral and basilar arteries. This artery-to-artery embolism may occur after local thrombosis in the upstream vessel or after spontaneous or traumatic dissection of the proximal arteries.[109] Prolonged hypotension can cause cerebral blindness as a result of bilateral watershed infarctions at the parieto-occipital junction (Fig. 4.22). More anterior infarctions in the distribution of the middle cerebral artery and its branches may result in visual field defects localizing to the parietal or temporal lobes, but these are rarely if ever clinically isolated. Occlusion of the distal anterior choroidal or lateral choroidal arteries may cause infarction of portions of the lateral geniculate body.[75,76,110] The optic tract is rarely involved in vascular lesions, although damage to the anterior choroidal artery during temporal lobectomy for epilepsy has led to vascular tract syndromes.[111]

Transient bilateral visual loss is commonly ascribed to vascular insufficiency, presumably of the vertebrobasilar system.[112,113] The pathogenesis may involve emboli that disintegrate or move downstream, transient compression of vascular structures, or cerebral vasospasm. One or several of these processes may underlie the transient cortical blindness that sometimes follows cerebral angiography, that occurs acutely in subarachnoid hemorrhage, or that may accompany hyperviscosity states. Occasionally, complete cerebral blindness clears, leaving a unilateral hemianopia.

Mass lesions are a common cause of retrochiasmal visual dysfunction, usually gradual and progressive[104,105] (Fig. 4.23). Associated signs and symptoms are common,[114] and may reflect nonspecific elevation of intracranial pressure, such as headache, nausea and vomiting, diplopia and VI nerve palsies, or they may have more localizing value if they suggest involvement of neighboring structures. Optic tract syndromes are usually the result of the same sort of compressive lesions that lead to chiasmal syndromes (see above). This is especially the case when the chiasm is prefixed (i.e., lies ante-

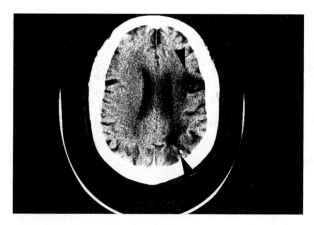

4.22 | Axial CT scan shows hypodense regions in the left brain (arrows) consistent with infarction in vascular "watershed" areas.

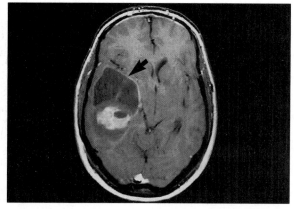

4.23 | T1-weighted axial MRI after the administration of gadolinium. There is a large, enhancing mass in the right temporal lobe (arrow) with a cystic component and significant mass effect. The patient had a left homonymous hemianopia and was found at surgery to have a glioblastoma multiforme.

rior to the sella). Causes include pituitary adenomas, meningiomas, cranio-pharyngiomas, internal carotid artery aneurysms, and intrinsic gliomas.[67,71] Neoplastic involvement of the temporal, parietal and occipital lobes is usually secondary to primary glioma, meningioma, or metastatic disease. Primary central nervous system lymphoma is increasing in incidence, especially since it is associated with the acquired immune deficiency syndrome.[115] Abscesses of bacterial, fungal, or parasitic origin must also be considered. Noninfectious inflammatory processes such as sarcoid may also act as intracerebral space-occupying lesions.[116] Arteriovenous malformations can present anywhere along the visual pathways and can result in dysfunction secondary to mass effect, ischemia, or local hemorrhage.[117] Intracerebral hemorrhages related to hypertension, amyloid angiopathy, systemic coagulopathies, infarctions, or tumors may present with more acute symptoms and signs that reflect their location and generalized elevation of intracranial pressure.

Traumatic injuries can cause damage to the retrochiasmal visual pathways. Penetrating injuries to the occipital and parietal lobes provided some of our earliest clinicoanatomic correlation.[118–122] Closed-head injury with contre-coup type damage can result in occipital lobe contusions, and subdural and epidural fluid collections can cause local compression (Fig. 4.24). Transient cortical blindness after head trauma usually lasts minutes to hours and is a well-recognized phenomenon.[123–126] The prognosis for complete recovery is excellent in children and adolescents but is more variable in adults.

Because the visual pathways are predominantly tracts of white matter, demyelinating disease would be expected to cause significant visual dysfunction. Diffuse abnormalities of myelin such as Schilder's disease, adrenoleukodystrophy, Pelizaeus–Merzbacher disease, and metachromatic leukodystrophy have resulted in hemianopias and cerebral blindness.[127] Similarly, progressive multifocal leukoencephalopathy, a demyelinating process associated with lymphoproliferative malignancies and the acquired immune deficiency syndrome, has a predilection for the white matter of the occipital

4.24 | Axial CT scan demonstrating a subdural collection of blood compressing the left occipital lobe (arrows). This patient had been in a motor vehicle accident and had a right homonymous hemianopia.

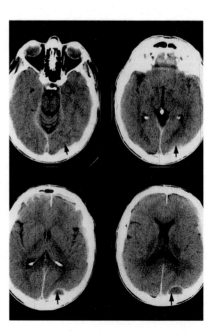

and parietal lobes[128-131] (Fig. 4.25). Clinical reports of retrochiasmal defects in multiple sclerosis are less common.[132]

Degenerative processes may severely disrupt the function of the cortical visual association areas. Alzheimer's disease often presents with disorders of visuospatial integration, including visual agnosia, spatial agnosia, alexia without agraphia, optic ataxia, prosopagnosia, constructional apraxia and deficits in visuospatial memory (see below).[133-135] The primary retrochiasmal visual pathways are usually spared early in the disease; later in the course of the illness, accurate visual field testing is difficult. Creutzfeld–Jakob disease, a spongiform degeneration caused by a slow virus, may present with cortical blindness, dementia, and a pronounced startle reaction (Heidenhain variant).[136-138]

Toxins may cause selective involvement of the visual system. Substances that have been implicated as the cause of cerebral blindness include carbon monoxide, nitrous oxide, ethanol, mercury, lead, cis-platinum, cyclosporin, methotrexate, and tansy tea.[139-142] A vascular pathogenesis may be responsible for some of these effects.

Other rare causes of cortical blindness include meningitis and encephalitis, subacute sclerosing panencephalitis, sudden elevation or reduction in intracranial pressure, cerebral angiography, electroshock, and hypoglycemia.[139,143-145] Rarely, transient cerebral blindness or hemianopia follows seizures, usually severe grand mal epilepsy.[146-149] Recovery may be prolonged over weeks. Even more unusual is true ictal visual loss in which the blindness or hemianopia is the clinical manifestation of seizure activity.[150-155]

Factitious visual loss may masquerade as cerebral blindness. Both conditions exhibit normal pupillary function, normal ocular examinations, and frequently isolated visual deficits without other neurologic abnormalities. When there is central visual sparing but severe peripheral field constriction, the visual field configuration may help to differentiate organic from functional visual loss. The visual fields in patients with bilateral occipital lobe damage may show macular sparing, but the degree of sparing in homonymous hemifields should be identical (Fig. 4.26). Factitious central sparing will not show these homonymous vertical notches. Furthermore, the presence of "tunnel vision," in which the size of the peripheral field does not enlarge with an increase in distance between the patient and the tangent screen, is nonphysiologic (Fig. 4.27). Various confrontational techniques can

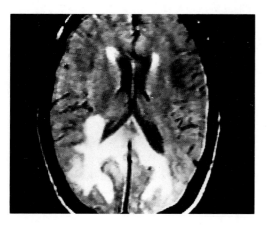

4.25 | Proton-density axial MRI with hyperintense white matter lesions, especially prominent in the parietal-occipital regions. The patient had AIDS and was cortically blind. Pathologic diagnosis of these lesions was progressive multifocal leukoencephalopathy (PML).

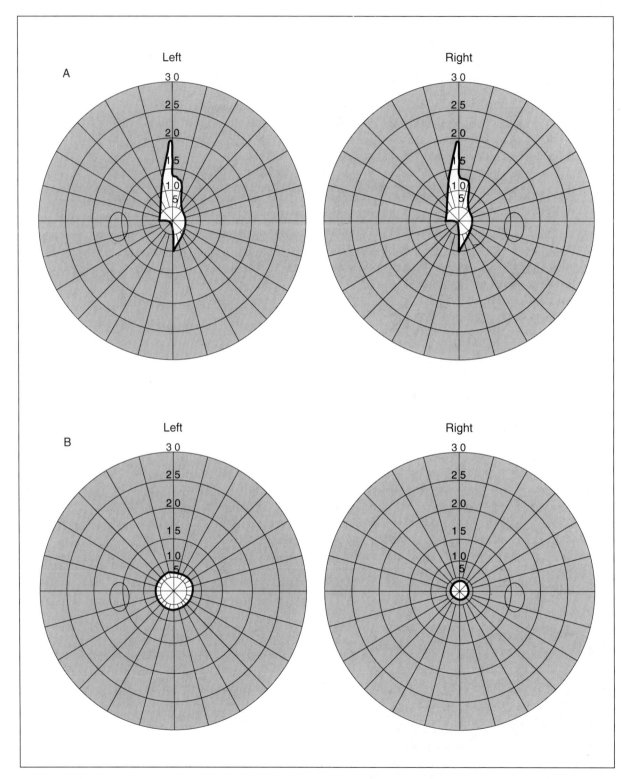

4.26 | Tangent screen visual fields with severe peripheral field constriction. *A*: Visual fields in a patient with bilateral occipital infarctions and bilateral macular sparing. Note the extreme congruity of the fields and the identical homonymous vertical notches. *B*: Visual fields in a patient with functional visual loss. Note that the fields do not respect the vertical meridian. (*A*, adapted from Lesell S, Lesell IM, Glaser JS: Topical diagnosis: Retrochiasmal visual pathways and higher cortical function, in Tasman W, Jaeger EA (eds): *Duane's Clinical Ophthalmology*, Vol 2. Philadelphia: JB Lippincott, 1991, 11.)

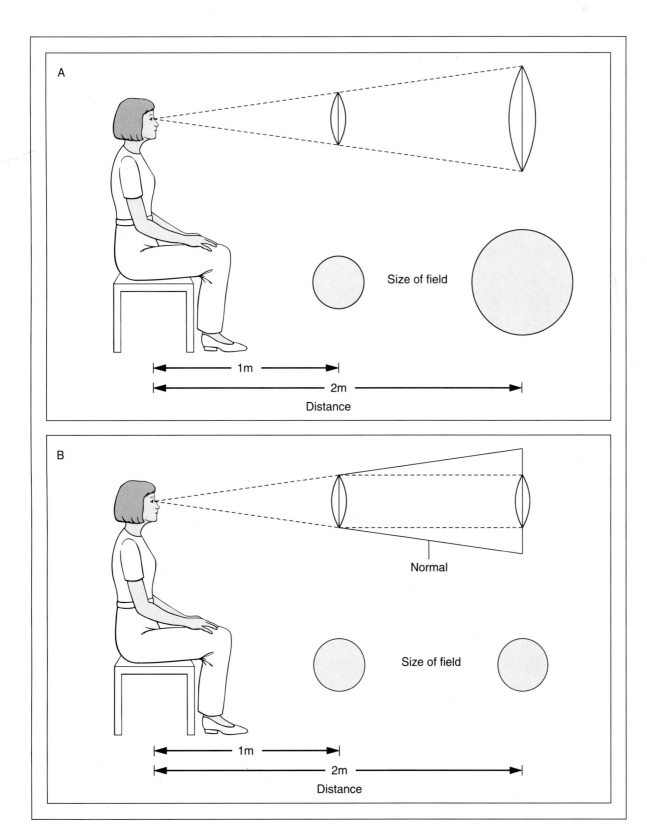

4.27 | Tangent screen visual fields in a normal patient (*A*) and in a patient with nonorganic visual dysfunction (*B*). The visual field in the patient with nonorganic visual dysfunction does not enlarge appropriately as the distance from the screen is increased; the size of the field remains the same, hence the designation of the fields in these patients as "tubular."

also be used to show that a patient's visual acuity or visual field is better than claimed. These include the presence of intact optokinetic responses in the "blind" patient or accurate localization of objects in the periphery in the patient with severe field constriction.

SPECIFIC SYNDROMES OF HIGHER VISUAL DYSFUNCTION

When the primary visual pathways are damaged anywhere from chiasm to striate cortex, visual field defects are the major demonstrable consequence. The remainder of the occipital lobes and portions of the posterior temporal and parietal lobes are also involved in visual function. These regions are broadly referred to as visual association areas. It is here that the primary visual information is processed, comprehended, and related to stored information reflecting previous visual and other sensory input. Some disorders of higher visual function are exquisitely localizable to specific visual association

FIGURE 4.28. Drugs Associated with Visual Hallucinations

Hallucinogens
  Dimethyltryptamine
  Harmine
  Ketamine hydrochloride
  LSD
  Mescaline
  Nitrous oxide
  Phencyclidine hydrochloride
    (PCP)
  Psilocybin
  Tetrahydrocannabinol

Stimulants
  Amphetamine
  Cocaine
  Methylphenidate

Anti-Parkinsonian Agents
  Amantadine hydrochloride
  Anticholinergic drugs
  Bromocriptine
  Levodopa
  Lisuride
  Mesulergine
  Pergolide mesylate

Antidepressants
  Amitriptyline hydrochloride
  Amoxapine
  Bupropion hydrochloride
  Doxepin hydrochloride

Imipramine hydrochloride
Lithium carbonate
Phenelzine sulfate

Anticonvulsants
  Ethosuximide
  Phenobarbital
  Phenytoin
  Primidone

Cardiovascular Agents
  Digitalis
  Disopyramide
  Methyldopa
  Propranolol hydrochloride
  Quinidine
  Reserpine
  Timolol

Antibiotics
  Antimalarial agents
  Cycloserine
  Isoniazid
  Podophyllum resin
  Procaine penicillin
  Sulfonamides
  Tetracycline

Hormonal Agents
  Levothyroxine sodium
  Steroidal agents

Analgesics and Nonsteroidal
Anti-Inflammatory Agents
  Indomethacin
  Nalorphine
  Narcotic agents
  Pentazocine
  Phenacetin
  Salicylates

Miscellaneous Agents
  Baclofen
  Bromide
  Cimetidine
  Clonazepam
  Diethylpropion
    hydrochloride
  Disulfiram
  Ephedrine
  Heavy metals
  Hexamethylamine
  Metrizamide
  Phenylephrine hydrochloride
  Promethazine hydrochloride
  Ranitidine
  Solvents
  Vincristine
  Volatile hydrocarbons

(From Cummings JL, Miller BL: Visual hallucinations. Clinical occurrence and use in differential diagnosis. *West J Med* 1987;146:46–51.)

areas. Others have yet to be localized or may suggest more generalized damage. Finally, some symptoms and signs are nonspecific reflections of disease in various different locations.

Visual hallucinations are the perception of visual images that cannot be verified by external examination of the patient's environment. They may be simple unformed visual phenomena, such as flashes of light, patterns, or colors, or more complex, formed images such as faces, objects, animals, recognizable people, or scenes. They are probably quite common, although a patient may be reluctant to report them. Both formed and unformed hallucinations can result either from direct insult to the brain or from a diminished input of normal visual information.[156,157]

A wide variety of medications, recreational drugs, and other ingested or injected agents has been associated with visual hallucinations[158] (Fig. 4.28). Images can be simple or complex and may occur with prolonged use, toxic levels, or withdrawal of these substances. Our understanding of cerebral function is not yet sophisticated enough to impart localizing value to the hallucinations associated with drugs.

Visual hallucinations secondary to "irritant" mechanisms from other causes may have greater localizing value. The nondominant hemisphere is most frequently involved.[122,156,159] When a structural lesion causes positive visual phenomena, the images are usually stereotyped and tend to be unformed when the lesion is occipital, but formed when the lesion is in the temporal lobe.[156] A common cause of unformed visual hallucinations is migraine with its often classic aura of fortification spectra followed by hemianopic visual loss and headache. Peduncular hallucinations are the rare visions of bright colors and animals reported by patients who have suffered midbrain infarction.[160–162]

Less stereotyped are the visual hallucinations of the visually deprived.[156,157,163] Release hallucinations are more common than those related to irritative lesions. They may be formed or unformed but this distinction has little practical localizing value, and the nature of the images may vary in the same patient. Abnormalities anywhere along the visual pathway from ocular surface to cerebral cortex may result in enough decreased visual input to allow hallucinations. The necessary reduction in visual acuity ranges from complete blindness to even mild impairment of central visual function.

Palinopsia, or visual perseveration, is the persistence of an image after the object of regard is no longer in view, beyond the normal physiologic afterimage.[164–169] The patient may complain of persistent images of objects just viewed even when looking elsewhere, or may report a stroboscopic view of a moving object (Fig. 4.29). Palinopsia usually occurs in association with other visual hallucinations or distortions. A hemianopia may be demonstrable. When a structural lesion is found to be the cause, it is most often located in the posterior nondominant cerebral hemisphere. Causes of palinopsia include structural abnormalities such as mass lesions, infarctions, focal trauma, demyelinating disease, and arteriovenous malformations. Palinopsia has also been associated with metabolic and anoxic encephalopathies, ingestions, migraine and seizure activity.

Micropsia (objects look smaller than in reality), macropsia (objects look larger than in reality), and metamorphopsia (distortion of shapes) of cerebral origin occur infrequently and have poor localizing value.[170–172] There are other rare phenomena of visual distortion that usually localize to the poste-

VISUAL HALLUCINATIONS AND VISUAL DISTORTIONS

rior cerebral hemispheres. Cerebral polyopia results in multiple perceived images, even with monocular occlusion, and is presumably of occipital lobe origin.[173,174] Distortion of edges, waviness of lines, halo effects, and motion of stationary objects have also been reported with posteriorly situated lesions.[175]

CEREBRAL DYSCHROMATOPSIA

The inability to differentiate colors is usually an inherited congenital abnormality. When it is acquired, dyschromatopsia usually reflects optic nerve or macular disease. Rarely, cerebral lesions cause an inability to differentiate colors, as demonstrated by errors on color-sorting tests and on reading the pseudoisochromatic color plates.[176-178] The lesions responsible for cerebral dyschromatopsia are located bilaterally at the inferior occipitotemporal junction. Usually there are associated bilateral superior homonymous field

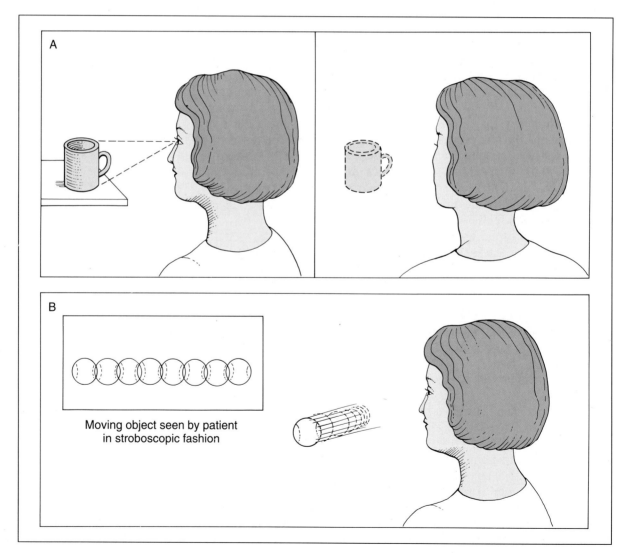

Moving object seen by patient
in stroboscopic fashion

4.29 | Palinopsia, or visual perseveration. *A*: A patient views an object and then continues to see this image when she looks away. *B*: Another patient might report a stroboscopic view of a moving object.

defects, reflecting involvement of the inferior optic radiations. Color-naming defects with preserved color differentiation and normal testing on the pseudoisochromatic plates suggest a lesion in the dominant hemisphere at the mesial occipitotemporal junction.[179] It is probable that color anomia is always associated with a right homonymous hemianopia.

Visual agnosia implies an intact and functioning primary visual apparatus but an inability to recognize an object's character, meaning, or relation to the observer or the environment.[176,180–187] In isolated visual agnosia, as soon as the object is presented to another sensory modality, such as touch or sound, recognition should be immediate. The anatomic substrate for this phenomenon is believed to be a disconnection between the primary visual cortex and regions in which previously encoded visual information is stored. Clinicopathologic correlation is rare, but bilateral occipitotemporal lesions interrupting visual–limbic connections have been proposed. On a practical level, there is unlikely to be visual agnosia without some associated visual field defect and/or abnormalities of mentation. Some specific forms that visual agnosia can take include body agnosia (an inability to recognize the various body parts), spatial agnosia (an inability to recognize the relationship in space of various parts of an object), symbolic agnosia (an inability to recognize the meaning of common symbols), and prosopagnosia (an inability to recognize familiar faces). Prosopagnosia typically accompanies cerebral dyschromatopsia and may therefore be associated with superior altitudinal visual field defects (i.e., bilateral superior homonymous quadrantinopias).[178,188,189]

Visual neglect implies an inattention to a hemifield in which there is no hemianopia.[190–192] Formal visual field testing demonstrates no abnormalities, but the presentation of spontaneous bihemifield stimuli results in the recognition of only one hemifield's stimulus. Ipsilateral neglect of other sensory modalities, such as touch, are often demonstrable. The lesions that cause visual neglect are most frequently located in the contralateral posterior parietal lobe, more often in the nondominant hemisphere. Other abnormalities of parietal lobe dysfunction, such as astereognosis, poor tactile discrimination, cortical sensory loss, and visuo–spatial difficulties, may be evident. The literature reports that neglect can be caused by lesions in areas other than the parietal lobe, including the frontal lobe, thalamus, internal capsule, and midbrain. These cases are less common but they suggest that several regions of the brain provide the network for visual and spatial attention, of which the nondominant parietal lobe is a prominent component.[192]

Some patients with posterior parietal lobe lesions of the nondominant hemisphere exhibit difficulty localizing objects in space.[193,194] Others do not appear able to direct their gaze or their touch to objects clearly seen and named.[195] These features are components of Balint syndrome, in which a patient cannot voluntarily move his eyes to an object clearly seen (psychic paralysis of gaze or optic apraxia), cannot grasp an object that he sees (optic ataxia), and cannot attend to the whole picture, especially when it is composed of multiple individual parts (simultagnosia).[196,197] The anatomic substrate for Balint syndrome is bilateral parieto-occipital lesions. In visual allesthesia, a rare abnormality of visual orientation, visual images are transposed

VISUAL AGNOSIA AND VISUAL NEGLECT

VISUAL DISORIENTATION

from one homonymous hemifield to the other, and even from lower to upper quadrants.[198,199]

EVALUATION AND MANAGEMENT

Because the majority of lesions that cause retrochiasmal visual dysfunction are either vascular or space-occupying, conventional neuroimaging can usually demonstrate the location and nature of the abnormality. Computed tomography typically fails to show evidence of an acute infarction unless it is very large, but within 3 to 4 days the damage is usually visible. Magnetic resonance imaging is more sensitive to early pathology. A vascular lesion may prompt cerebral angiography and a systemic work-up to help establish the underlying cause. Mass lesions may require biopsy to determine the tissue type, consequent prognosis, and treatment plan. Demyelinating lesions may be apparent only on magnetic resonance imaging, as the latter is exquisitely sensitive to abnormalities of white matter. Degenerative diseases such as Alzheimer's may have normal neuroimaging studies until late in their course, when nonspecific atrophy may supervene. If a fixed deficit localizing to the retrochiasmal pathways is demonstrated clinically, but no abnormalities are seen on neuroimaging, an electroencephalogram and lumbar puncture for CSF analysis are indicated. If factitious visual loss is suspected but not conclusively demonstrated on examination, pattern visual evoked responses may be helpful. Responses of completely normal amplitude and latency are unusual in the truly blind patient. However, abnormal responses do not necessarily indicate organic damage, since normal volunteers have been able to alter the configuration and latency of their responses.[200,201]

The evaluation of transient cerebral visual loss depends on the age of the patient, the underlying medical history, and the clinical setting. Suspicion of a vascular cause may prompt noninvasive transcranial Doppler ultrasound visualization of the vertebrobasilar circulation and/or cerebral angiography.

Management of the patient with a disorder of retrochiasmal visual dysfunction is determined by the nature and location of the underlying lesion. Although some improvement in visual field deficits can occur after cerebral infarction, the majority of cases have abnormalities that are maximal at onset and remain stable thereafter. Hemianopias secondary to hemorrhage have a greater chance of improvement and even of resolution. Similarly, when compressive lesions are removed there may be complete recovery of visual field, especially if much of the effect was produced by surrounding edema. Unfortunately, surgery itself may cause more extensive and permanent damage to the visual pathways. The prognosis for recovery of vision in patients with cortical blindness is also variable. As noted above, the young patient with cerebral blindness after head trauma has an excellent prognosis. Poor prognosis in cortical blindness is associated with stroke as the underlying cause, age greater than 40, severe visual impairment, associated cognitive, language, or memory impairment, and bilateral abnormalities on computed tomography.[202]

5 | THE PUPIL
Joel M. Weinstein

ANATOMY OF THE IRIS

The size of the pupillary aperture is controlled by two opposing smooth muscles, the dilator and the sphincter[1] (Fig. 5.1). The dilator muscle originates at the iris root and lies within the cytoplasm of the anterior portion of the anterior layer of the iris pigment epithelium. This radially oriented muscle terminates approximately 2 mm from the pupillary margin. Shortening of the radially oriented dilator muscle widens the pupillary aperture. The iris sphincter muscle lies more superficially in the iris stroma, running in a circumferential fashion around the pupillary aperture. The sphincter muscle occupies the area within 2–3 mm of the pupillary margin. Contraction of the circular sphincter in a "coil-spring" fashion serves to narrow the pupillary aperture.

ANATOMY AND PHYSIOLOGY OF THE PUPILLARY LIGHT AND NEAR REFLEXES

The pupillary sphincter changes its tonus in response to two types of physiologic stimuli: changes in the level of ambient retinal illumination (the light reflex) and changes in viewing distance as part of the near triad, which consists of accommodation, convergence, and miosis (the near reflex). As will be discussed, the pupillary light reflex may be impaired with relative sparing of the near reflex. This may occur in dorsal midbrain disease and with lesions of the ciliary ganglion or short posterior ciliary nerves (see below).

The pupillary light reflex (Fig. 5.2) begins in the retina with transduction of light energy by photoreceptors. The photoreceptors synapse with bipolar cells, which communicate with each other via horizontal and amacrine cells. The bipolar cells then synapse with ganglion cells. Axons of ganglion cells that subserve the pupillary reflex, like ganglion cells that subserve vision, undergo a hemidecussation in the optic chiasm. In the optic tract, some ganglion cell axons appear to bifurcate, projecting both to the lateral geniculate body (subserving vision) and to the pretectum (subserving the pupillary light reflex).[2,3] These axons leave the posterior optic tract, enter the pretectal area of the midbrain, and synapse in the pretectal olivary and sublentiform nuclei.[4] Each pretectal nucleus is an analogue of the lateral geniculate body, in that it receives light input from the opposite hemifield, just as each lateral geniculate subserves vision from the opposite hemifield. The pretectal nuclei distribute their input more or less equally between the two Edinger–Westphal nuclei.[5,6] The result of this distribution is that unequal input arising from lesions of one optic nerve or one optic tract do not result in different sized pupils, i.e., the afferent input, no matter what its source, is equally distributed to both III nerves. The Edinger–Westphal nucleus is the autonomic subnucleus of the III nerve and gives rise to pupillomotor and ciliary muscle innervation. The preganglionic fibers to the pupil follow the III nerve into the orbit and synapse in the ciliary ganglion. Postganglionic fibers follow the short posterior ciliary nerves and run in the suprachoroidal space to innervate the pupillary sphincter. Further details of the pathway from the III nerve to the pupil are discussed below.

The neuroanatomic pathway for the near reflex has not been fully elucidated. It is believed to involve a closed feedback loop which begins with estimation of target distance by visual association areas within the occipital and posterior parietal lobes. This information is relayed to one or more near reflex centers somewhere in the rostral midbrain which instruct the III nerve nuclei to increase or decrease the tonus of the intrinsic and extrinsic muscles

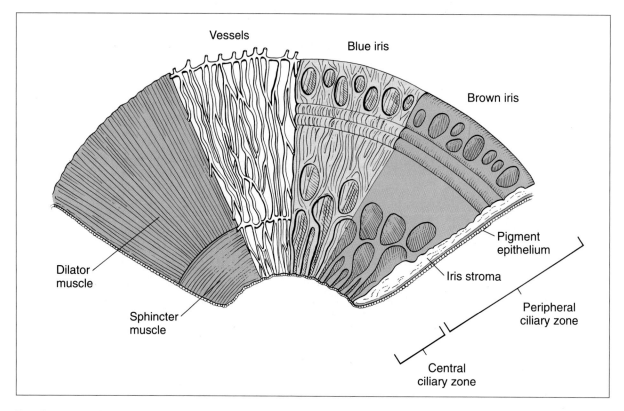

5.1 | Structure of the iris, including sphincter and dilator muscles.

of the eye that regulate accommodation, convergence, and miosis.[7] Continuous feedback to the visual cortex serves to complete the closed loop and fine tune the reflex.

The cholinergic innervation of the iris sphincter consists of three components: a parasympathetic motor nerve ending; a myoneural junction consisting of pre- and postsynaptic components with postsynaptic muscarinic receptors; and iris smooth muscle (sphincter).[8] Action potentials are initiated via release of acetylcholine, which is stored in vesicles of all presynaptic cholinergic nerve terminals. The contents of these vesicles enter the synaptic cleft, causing stimulation of the postsynaptic cholinergic receptors. Termination of a parasympathetic action potential is accomplished when acetyl-

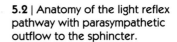

PHARMACOLOGY OF THE PARASYMPATHETIC SYSTEM

5.2 | Anatomy of the light reflex pathway with parasympathetic outflow to the sphincter.

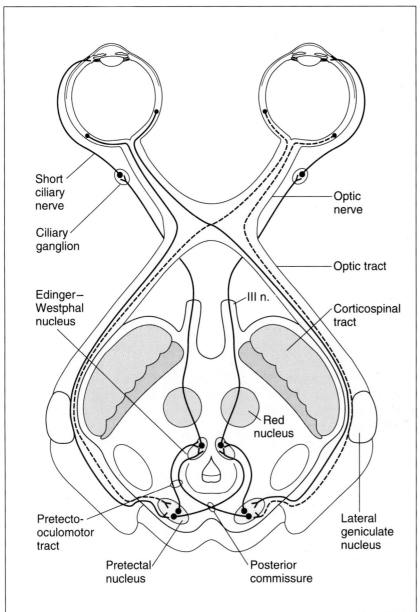

choline is hydrolyzed by the enzyme acetylcholinesterase. Significant levels of acetylcholinesterase are present in both iris sphincter and ciliary smooth muscle, as well as in other ocular tissues including corneal epithelium, retina, and choroid.

Pharmacologic agents that affect the sphincter muscle can be divided into several categories: direct-acting muscarinic agonists, such as acetylcholine and pilocarpine; indirect-acting muscarinic agonists (i.e., cholinesterase inhibitors); and muscarinic antagonists (e.g., atropine). The commonly used drugs are listed in Figure 5.3 and their properties are discussed below.[8-10]

DIRECT-ACTING MUSCARINIC AGONISTS

Acetylcholine is not used topically but is an extremely useful adjunct to intraocular surgery. When instilled intracamerally in a concentration of 1:1,000, it results in prompt miosis to approximately 2 mm. The miotic action lasts approximately 10 minutes.

Pilocarpine acts directly on muscarinic receptors in the pupillary sphincter muscle. Pilocarpine is, of course, invaluable in the treatment of glaucoma, and from the standpoint of pupillary disorders, it is the drug of choice for the diagnosis of tonic pupils (see below). Either a 0.08% or a 0.10% solution can be employed in the diagnosis of unilateral tonic pupils. The side effects of topical pilocarpine are related to stimulation of other systemic muscarinic receptors. These include lacrimation, salivation, sweating, vomiting, and diarrhea. These side effects are uncommon in the doses used either in pupillary drug testing or in the treatment of glaucoma.

Carbachol is a direct-acting cholinergic agent which actually combines the properties of acetylcholine (direct agonist) and physostigmine (cholinesterase inhibitor). It is not used in the diagnosis of pupillary disorders.

Methacholine bromide is very similar in its pharmacologic activity to acetylcholine. This drug has been used topically in the diagnosis of Adie's tonic pupil and in the diagnosis of familial dysautonomia. It is not generally available for ophthalmic use and has been demonstrated to be less effective than dilute pilocarpine in the diagnosis of tonic pupils. For this reason, methacholine bromide is rarely used for the diagnosis of pupillary disorders.

INDIRECT-ACTING MUSCARINIC AGONISTS

The indirect agonists produce ocular effects that are similar to those of direct-acting agents, although their mechanism of action is different. These drugs (listed in Figure 5.3) prevent the degradation of acetylcholine by the enzyme acetylcholinesterase, thereby producing miosis, ciliary muscle contraction, and ocular hypotension. These agents have been useful in the treatment of glaucoma, accommodative esotropia with a high AC/A ratio, and louse blepharitis.

These agents compete with acetylcholine for muscarinic receptor sites on the sphincter muscle. Some pharmacologists have suggested that a noncompetitive antagonist effect at another receptor site may also be present. Muscarinic antagonists are usually subdivided into naturally occurring agents, such as atropine or scopolamine, and synthetic agents, such as cyclopentolate, homatropine, and tropicamide. Of these, atropine is the most potent and long-lasting cycloplegic, requiring an average of 12 days for full recovery. The cycloplegic affect of cyclopentolate is superior to both tropicamide and homatropine and has the advantage over atropine of being short acting.[9,10] Because the antimuscarinic activity of these drugs is competitive, it can be reversed, at least in part, by muscarinic agonists. The relative mydriatic and cycloplegic potency of various muscarinic antagonists is shown in Figures 5.4 and 5.5.

MUSCARINIC ANTAGONISTS

FIGURE 5.3. Cholinergic Agents Affecting the Pupil

DIRECT-ACTING MUSCARINIC AGONISTS

Acetylcholine
Pilocarpine
Methacholine bromide

INDIRECT-ACTING MUSCARINIC AGENTS (CHOLINESTERASE INHIBITORS)

Diisopropyl fluorophosphate (DFP)
Echothiophate (phospholine)
Neostigmine*

MUSCARINIC ANTAGONISTS

Atropine
Scopolamine
Homatropine
Tropicamide
Cyclopentolate

*Not administered topically.

FIGURE 5.4. Comparisons of Mydriatic Effects of Tropicamide 0.5% and Homatropine 2%

	AVERAGE TIME IN MINUTES			
	LIGHT IRIDES		DARK IRIDES	
	Tropicamide	Homatropine	Tropicamide	Homatropine
Latency	7.1	14.3	6.4	14.2
Maximal effect	36.8	68.0	42.4	78.4
Half recovery	151.8	420.0	186.6	425.4
90% recovery	451.8	1192.8	489.0	1190.4

(Data from Gambill HD, Ogle KN, Kearns TP: Mydriatic effect of four drugs determined with pupillograph. *Arch Ophthalmol* 1967;77:740. Copyright 1967, American Medical Association.)

ANATOMY AND PHYSIOLOGY OF THE SYMPATHETIC SYSTEM

The iris dilator muscle is controlled by the sympathetic nervous system. The tonus of the dilator muscle is, for all practical purposes, independent of light and near stimuli. The tonus of the dilator muscle changes in response to the level of circulating catecholamines and discharge from the sympathetic nervous system. The sympathetic pathway to the eye is illustrated in Figure 5.6. The first neuron of this three-neuron chain begins in the posterolateral hypothalamus on the same side as the dilator muscle.[11] This first-order or "central" neuron descends through the brain stem and synapses in the intermediolateral gray matter of the lower cervical and upper thoracic spinal cord (the ciliospinal center of Budge).[12]

The second-order or "preganglionic" neuron is situated in the intermediolateral gray and gives rise to an axon that leaves the spinal cord with the ventral roots between C8 and T2. These fibers pass over the apex of the lung and ascend in the cervical sympathetic plexus, passing through the stellate (inferior cervical) ganglion and finally synapsing in the superior cervical ganglion at the level of the angle of the jaw.[13,14]

Third order or "postganglionic" neurons originate in the superior cervical ganglion and follow the neural plexus along the internal carotid artery.[13] Within the cavernous sinus, the sympathetic fibers pass very close to the VI nerve (perhaps joining it briefly in some individuals)[15] and enter the orbit along with the nasociliary branch of V1. Fibers to the dilator muscle enter the globe with the long ciliary nerves. Postganglionic sympathetic fibers regulating facial sweating and vasoconstriction also originate in the superior cervical ganglion but follow the external carotid artery and its branches to the face, except for a small patch on the forehead which in some individuals

FIGURE 5.5. Residual Accommodation (Prince Rule) in Subjects 4 to 9 Years of Age After a Single Drop

Cycloplegic	Race	No. Subjects	DIOPTERS OF RESIDUAL ACCOMMODATION — MINUTES AFTER DROP				
			15	30	60	90	120
1% Tropicamide	White	22	4.2	0.4	3.7	6.4	5.6
	Black	14	4.4	2.6	5.3	8.0	8.2
1% Cyclopentolate	White	8	4.8	4.0	4.1	4.7	4.8
	Black	8	4.8	4.2	3.3	3.1	5.0
5% Homatropine	White	5	7.6	6.3	5.9	5.5	5.4
	Black	5	8.0	6.4	5.9	5.6	5.5

(Data from Merill DL, Goldberg G, Zavell S: *bis*-Tropicamide, a new parasympatholytic. *Curr Ther Res 1960;2:43.*)

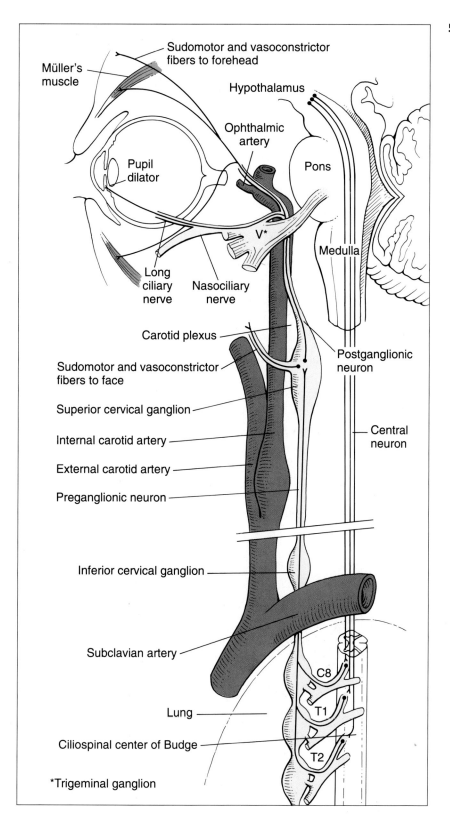

Müller's muscle

Sudomotor and vasoconstrictor fibers to forehead

Hypothalamus

Ophthalmic artery

Pupil dilator

Pons

Long ciliary nerve

Nasociliary nerve

V*

Medulla

Carotid plexus

Sudomotor and vasoconstrictor fibers to face

Postganglionic neuron

Superior cervical ganglion

Internal carotid artery

External carotid artery

Central neuron

Preganglionic neuron

Inferior cervical ganglion

Subclavian artery

C8

Lung

T1

Ciliospinal center of Budge

T2

*Trigeminal ganglion

5.6 | Oculosympathetic pathway.

may be supplied by fibers that follow the internal carotid. This anatomic variation may have some clinical significance in localizing the site of the lesion producing Horner syndrome (see below).

PHARMACOLOGY OF THE SYMPATHETIC NERVOUS SYSTEM

The iris dilator muscle contains alpha-adrenergic receptors and hence responds most strongly to adrenergic agents with primarily alpha-agonist properties. Among these, phenylephrine has found the most widespread clinical use. Clinical studies have demonstrated that the 2.5% solution is almost as effective as the 10% solution and produces fewer cardiovascular side effects.[17] In premature neonates, in whom a single drop of the 2.5% solution may produce serious cardiovascular side effects, the 1% solution is commonly used and has been shown to be equally effective.[18]

Sympathetic action potentials are terminated by reuptake of approximately 98% of released norepinephrine back into the presynaptic nerve terminal (Fig. 5.7). When the entire three neuron sympathetic pathway to the pupil is intact, the resting tonus of the dilator muscle is maintained by a continuous balance between release and reuptake of norepinephrine. *Cocaine* exerts its agonist effect by preventing reuptake of norepinephrine, allowing accumulation of the neurotransmitter and continuous stimulation of the postsynaptic receptors. Cocaine will dilate the pupil subnormally if a lesion at any point in the sympathetic pathway interrupts the tonic release of norepinephrine, preventing accumulation of neurotransmitter (see Fig. 5.7). All sympathetically denervated pupils, no matter where the site of the lesion,

5.7 | Pharmacology of the postganglionic neuron and neuromuscular junction. OH-AMP is hydroxyamphetamine; NE is norepinephrine.

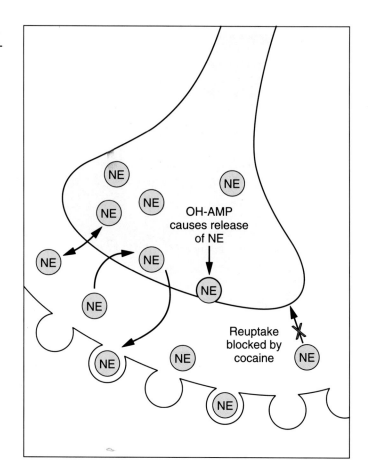

show a relatively poor dilatation to cocaine compared with the fellow eye.[19] One drop of 10% cocaine is placed in each eye and repeated in about 5 minutes. The results are interpreted at 45 minutes. More than 0.8 mm of post-test anisocoria (regardless of pre-test pupillary size) is considered a positive result (mean odds ratio of 1,050:1 that Horner syndrome is present, lower 95% confidence limit = 37:1).[19]

Hydroxyamphetamine dilates the pupil by releasing norepinephrine from postganglionic neurons. A lesion of the sympathetic pathway affecting the postganglionic neuron will impair pupillary dilatation by hydroxyamphetamine (see Fig. 5.7). Lesions of the central or preganglionic neuron, on the other hand, have little or no effect on the activity of topically applied hydroxyamphetamine. Hydroxyamphetamine therefore differentiates between postganglionic lesions, on the one hand, which dilate poorly to hydroxyamphetamine, and central or preganglionic lesions, on the other hand, which dilate normally to hydroxyamphetamine. On the basis of clinical data and pharmacologic testing in 54 patients with Horner syndrome, Cremer et al[20] concluded that after instillation of 1% hydroxyamphetamine, a difference in dilation of 1.0 mm indicates an 85% probability of a postganglionic lesion; a difference of 1.5 mm would correspond to a 96% probability of a postganglionic lesion.

No pharmacologic test is available that can differentiate a central from a preganglionic lesion. This must be done on the basis of other clinical data (i.e., the presence of hypothalamic, brain stem, or spinal cord symptoms in the case of a central lesion versus chest or neck signs and/or symptoms in a preganglionic lesion). This clinical differentiation is usually not difficult.

The hydroxyamphetamine and cocaine tests should not be done on the same day, because cocaine may inhibit uptake of hydroxyamphetamine by postganglionic nerve endings, yielding spurious results. Although some degree of denervation supersensitivity to dilute adrenergic agents is found in patients with postganglionic lesions, preganglionic lesions can also display this property. The degree of overlap may preclude differentiation, and supersensitivity testing has been largely abandoned in favor of the hydroxyamphetamine test.

PUPILLARY ABNORMALITIES
SIMPLE ANISOCORIA

Approximately 15% of the normal population has clinically detectable anisocoria.[21] The difference in pupillary diameter is usually in the range of 0.3–0.7 mm. Rarely is the difference greater than 1.0 mm. The anisocoria in these normal individuals is either equal in light and dark or is slightly greater in darkness. The designation "simple anisocoria" has been applied to the pupils in these normal individuals. Although the anisocoria, once present, is usually unchanged on future examinations, the degree of anisocoria may vary in some patients, and the size of the pupils may even reverse, with the originally larger pupil becoming the smaller of the two.

Differences that help distinguish between simple anisocoria and Horner syndrome include lack of ptosis; no change in anisocoria between light and dark (although many patients do have more anisocoria in darkness, as is seen in Horner syndrome); no "dilation lag" compared with the larger pupil (can be detected by flash Polaroid® photos); and a normal response to cocaine.[22] Many patients referred for evaluation of Horner syndrome actually have physiologic anisocoria and a non-neurologic cause of ptosis, such as chronic blepharitis or age-related levator dehiscence. The cocaine test is useful in convincing referring physicians that the ptosis and anisocoria are nonneurogenic.[23] Old photographs, such as on a driver's license or other identification card, can also be useful.

ABNORMALITIES OF THE AFFERENT PUPILLARY PATHWAY

A relative afferent pupillary defect (RAPD) is an extremely sensitive indicator of optic nerve disease and may be found in the presence of normal or minimally impaired visual acuity. Of note, the term "Marcus Gunn pupil" has sometimes been incorrectly applied to RAPDs demonstrated by Levitan's swinging flashlight test, described below. Marcus Gunn actually described "secondary dilation under continued exposure"[24] (to light) in an eye with an impaired optic nerve. For all practical purposes, afferent pupillary defects are not found in eyes with cataract, refractive error, or mild macular disease. When present, this sign to the clinician indicates impaired function of the retina or optic nerve of one eye *relative* to the other eye (Fig. 5.8).

Proper technique for RAPD testing is crucial.[25] Testing should be performed in a semidarkened room with the patient fixating at a distance. A bright light is used and should be alternated from one eye to the other every 2–4 seconds (Fig. 5.9A). The normal response to the swinging flashlight consists of a brief constriction of the stimulated pupil, followed by redilatation, whereupon the pupils reach a stable diameter after some oscillation (hippus). When an afferent defect is present, both pupils are larger when the defective eye is stimulated and smaller when the good eye is stimulated. Only one working iris sphincter is required to perform the test, which can be carried out in the presence of unilateral posterior synechiae, III nerve palsy, corneal opacities, or hyphema. Only the reaction of the working pupil needs to be observed by using a dim side light while each eye is alternately illuminated with the swinging flashlight. The afferent pupil defect is on the side which, when stimulated, results in dilatation of the observed pupil.

Considerable controversy has surrounded the question of how bright a light should be used to perform the swinging flashlight test. The answer to this question appears to be that brighter is not necessarily better. Rizzo et al[26] have demonstrated that a very bright light may mask some RAPDs by creating a maximal response in the defective pupil that almost equals the normal response. In such cases, a midrange light intensity may be more effective in bringing out mild asymmetry. It is therefore probably worthwhile to use a light with a variable rheostat, e.g., a muscle light or a Finoff transilluminator.

FIGURE 5.8. Causes of RAPD by Frequency

DISEASES THAT OFTEN CAUSE RAPDs	DISEASES THAT SOMETIMES CAUSE RAPDs	DISEASES THAT ALMOST NEVER CAUSE RAPDs
Compressive optic neuropathy	Macular disease	Cataract
Ischemic optic neuropathy	Retinal detachment	Corneal opacity
Optic neuritis	Branch vein occlusion	Hyphema
Optic nerve tumors	Branch retinal artery occlusion	Vitreous hemorrhage (unless very dense)
	Amblyopia	
	Glaucoma	

SWINGING FLASHLIGHT TEST

Intact optic nerve

Defective optic nerve

R

L

1. Room light

2. Right (normal) eye illuminated. Strong pupillomotor input from intact optic nerve.

3. Left (abnormal) eye illuminated. Weak pupillomotor input from defective optic nerve.

A

MEASUREMENT OF THE RELATIVE AFFERENT PUPIL DEFECT

0.3 log u filter

4. 0.3 log u filter over "good" eye.

0.3 log u filter

5. Pupils still dilate when the "defective" left eye is illuminated, indicating that a stronger filter is needed over the good eye to balance the pupillomotor input.

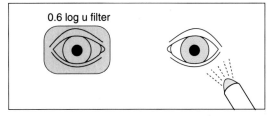

0.6 log u filter

6. Pupillary reactions are symmetric with 0.6 log unit filter over OD. Therefore, measurement of RAPD for OS = 0.6 log u.

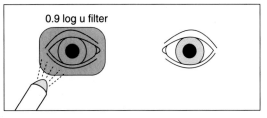

0.9 log u filter

7. A stronger filter over the good eye actually results in reversing the RAPD, indicating that 0.6 log u was the correct measurement.

B

5.9 | A: The swinging flashlight test in a patient with a left optic nerve lesion. 1: In room light, both pupils are approximately 4 mm. 2: With the normal (right) right eye illuminated, the pupils constrict to 2 mm. 3: When the flashlight is swung over to illuminate the left eye, both pupils dilate to 5 mm. *B:* Measurement of a relative afferent pupil defect. 4: As in 1, a swinging flashlight test is performed to determine whether either eye has an afferent pupil defect. 5: A 0.3 log unit neutral density filter is placed over the good eye. A swinging flashlight test is performed as in 1. The pupil in the "defective" left eye still dilates when the swinging flashlight test is performed, indicating that a stronger filter is needed over the good eye to balance the pupillomotor input. 6: A 0.6 log unit filter is placed over the right eye and a swinging flashlight test is again performed. The pupillary reactions are now symmetric. Therefore, a 0.6 log unit RAPD is present in the left eye. 7: A 0.9 log unit filter is placed over the right eye and the swinging flashlight test is again performed. As expected, the RAPD is now reversed and the right pupil dilates, indicating that 0.6 log unit was the correct measurement.

When a small RAPD is suspected and is not adequately demonstrated with a bright light, a lower setting on the rheostat can be tried.

A fully developed, "barn-door" RAPD is characterized by obvious dilatation of the affected pupil when the light is swung from the normal to the defective eye. But which component of the pupillary response is most useful for detecting smaller afferent defects? The possibilities include amplitude of initial constriction, amount of redilatation, final size after dilation, and minimum size. Any one of these may be observed clinically during the swinging flashlight test, but keeping track of all four simultaneously in both eyes is impossible. According to Cox, "although clinicians have been looking at pupils for years, no one has shown what component of the pupillary response is most useful for detecting small afferent pupillary defects."[27] To answer this question, Cox simulated RAPDs in normal subjects by using a neutral-density filter over one eye.[27] His conclusion: "To detect a relative afferent pupillary defect, the clinician should look for a difference in amplitude of the initial constriction of the two pupils during the alternating light test, and a pupil defect should be diagnosed when the consensual response is greater than the direct response." In other words, when a small RAPD is suspected the clinician should focus attention on the suspected defective eye, which can be illuminated by a dim side light. As the bright light is alternated between the two eyes, the responses of the defective eye to direct and consensual illumination are compared. If the initial constriction to consensual stimulation exceeds that for direct stimulation, an RAPD is present. If the initial constriction is not well seen (i.e., is too small), a brighter light can be used or the light may be alternated more slowly.

An RAPD can be quantified by "partial occlusion" of the good eye with a neutral density filter (Fig. 5.9B). The filter absorbs some of the incident light and reduces the response of the good eye. The swinging flashlight test is performed in the usual manner and the filter is increased or decreased until the RAPD is eliminated. This measurement can then be compared with later measurements as an index of recovery or progression of optic nerve (or retinal) disease. Thompson and colleagues have provided excellent discussions of the fine points and possible pitfalls of quantitative RAPD testing.[25,28]

It is important to remember that unilateral optic nerve disease does not result in anisocoria. This is because there is summation in the midbrain of all input from both optic nerves, followed by distribution of equal output to each oculomotor nucleus (see Fig. 5.2). It is also important to keep in mind that the afferent pupillary defect is really a relative test, i.e., a comparison of the pupillomotor input between the two optic nerves. Asymmetric optic nerve disease (e.g., asymmetric chiasmal compression) will give rise to an afferent pupil defect. Lesions of the optic tract may also cause afferent pupil defects.[29] These lesions tend to produce incongruous (i.e., asymmetric) homonymous hemianopias with an afferent pupil defect on the side of greater field loss. When a tract lesion produces a complete homonymous hemianopia, the field loss in the ipsilateral eye (i.e., the eye with a temporal field defect) is greater than the field loss in the eye with the nasal defect. This asymmetry is often sufficient to produce a small but easily detectable afferent pupillary defect. Symmetric optic nerve disease may mask an afferent pupil defect, leading to the incorrect conclusion that both optic nerves are normal. For example, in patients with acute optic neuritis associated with multiple sclerosis, a relative afferent pupil defect may not be found, or may be smaller than expected, due to subclinical optic neuropathy on the asymptomatic side.[30]

Although afferent pupil defects are usually considered to be characteristic of optic nerve disease, this sign may also be present in retinal lesions including detachment,[31] age-related macular degeneration,[32] histoplasmosis,[33] and retinal vein occlusion.[34] Although the mechanism is not clear, afferent pupil defects may be seen in some patients with amblyopia.[35] The severity of the RAPD is not related to the degree of amblyopia. Although opacities of the ocular media, such as cataracts and corneal opacities, filter a significant fraction of incoming light, they do not produce an RAPD. Recent evidence reported by Sadun et al[36] suggests that filtering of incoming light can be compensated by adaptation, i.e., increased sensitivity, both within the retina and possibly in the midbrain as well.

Whereas afferent defects are characterized by a pupil that responds better to consensual than to direct stimulation, efferent defects are characterized by pupils that respond poorly to both direct and consensual stimulation. Abnormalities of the efferent pathway may be caused by lesions anywhere from the midbrain to the pupillary sphincter muscle (see Fig. 5.2). Before an etiologic diagnosis is possible, the clinician must localize the lesion by clinical, radiologic and pharmacologic methods. The classification scheme outlined below is useful for that purpose.

Lesions of the dorsal midbrain often produce pupillary light–near dissociation, with impairment of the light reflex and relative sparing of the near response.[37] As illustrated in Figure 5.10, compression of the dorsal midbrain can selectively damage the dorsally located light reflex fibers in and around the posterior commissure, while leaving the more ventrally located near reflex fibers intact. The most frequent cause is a tumor of the pineal gland. Other causes include hydrocephalus and metastatic tumors in and around the periaqueductal area. The pupils in this syndrome are usually large, may be slightly unequal, and are often oval in shape. Light–near dissociation is only one component of the dorsal midbrain syndrome (Parinaud syndrome). Other components of the fully developed dorsal midbrain syndrome include a supranuclear upgaze palsy, impaired convergence, convergence-retraction nystagmus on attempted upgaze, and pseudoabducens paresis due to inappropriate convergence on attempted lateral gaze.

ABNORMALITIES OF THE EFFERENT PUPILLARY PATHWAY

DORSAL MIDBRAIN LESIONS PRODUCING LIGHT–NEAR DISSOCIATION

Perhaps the best known, albeit quite rare, form of light–near dissociation is the Argyll–Robertson pupil.[38] Argyll–Robertson pupils are small, often irregular in shape, and dilate poorly to all mydriatics. The condition is frequently bilateral, and the vast majority of patients have neurosyphilis. Good vision in both eyes is a prerequisite for this diagnosis, since optic neuropathy must be ruled out as a cause for impairment of the pupillary light reflex. Impairment of the light reflex is probably due to disconnection of the Edinger–Westphal nuclei from the pretectal nuclei (see Fig. 5.2). It should be remembered that tonic pupils resulting from lesions of the ciliary ganglion and/or the short posterior ciliary nerves (see below) also exhibit light–near dissociation.

LESIONS OF THE III NERVE

Efferent pupil defects of neurogenic origin may occur as part of a III nerve palsy or as an isolated internal ophthalmoplegia. The pupillary fibers of the III nerve arise from the Edinger–Westphal subnucleus, a midline structure that innervates both pupils (see Fig. 5.2). Nuclear lesions affecting the III nerve therefore cause bilateral (sometimes asymmetric) pupillary involvement if the pupils are involved at all. As shown in Figure 5.11, the fascicular portion of the III nerve (the portion within the midbrain) passes through the red nucleus and the corticospinal tracts, then emerges in the interpeduncular cistern. Midbrain lesions of various causes may result in a nuclear or fascicu-

5.10 | Light–near dissociation. The fibers mediating the near response are thought to be more ventrally located in the midbrain and therefore are spared with dorsal midbrain lesions (e.g., pinealoma).

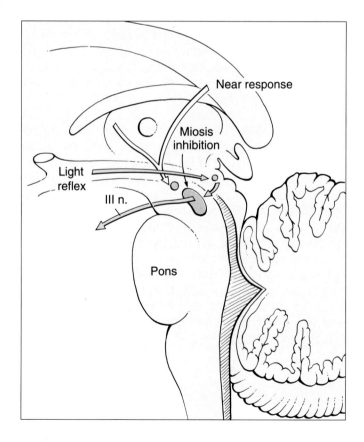

lar III nerve palsy with associated brain stem signs, including contralateral tremor due to involvement of the red nucleus (Benedikt syndrome) and contralateral hemiparesis due to involvement of the corticospinal tracts (Weber syndrome). Third nerve palsies caused by fascicular lesions often involve the pupil, although partial sparing of one or more extraocular muscles is not uncommon. Recent evidence, however, suggests that midbrain ischemia is a frequent cause of pupil-sparing III nerve palsy in diabetic patients.[39,40] These findings contradict earlier autopsy studies demonstrating infarction of the subarachnoid or intracavernous portion of the nerve in three patients.[41-44]

The pupillary fibers occupy the dorsomedial portion of the III nerve, where their superficial location renders them vulnerable to external compres-

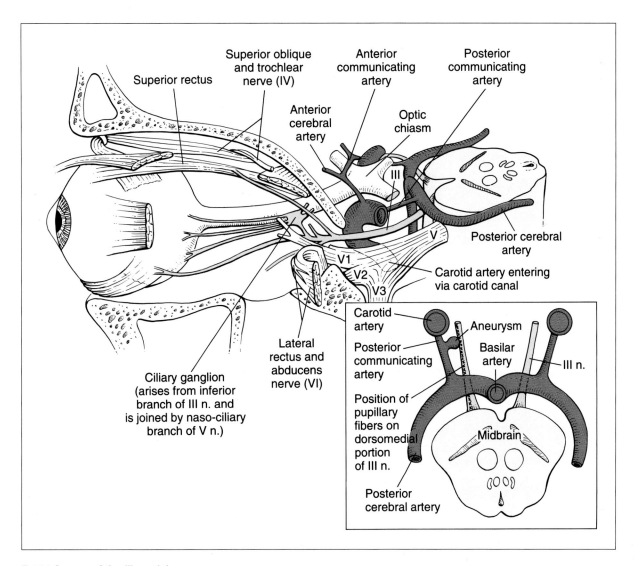

5.11 | Course of the III cranial nerve.

sion (see Fig. 5.11, inset). The most common cause of III nerve compression is an aneurysm of the posterior communicating artery at its junction with the internal carotid artery (ICPC aneurysm). Aneurysms at this location usually point downward and medially, coming into immediate contact with the pupillary fibers of the III nerve. Pupil sparing, therefore, is uncommon in III nerve palsy resulting from ICPC aneurysms.[45]

Several authors have reviewed the issues involved in managing patients with pupil-sparing III nerve palsy.[44-47] A complete review of this problem is beyond the scope of this chapter. The critical question, of course, is whether or not the palsy represents an ischemic process, with an excellent prognosis for recovery, or whether it represents a compressive lesion, possibly an ICPC aneurysm, which may be immediately life-threatening. Although the problem is still quite controversial and the management of each patient must be individualized, the following guidelines are helpful. First, the vast majority (greater than 90%) of patients with ischemic III nerve palsies are diabetic. The diagnosis of ischemic III nerve palsy should be viewed with caution in patients without diabetes mellitus. The approximately 10% of patients with nondiabetic ischemic III nerve palsy are usually elderly and/or have a well-documented history of long-standing hypertension or arteriosclerotic cardiovascular disease, often with prior cardiovascular complications. Second, pupil-sparing ischemic III nerve palsies involve *all* of the extraocular muscles. Therefore, the term "pupil sparing" should not be applied to *partial* III nerve palsies that spare one or more extraocular muscles. Partial III nerve palsies of this type should be considered nonischemic (but not necessarily aneurysmal) until proven otherwise. Third, III nerve palsy due to migraine is basically a disease of children and this diagnosis should be regarded with suspicion in anyone over the age of 20. Finally, high-resolution magnetic resonance imaging is *not* an adequate substitute for cerebral angiography which is, to date, the only test capable, when performed adequately, of ruling out an aneurysm as the cause of III nerve palsy. In summary, patients who are not diabetic or do not have well-established cardiovascular disease, as well as those with other atypical features mentioned above, should usually undergo neuroradiologic studies, including arteriography, to rule out an aneurysm or other compressive lesion. However, the advent of noninvasive magnetic resonance angiography may greatly simplify the management of these patients, perhaps even obviating standard angiography, over the next few years.

Aberrant regeneration of the III nerve may affect the eyelid (pseudo-Graefe sign) or the pupil and is almost always a sign of chronic compression. Aberrant regeneration involving the pupil is manifested by constriction of the affected pupil when the eye moves up, down, or medially, activating one of the muscles innervated by the III nerve.[48] In patients with aberrant regeneration, axons destined for one of the extraocular muscles become "miswired," making their way instead to the ciliary ganglion. This miswiring, and hence the aberrant sphincter response, is often limited to one or more segments of the pupillary sphincter. Therefore, different areas of the sphincter may constrict, depending on the direction of intended gaze. Aberrant regeneration is characteristic of compressive lesions and does not occur as a sequela of ischemic III nerve palsy. Patients with slowly evolving compressive III nerve lesions may have only minimal paresis and little or no diplopia, due to a balance between injury and regrowth of axons. In such cases the presence of aberrant regeneration provides a clue to the existence of a long-standing compressive III nerve palsy.

The III nerve enters the cavernous sinus where it lies in the lateral wall (see Fig. 5.11, inset). Mass lesions within the cavernous sinus typically produce pupil-involving III nerve palsies. These include intracavernous carotid aneurysms, sphenoid meningiomas, lymphomas, pituitary adenomas, and metastases.[49,50] Lesions within the cavernous sinus may involve both the III nerve and the sympathetic fibers to the pupillary dilator muscle, producing a III nerve palsy with a nondilated pupil which is nevertheless fixed to light. This should, of course, not be confused with a pupil-sparing III nerve palsy. Simultaneous involvement of the sympathetic innervation to the pupil, which can be confirmed by cocaine testing, exquisitely localizes the lesion to the cavernous sinus.

The III nerve passes through the superior orbital fissure and into the orbit, where the pupillary fibers synapse in the ciliary ganglion (Fig. 5.12). The ciliary ganglion may be affected by benign or malignant orbital tumors, orbital infection, inflammation (orbital pseudotumor), or orbital trauma (for a more extensive list, see Figure 5.13).[51] As shown in Figure 5.12, the motor root to the ciliary ganglion arises from the inferior division of the III nerve as it courses along the lateral border of the inferior rectus muscle on its way to

TONIC PUPILS

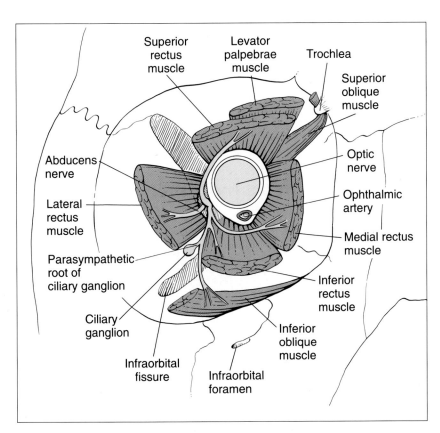

5.12 | Motor root of the ciliary ganglion and its relationship to the extraocular muscles.

innervate the inferior oblique. Trauma to the orbital floor, including entrapment of the inferior rectus muscle, may produce traction on the motor root, causing pupillary paresis. Lesions of the ciliary ganglion and/or short posterior ciliary nerves (of any etiology) produce a characteristic pupillary abnormality, the tonic pupil, characterized by a segmental palsy of the iris sphincter (Fig. 5.14); a tonic response to both light and near (see below); light–near dissociation (i.e., the light reflex is usually affected to a greater extent than the near reflex); and denervation supersensitivity to dilute cholinergic agents.[51,52]

The most common cause of isolated internal ophthalmoplegia is Adie's tonic pupil syndrome.[51,52] The typical patient is a woman, aged 20 to 40, complaining of unilateral blurred vision at near, or in whom an asymptomatic anisocoria has been noted. In the earliest stage the involved pupil is dilated and reacts poorly to light. The near response tends to be slow and tonic but is usually better than the light response. A "tonic" near response is one in which the pupil remains constricted long after the patient has discontinued accommodative effort, i.e., there is a delayed and prolonged relaxation of the sphincter after an accommodative response. For reasons that are unclear, deep tendon reflexes are diminished in most patients. The hyporeflexia is usually diffuse but may spare one or more reflexes and may be asymmetric.

The sphincter palsy is almost always segmental, i.e., the response is preserved in some segments and impaired in others (see Fig. 5.14). This is most easily observed with slit lamp magnification as "bunching up" of the iris stroma and pupillary margin in segments with intact innervation and spreading of the stroma in flaccid segments. The radial strands of the iris stroma are tugged towards areas of working sphincter. Like the near response, the light response is usually tonic. This segmental tonic response has caused

FIGURE 5.13. Tonic Pupil Causes

INFLAMMATORY
Herpes zoster
Chickenpox
Measles
Sarcoidosis

TRAUMA
Orbital floor fracture
Penetrating orbital trauma

ORBITAL TUMOR

GENERALIZED PERIPHERAL NEUROPATHY
Alcoholism
Diabetes mellitus
Guillain–Barré syndrome
Shy–Drager syndrome
Amyloidosis
Charcot–Marie–Tooth
   disease
Trichloroethylene
   intoxication

IDIOPATHIC
Adie's tonic pupil syndrome

some observers to characterize the movement of the iris as "vermiform." Another common feature of Adie's pupils is depigmentation of the iris collarette at the pupillary margin.

Denervation supersensitivity to dilute pilocarpine is present in 80%–90% of patients with Adie's syndrome.[52] Pilocarpine 1/8% is the drug of choice; one drop is instilled in each eye and repeated 5 minutes later. The test should not be performed within 24 hours of other procedures that might affect corneal permeability, such as applanation or instillation of anesthetic drops. Pupil diameter is reevaluated at 45 minutes. A change in anisocoria of 1 mm or more compared with pre-test measurement is considered a positive result. When bilateral tonic pupils are suspected, a comparative test with pilocarpine 1/8% would not be useful. Instead, pilocarpine 1/16% is instilled bilaterally (twice at 5 minutes apart). Normal pupils respond little, if at all, to this dilute solution and >1 mm of constriction of *either* pupil is considered highly probable for a tonic pupil.

In an interesting but unusual variant of Adie's syndrome, the pupil may be spared and the ciliary muscle alone may be denervated, resulting in accommodative paresis.[53] The ciliary muscle in these patients is supersensitive to dilute pilocarpine, resulting in an induced myopia and, in some cases, an induced astigmatism caused by the segmental nature of the ciliary muscle palsy.

The character of Adie's pupil changes with time.[52] Approximately 50% of patients will recover almost full accommodation within 2 years. With time, the Adie's pupil becomes smaller and may actually become smaller than the normal pupil, although the tonic near response, the poor light response, the segmental nature of the palsy, and the denervation supersensitivity all persist. Palsy of previously normal segments often occurs. Involvement of the second eye is common and occurs at the rate of approximately 5% per year, so that after 10 years a patient who began with a unilateral Adie's pupil has about a 50% chance of bilateral involvement.

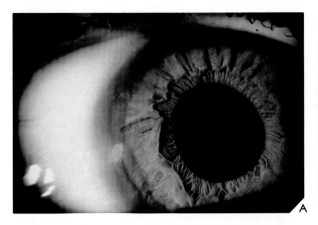
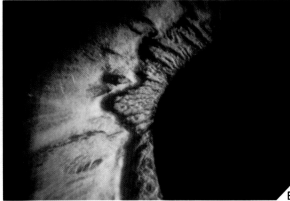

5.14 | *A:* Segmental palsy of the iris sphincter in a patient with Adie's syndrome. The pupillary margin is flattened from 1 o'clock to 5 o'clock due to paralysis of the iris sphincter, while the margin is "bunched up" from 7 o'clock to 10 o'clock in the area of working sphincter. The radial iris markings are dragged toward the areas of intact sphincter. *B:* Enlargement of pupillary border, showing "bunching up" from 7 to 10 o'clock.

Although the cause of Adie's syndrome is unknown, the site of pathology is almost certainly the ciliary ganglion and/or the short posterior ciliary nerves. This view is supported by both histologic[54] and physiologic evidence.[55] Many patients with Adie's syndrome have mildly impaired corneal sensation,[55] presumably due to involvement of trigeminal branches to the short posterior ciliary nerves that pass through the ciliary ganglion without synapsing. The presence of denervation supersensitivity also supports a postganglionic lesion, although preganglionic lesions due to III nerve palsy may produce supersensitivity.[56,57] The light–near dissociation that occurs in Adie's syndrome is believed to be due to aberrant regeneration in a mixed nerve (the posterior ciliary nerve) that serves both accommodation and pupil constriction. Accommodative fibers in these short ciliary nerves outnumber light reflex fibers by approximately 30 to 1. When axonal (or ciliary ganglion) damage occurs, followed by regeneration, these odds overwhelmingly favor appropriate reinnervation of the ciliary muscle by an accommodative axon. If reinnervation of the iris sphincter occurs, the odds are 30 to 1 in favor of reinnervation by an accommodative axon rather than by an axon driven by the light reflex. It is felt that this phenomenon is the basis for the recovery of accommodation and the pupillary light–near dissociation.

PHARMACOLOGIC PARESIS: THE FIXED, DILATED PUPIL

Pharmacologic sphincter paresis, inadvertent or otherwise, is common in neurophthalmologic practice. This may occur as part of a behavioral disorder or when pharmacists, nurses, or other medical personnel inadvertently handle cycloplegic drops or other anticholinergic substances. In this setting, the ophthalmologist is faced with the differential diagnosis of a pupil that is fixed to both light and near. The differential diagnosis of isolated mydriasis includes all of the causes of sphincter paresis, beginning in the midbrain and ending at the pupillary sphincter. These include: dorsal midbrain compression; early III nerve palsy due to a midbrain (nuclear or fascicular) or extra-axial lesion; a lesion involving the ciliary ganglion or short posterior ciliary nerves; pharmacologic sphincter paresis; and damage to the pupillary sphincter muscle from either inflammation or trauma. Myopathic injuries can usually be ruled out with certainty by inspection of the iris and anterior segment during slit-lamp examination. Dorsal midbrain lesions virtually always cause bilateral pupillary abnormalities. Pupillary light–near dissociation is usually present, at least in the early stages. Other signs of dorsal midbrain compression include upgaze paresis, with convergence–retraction nystagmus on attempted upgaze, and pseudoabducens paresis. Compression of the III nerve rarely produces isolated pupillary paresis without extraocular muscle abnormalities. Even in the acute phase of transtentorial herniation, extraocular muscle abnormalities follow within hours of the pupillary abnormality, if not sooner. Patients with this problem are neurologically quite ill. The differential diagnosis of isolated pupillary mydriasis usually comes down to one of tonic pupil versus pharmacologic paresis. The pharmacologic differentiation should proceed as outlined below.

Pilocarpine 1/8% should be used first to diagnose a tonic pupil. This will be positive in at least 85% of patients with this disorder. If supersensitivity is present, no further testing is needed. If supersensitivity is not present, then 1% pilocarpine should be instilled bilaterally. If both pupils react equally to this agent, pharmacologic paresis, sphincter damage, and sphincter inflammation are ruled out. "Equal" reaction means the same change in pupillary size in each eye, e.g., a change from 7 mm to 4 mm in one eye and a change from 6 mm to 3 mm in the other eye. A difference of more than 1 mm after installation of pilocarpine 0.125% is highly suggestive of pharmacologic paresis. If neither pupil constricts more than 1 mm to pilocarpine 1%, pilocarpine 4% is used and a differential response is again looked for. More than 1 mm difference in the response to 4% pilocarpine is considered indicative of pharmacologic paresis.

The syndrome of ptosis, miosis, and facial anhydrosis was correctly ascribed to a lesion of the sympathetic pathway by Friedrich Horner in 1858.[58] Other inconstant features, including elevation of the lower lid ("upside-down ptosis"), ocular hypotony, and conjunctival hyperemia in the acute stage were subsequently noted. Although the complete triad of ptosis, miosis, and facial anhydrosis is diagnostic, lesions distal to the superior cervical ganglion usually spare the sweating and vasoconstrictor fibers (see Figure 5.6 and the section on sympathetic nervous system anatomy above), leaving only ptosis and miosis. In addition, sweating can be difficult to assess in a dry, air-conditioned office or hospital. Pharmacologic testing should therefore be used to confirm the presence of Horner syndrome and to localize the lesion in these patients. Many patients referred for evaluation of "Horner syndrome" actually have pseudo-Horner syndrome, with miosis due to physiologic anisocoria and ptosis due to a non-neurologic cause, such as blepharochalasis, age-related levator dehiscence, or old trauma.[23] These patients are often seen in the setting of evaluation for headache or other neurologic complaints in which the presence of Horner syndrome would significantly affect diagnosis and management. Pharmacologic confirmation of the diagnosis is particularly important in these patients.

When observed in room light, the anisocoria in Horner syndrome may be as little as 1 mm or even slightly less. Placing the patient in darkness accentuates the anisocoria by turning off the sphincter muscles and directly comparing the strength of the two dilator muscles. Anisocoria that does not increase in darkness is not likely to be due to Horner syndrome. In addition to increased anisocoria in darkness, the Horner pupil dilates more slowly than normal, often requiring a full 15 seconds to dilate completely. This "dilatation lag" is specific for Horner syndrome and can be detected with flash Polaroid® photos from which measurements of pupillary size can be made. This "poor man's pupillography" can be a reasonable substitute for pharmacologic confirmation if performed carefully. The technique is simple and inexpensive and is described in detail by Pilley and Thompson.[59]

Lesions of the sympathetic pathway to the eye can be classified anatomically as *central, preganglionic,* or *postganglionic.* Anatomic localization by clinical and pharmacologic criteria is extremely useful in diagnosing the underlying cause of the lesion. Central lesions causing Horner syndrome originate in the hypothalamus, brain stem, or the cervical or upper thoracic spinal cord. Perhaps the most characteristic syndrome involving the central sympathetic pathway is Wallenberg lateral medullary syndrome. The syndrome includes *ipsi*lateral Horner syndrome, facial hemianesthesia, paresis of IX–XII cranial nerves (one or more), and *contra*lateral body hemianesthesia. It is caused by infarction of the lateral medulla, including the sympathetic

ABNORMALITIES OF THE SYMPATHETIC PATHWAY (HORNER SYNDROME)

pathway, the lower cranial nerve nuclei, the spinal tract and/or nucleus of the trigeminal nerve (*ipsi*lateral facial hemianesthesia), and the ascending spinothalamic tract (*contra*lateral body hemianesthesia). Lateral medullary infarction is usually caused by thrombosis of the posterior inferior cerebellar artery (PICA) or its parent vertebral artery. As noted earlier, pupils with central Horner syndrome fail to dilate to cocaine but dilate normally to hydroxyamphetamine.[60]

Preganglionic Horner syndrome originates from lesions in the neck or chest. The best-known cause is a tumor at the apex of the lung (Pancoast syndrome). The vast majority of patients with tumors in this location have symptoms of compression of the brachial plexus, especially pain in the hand or arm.[61] All patients with pharmacologic evidence of preganglionic Horner syndrome require detailed imaging studies (magnetic resonance imaging or computerized tomography) of the chest and neck to rule out neoplasia. As noted earlier, pupils in patients with preganglionic and central lesions dilate normally to hydroxyamphetamine, and clinical criteria must be used to differentiate the two. However, this differentiation can usually be made quite reliably.

Postganglionic Horner syndrome originates from a lesion along the course of the carotid artery in the neck or at the base of the skull, or from a lesion within the cavernous sinus or at the orbital apex. Dissecting aneurysms of the carotid artery usually occur in the subcranial portion of the vessel and are characterized by the acute onset of pain and Horner syndrome, the latter occurring in about 20% of patients.[61,62] The pain may be referred to the neck, jaw, pharynx, ear, cheek, or almost any craniofacial location. Dysgeusia, or a sensation of unpleasant taste, is sometimes present. Although most of these dissections are nonprogressive and self-healing, it is important to think of the syndrome in the setting of acute craniofacial pain and Horner syndrome and to rule out more dangerous disorders. The diagnosis can often be made by the noninvasive technique of magnetic resonance angiography.

In 1924, Raeder described two syndromes to which his name was subsequently attached.[63] The first type of patient described by Raeder (subsequently referred to as "Raeder's Type I") presented with Horner syndrome, *chronic* facial pain (often in the periorbital region), and trigeminal hypesthesia. These patients had tumors or space-occupying lesions at the base of the skull, involving the trigeminal ganglion or its branches and the sympathetic plexus on the carotid artery. The mass was often located near the fossa containing the trigeminal ganglion (Meckel's cave), and adjacent to the carotid artery carrying the sympathetic plexus. The second type of patient described by Raeder ("Raeder's Type II") had what we would now recognize as the cluster headache syndrome, i.e., *intermittent* periorbital headaches clustering in time and accompanied during one or more episodes by Horner syndrome, which might become permanent. The critical differentiating factors between the two types of patients are the presence of trigeminal hypesthesia and the more or less continuous character of the pain associated with paratrigeminal masses. The eponyms Raeder's Type I and Type II serve no useful purpose. Some patients with tumors at the base of the skull are unfortunately labeled by clinicians as "Raeder's syndrome," with the inference that their problem is benign. It seems more logical to discard the term "Raeder's syndrome" altogether and to remember that postganglionic Horner syndrome may be caused by a benign vascular headache syndrome or by lesions at the base of the skull that are frequently malignant. Although the absence of trigeminal hypesthesia is reassuring, most patients with postganglionic Horner syndrome should probably undergo detailed magnetic resonance imaging of the base of the skull.

Congenital Horner syndrome, or Horner syndrome occurring in the first 2 years of life, is often marked by hypochromia of the affected iris.[16] The reason for this is not clear, but electron microscopic studies have demonstrated adrenergic nerve terminals associated with iris melanocytes. Perhaps the trophic influence of the sympathetic nervous system is required for melanocytic growth, which normally occurs in the iris stroma during early childhood. It is also important to note that testing with hydroxyamphetamine may not be reliable in early childhood.[16] Preganglionic lesions (e.g., chest tumors) frequently produce a Horner syndrome which behaves pharmacologically as though the lesion were postganglionic, i.e., the pupil fails to dilate to hydroxyamphetamine. This phenomenon has been attributed to transsynaptic degeneration of the postganglionic neuron after early preganglionic lesions, a phenomenon that has been abundantly documented in experimental animals. An acquired Horner syndrome in the first few years of life is an ominous occurrence and is most frequently caused by neuroblastoma involving the sympathetic chain in the chest or neck.[64] These tumors may be difficult to detect, and the assistance of a pediatric oncologist should be sought in children with acquired Horner syndrome. Horner syndrome that is present at birth, on the other hand, is almost always benign and a cause is rarely found. Cases of intrauterine or infantile neuroblastoma associated with congenital Horner syndrome have been described, however, and therefore a pediatric evaluation is advisable. Early detection of neuroblastoma significantly improves prognosis for life, whereas the presence of metastases to bony structures, including the orbit, is associated with a much more guarded prognosis.[56]

MISCELLANEOUS PUPILLARY DISORDERS
PARADOXICAL PUPILS

In 1977, Baricks et al[65] reported pupillary constriction in darkness in three patients with congenital stationary night blindness. Flynn et al[66] subsequently described the same phenomenon in patients with congenital achromatopsia. Later reports documented this phenomenon in patients with dominant optic atrophy and bilateral optic neuritis. All of these patients had pupils that paradoxically *constricted* in darkness. Most recently, Frank et al[67] have suggested that this phenomenon may occur more frequently than has been recognized. The authors documented paradoxic pupillary response in patients with optic nerve coloboma, optic nerve hypoplasia, congenital nystagmus, retinitis pigmentosa, Leber's congenital amaurosis, Best's disease, macular dystrophy, albinism, and strabismic amblyopia.

OCULOMOTOR PALSY WITH CYCLIC SPASMS

In 1975 Loewenfeld and Thompson reviewed 54 cases of this unusual syndrome associated with III nerve palsy.[68] Almost all patients had the onset of their deficit before the age of 2. Although other congenital neurologic deficits may be present in these patients, the syndrome has not been associated with an acquired neurologic disorder. This rare disorder consists of alternating spastic and paretic phases of III nerve dysfunction. During the paretic phase a typical complete III nerve palsy involving the pupil is present. In the spastic phase the eye returns to the midline and the pupil constricts, usually becoming smaller than the normal pupil. The spastic phases typically occur about every 2 minutes and last from 10 to 30 seconds, followed by recurrence of the paretic phase.

INTERMITTENT UNILATERAL MYDRIASIS

Several authors have described transient pupillary dilation in young adults, frequently women, in association with headaches and blurred vision.[69,70] These patients have not had evidence of oculomotor dysfunction to suggest that the pupillary dilation is part of a III nerve palsy. This condition is at times referred to as "springing pupil." In many patients a history compatible with migraine is present. It is unclear whether this disorder represents increased sympathetic activity or decreased parasympathetic activity.

Unilateral mydriasis has also been reported without an accompanying headache and in patients without a prior history of migraine-like episodes. Patients who have had episodes of dilatation, with or without headache, have had normal systemic and neurologic examinations and no neurologic disorder has subsequently been found. In 1983, Thompson et al[71] reported 26 cases of a disorder he called "tadpole pupils." These pupils were segmentally dilated and peaked in one direction. The episodes of dilatation occurred several times daily and lasted about 1 minute. The condition usually persisted for several weeks. The authors noted that some of these individuals demonstrated pharmacologic evidence of pupillary denervation and suggested that the episodes of dilatation represent brief spasms of the dilator muscle.

6 | THE EFFERENT VISUAL SYSTEM

Lyn A. Sedwick

ANATOMY AND PHYSIOLOGY

SUPRANUCLEAR CONTROL CENTERS

Centers in the cerebral hemispheres, brainstem, and cerebellum exert supranuclear control over movements of the extraocular muscles. Saccades are generated in the contralateral premotor cortex of the frontal lobes in an area called the frontal eye field (FEF) (Fig. 6.1). The FEF receives projections from the region of the parieto–occipital–temporal junction (see Fig. 6.1). The primary pathways from the frontal eye fields are to the paramedian pontine reticular formation (PPRF) to initiate horizontal movements and either through the PPRF or directly to the rostral interstitial nucleus of the medial longitudinal fasciculus (riMLF) in the midbrain, which is the final processing area for vertical eye movements (see Fig. 6.1). The superior colliculi (SC) are also able to generate saccades (independent of the frontal eye fields) and they receive input from the retina and visual cortex. The superior colliculi also project to these same vertical and horizontal control centers. The FEF and SC represent parallel pathways for the initiation of saccades, each responding to a different physiologic need (e.g., foveating, reflexive, random). Ablation of both the FEF and SC is required to alter profoundly and selectively supranuclear vertical or horizontal saccades. The cerebellum is important to the control of saccadic movements, with the dorsal cerebellum and flocculus most strongly implicated in conjugate eye movements on the basis of experimental data obtained in monkey studies.

The neuroanatomic substrates of smooth pursuit movements are not as well understood as those of saccades. On the basis of experimental and clinical data, there appear to be visual tracking neurons in the inferior parietal lobule, which project in an unknown fashion to the brainstem nuclei. The control appears to be ipsilateral. The FEF and SC may also play a role in pursuit, because ablation of these centers limits pursuit movements and abolishes saccades. The dorsal pontine nuclei, the

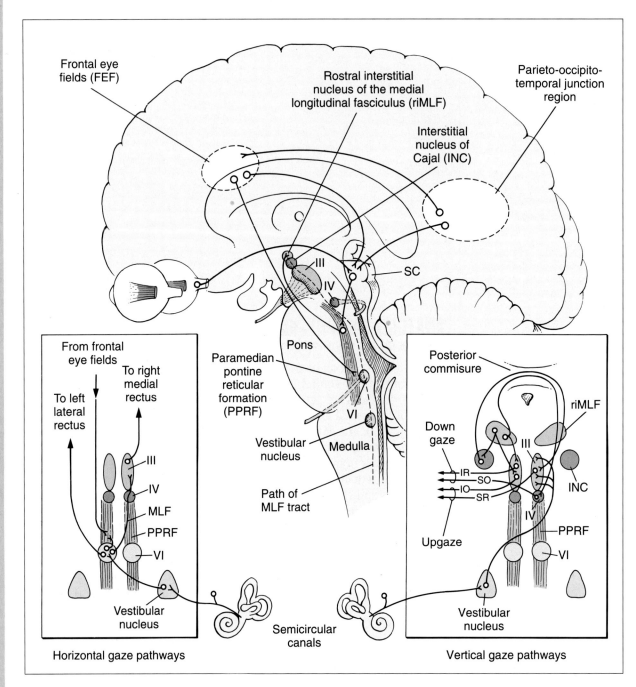

6.1 | Supranuclear and internuclear pathways for ocular motility. The medial longitudinal fasciculus (MLF) and paramedian pontine reticular formation (PPRF) are shown in several projections. Pathways of input are marked by small circles at origin and inverted arrow at destination, connected by a line depicting probable or known course.

cerebellum (flocculus), and the vestibular nuclei all are involved in the generation of smooth pursuit movements. The abducens nucleus contains both motor neurons and interneurons and is the final common center for horizontal conjugate movements. The rostral interstitial nucleus of the MLF (riMLF) in the midbrain serves a similar role for vertical eye movements.

The anlage controlling vergence movements is entirely unknown. It is possible that certain parietal and occipital areas respond to visual stimulation and thus produce convergence or divergence movements to attain an object of regard. There are groups of cells in and around the III nerve nucleus that induce both active divergence and convergence. The cerebellum probably contains neurons that facilitate vergence movements.

The vestibular system helps to coordinate ocular and head movements to attain or maintain an object of regard or to stabilize eye movements in response to body movements. Stimulation of the semicircular canals and the otolith organs induces vestibular eye movements that relay through the vestibular nuclei in the pons to the III, IV, and VI cranial nerves (see Fig. 6.1).

BRAINSTEM AND INTRACRANIAL ANATOMY

The major areas of interest to ocular motility in the brainstem are the mesencephalon (midbrain) and the pons. The III and IV cranial nerve nuclei are located beneath the periaqueductal gray matter of the rostral midbrain, the III nerve nucleus at the level of the superior colliculus, and the IV nerve nucleus at the level of the inferior colliculus (Fig. 6.2). The VI nerve nucleus lies beneath the floor of the fourth ventricle in the caudal portion of the paramedian pontine tegmentum. The medial longitudinal fasciculus (MLF), which connects the three ocular motor nerves, passes lateral to the III and IV nerve nuclei but medial to the VI nerve nucleus.

The III nerve nucleus is a complex structure consisting of subnuclei which project to individual extraocular muscles (i.e., the inferior oblique, inferior rectus, superior rectus, medial rectus, and levator) as well as to the parasympathetically innervated structures. The levator muscles share a midline central subnucleus, the central caudal nucleus, which possesses both crossed and uncrossed axonal projections. The superior rectus has only a crossed projection, i.e., the right subnucleus innervates the left superior rectus muscle. The other individual extraocular muscles are subserved by individual subnuclei with uncrossed projections. The midline Edinger–Westphal nucleus is a paired structure which gives rise to ipsilateral parasympathetic outflow to the pupil and ciliary muscle.

The location of the IV nerve nucleus is almost contiguous with the caudal end of the III nerve nucleus in the midbrain. The trochlear nerve innervates only the contralateral superior oblique muscle and is the only cranial nerve to exit the brainstem dorsally, decussating in the medullary velum (Fig. 6.3).

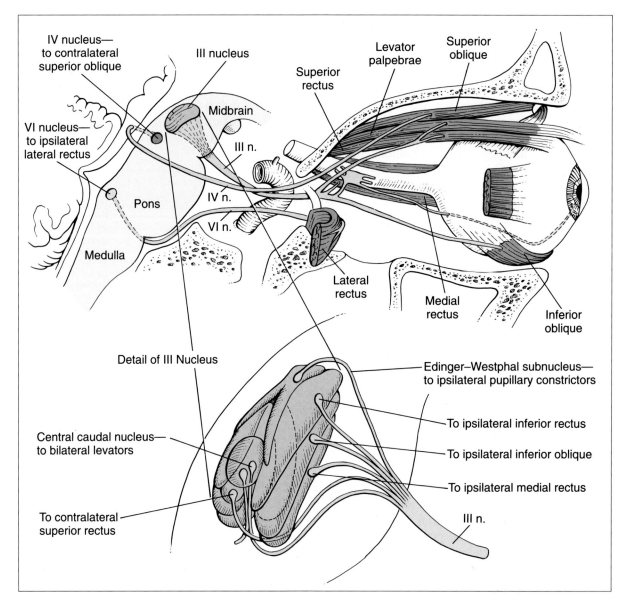

6.2 | Cutaway and sagittal section of brainstem showing organization of the nucleus of III, as well as pathways of III, IV, and VI nerves from their nuclei to the extraocular muscles. Note projections for III nerve, except for fibers from superior rectus subnucleus which are crossed, and fibers from midline central caudal levator nucleus, which are shared. Sixth nerve projection is uncrossed, IV nerve projection is crossed.

The VI nerve nucleus is now known to contain two kinds of neurons: motor neurons that innervate the ipsilateral lateral rectus muscle and interneurons that innervate the contralateral medial rectus via the medial longitudinal fasciculus (MLF). The abducens nucleus and fascicle are in proximity to many important structures in the pons, including the facial nerve, the MLF, the parapontine reticular formation, vestibular nuclei, mesen-

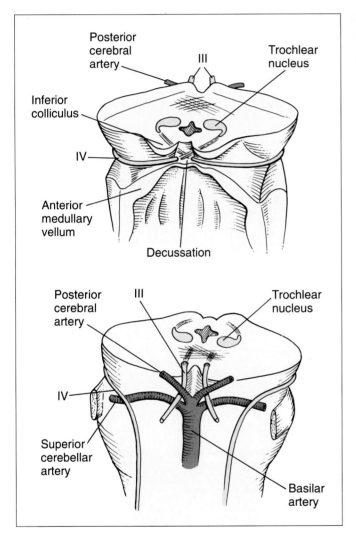

6.3 | Posterior and anterior view of mesencephalon. The IV nerve exits and curves forward to almost approximate the course of the intracranial III nerve.

cephalic root of the trigeminal nerve, oculosympathetic fibers, and the peduncle. Therefore, the neurologic findings that accompany VI nerve palsies are important in localizing lesions (Fig. 6.4).

The III nerve runs ventrally through the midbrain, passing through the red nucleus and cerebral peduncles to emerge in the interpeduncular fossa

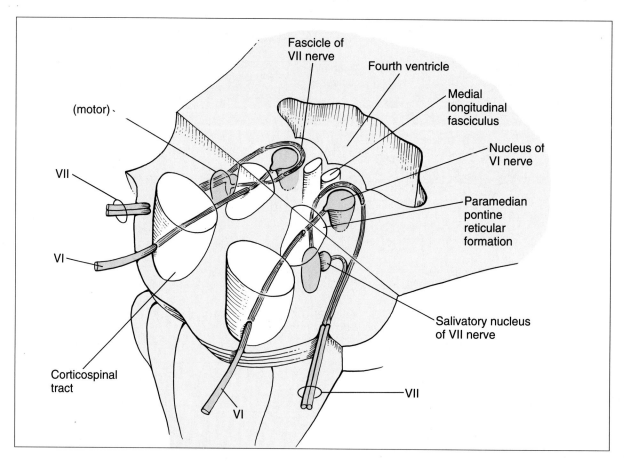

6.4 | Axial section through pons, showing VI nerve nucleus and vicinity. Note the close association of the VI nerve nucleus, the loop of motor VII nerve fasciculus, the paramedian pontine reticular formation, and the medial longitudinal fasciculus.

between the midbrain and pons (Fig. 6.5). It passes between the posterior cerebral and superior cerebellar arteries anteriorly to the cavernous sinus. The IV nerve exits the midbrain posteriorly and dorsally at the level of the inferior colliculus (see Fig. 6.3). After decussation in the anterior medullary velum, the nerve then curves around the cerebral peduncles to run laterally

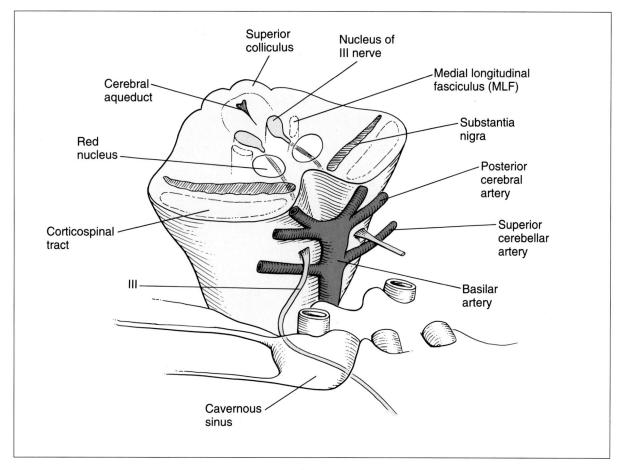

6.5 | Axial section through the mesencephalon, showing the fascicular and intracranial course of III nerve. Note proximity to red nucleus and corticospinal tracts.

to the III nerve between the posterior cerebral and superior cerebellar arteries (see Fig. 6.3). The VI nerve axons run ventrally through the pons and emerge at the junction of the pons and the pyramid of the medulla (Fig. 6.6). The VI nerve runs anteriorly and pierces the dura lateral to the dorsum sellae. It is tethered to the apex of the petrous pyramid and it continues forward and up between the apex of the petrous bone and dura until it turns 90 degrees to enter the cavernous sinus (see Fig. 6.6).

CAVERNOUS SINUS AND ORBITAL ANATOMY

The cavernous sinus is of clinical importance because it confines within a relatively nonexpandable space all of the ocular motor nerves, the oculosympathetic fibers, the first and second divisions of the trigeminal nerve, and the carotid artery (Fig. 6.7). The III and IV nerves are embedded in the lateral wall of the cavernous sinus, whereas the VI nerve is located within the sinus itself, adjacent to the intracavernous carotid artery (see Fig. 6.7). All of the ocular motor nerves travel anteriorly through the cavernous sinus and via the superior orbital fissure into the orbit.

Close to the superior orbital fissure, the ocular motor nerve splits into an inferior and a superior division. The superior division supplies the superior rectus and levator muscles and the inferior division goes to the inferior

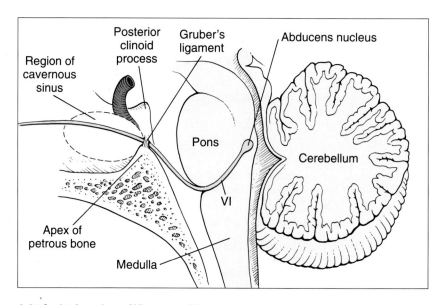

6.6 | Sagittal section of VI nerve exiting pons and coursing upward to the posterior clinoid.

rectus, inferior oblique, and medial rectus muscles. The parasympathetic fibers of the III nerve travel with the inferior division and join the nerve to the inferior oblique before entering the ciliary ganglion.

The IV nerve also enters the orbit through the superior orbital fissure lateral to the tendinous ring. It then crosses the superior orbit and runs medially along the roof of the orbit across the levator and superior rectus muscles to the superior oblique muscle, which it enters proximal to the trochlea. The VI nerve also enters the orbit in the superior orbital fissure and runs through the tendinous ring. It then enters the lateral rectus muscle.

BRAINSTEM DISORDERS

Because of the unusual nature of the III nerve subnuclei, a complete unilateral nuclear III nerve palsy must result in contralateral superior rectus weakness, normal ipsilateral superior rectus function, bilateral ptosis, ipsilateral dysfunction of the medial rectus, inferior rectus, and inferior oblique muscles, and ipsilateral pupillary mydriasis. Nuclear lesions not affecting the most caudal end of the nucleus can spare levator function.[1] Until recently, verified individual subnuclear paresis had not been reported. A recent case, however, confirmed by histopathology the presence of a metastatic lesion in one subnucleus in a patient with esophageal carcinoma, which produced an

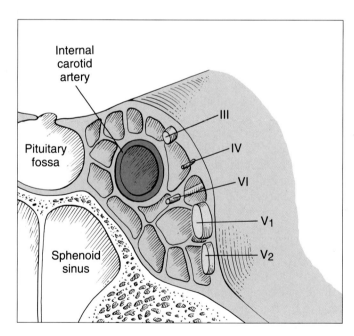

6.7 | Coronal, slightly oblique cross-section of mid-cavernous sinus. Sixth nerve is "free" in the sinus, but III and IV nerves are embedded in the wall. V_1 and V_2 are sensory branches of the trigeminal nerve.

Internal carotid artery

Pituitary fossa

Sphenoid sinus

III

IV

VI

V_1

V_2

isolated inferior rectus palsy.[2] Several reports have demonstrated partial III nerve palsy from fascicular lesions that may selectively impair both extraocular muscle function and pupillomotor fibers.[3-7] Fascicular lesions can be, but are not always, accompanied by clinical signs of involvement of adjacent midbrain structures. When the lesion involves the fascicular III nerve, red nucleus, and nearby medial lemniscus, the resulting ipsilateral III nerve palsy and the contralateral loss of sensation and tremor or abnormal movement in the arm and leg comprises Benedikt syndrome.[8] Lesions that involve the cerebral peduncle and III nerve fascicle, producing spastic paralysis of the contralateral arm and leg with ipsilateral III nerve palsy, are termed Weber's syndrome. Both of these syndromes are most commonly caused by infarction, hemorrhage, or tumor.

Brainstem lesions involving the IV nerve are rarer than those affecting the III and VI cranial nerves. They can be secondary to infarction, trauma, demyelination, or tumor. This nerve is much more commonly injured peripherally, most typically as a result of trauma. A superior oblique paresis and Horner's syndrome contralateral to it as a result of a brainstem lesion have been reported.[9]

Vertical misalignment accompanying a brainstem lesion can be due to dysfunction of the III and IV cranial nerves or can be the nonspecific result of a so-called "skew deviation." It is probably a supranuclear disorder arising from imbalance of otolith inputs that cross in the medulla and ascend in the medial longitudinal fasciculus. Skew deviation can be caused by lesions anywhere in the midbrain, medulla, or pons.[10] The hypertropia may be comitant or incomitant. When it is associated with an internuclear ophthalmoplegia, the higher eye is usually on the side of the lesion. Infarction is the leading cause of skew, but metastatic tumor and multiple sclerosis are other common causes.[10]

A lesion of the VI nerve nucleus produces an ipsilateral gaze palsy as these neurons are anatomically inseparable from those that control abduction at the nuclear level. A horizontal gaze palsy can be produced by a lesion either of the VI nerve nucleus or of the parapontine reticular formation (PPRF). In theory, these lesions can be distinguished from each other in that a vestibular stimulus will overcome the gaze paresis with PPRF lesions but not with nuclear abducens lesions. Duane's syndrome is a congenital abnormality of the VI nerve nucleus in which motor neurons are affected but interneurons are spared. This explains the presence of an abduction deficit rather than gaze palsy.[11] The fascicles of the motor root of the facial nerve are frequently involved by lesions that affect the VI nerve nucleus, since the latter lies in the genu of the facial nerve. When the VI nerve nucleus and the nearby medial longitudinal fasciculus are affected, in addition to an ipsilateral gaze palsy and abduction deficit, there is an ipsilateral internuclear ophthalmoplegia (one-and-a-half syndrome),[12] such that the only remaining horizontal movement is abduction of the contralateral eye. Fascicular VI nerve lesions can result in an "isolated" VI nerve paresis,[13] but it is much more likely that there will be involvement of other nearby structures, producing associated symptoms. A lesion involving the fascicular VI nerve and pyramidal tract results in an ipsilateral lateral rectus paresis and contralateral hemiplegia. When the lesion extends laterally to include the fascicular VII nerve, it is called Millard–Gubler syndrome. If the lesion extends dorsally into the tegmentum to involve medial lemniscus, crossed sensory symptoms ensue. A gaze palsy may be present, as may a Horner's syndrome, and this combination of findings is called the syndrome of Foville.

Nuclear and perinuclear lesions of the VI nerve most commonly arise from intrinsic tumor, infarction, or demyelination. Fascicular lesions are usually secondary to vascular disease, although demyelination and tumor are occasional causes.

Other forms of esotropia can result from brainstem lesions, including divergence paralysis and convergence spasm. Divergence paralysis is defined as an acquired comitant esotropia at distance but not at near, with normal ocular ductions and versions. The anatomic location of the lesion causing divergence paresis or paralysis is controversial, but most feel that it results from a lesion in a specific "divergence center" in the brainstem, possibly in the mesencephalon or in the pons near the VI nerve nucleus.[14] Some feel that divergence paralysis represents minimal bilateral abducens pareses. Causes of divergence paralysis are head trauma, increased intracranial pressure, and multiple sclerosis.[15] Thalamic esotropia is believed to be due to supranuclear disinhibition of the medial rectus subnucleus, leading to esotropia, and possibly to convergence spasm. The esotropic eye is often hypotropic as well. The common cause of thalamic esotropia is hemorrhagic infarction.

7 | DISORDERS OF OCULAR MOTILITY

Steven A. Newman

The ocular motor cranial nerves (III, IV, VI) are the peripheral projection of the efferent visual system and thus the beginning of the final common pathways responsible for ocular motility. Dysfunction of one or more of these nerves leads to breakdown of normal globe motion. Although the inability to stabilize a target on the retina or failure to align the object of interest with the macula may produce symptoms of blurred vision, the most common symptom associated with ocular motor nerve dysfunction (ophthalmoplegia) is diplopia. Diplopia occurs when a single object projects onto noncorresponding retinal points. It should be noted that ocular misalignment (strabismus) does not always lead to double vision. For example, poor acuity in one or both eyes may permit lack of alignment to go unnoticed. An even more common cause for lack of expected double vision is the development of a suppression scotoma. This adaptive mechanism, operating efficiently only during childhood, essentially shuts off the afferent input from one eye when the visual axes are misaligned. As the individual ages this potential adaptation is lost. Early development of persistent suppression can lead to arrested visual maturation and permanent amblyopia.

COMITANT AND INCOMITANT DEVIATIONS

Variability in the amount of visual axis misalignment can usually separate a cranial nerve palsy from congenital strabismus. A deviation is said to be *comitant* when it is essentially unchanged in all fields of gaze. When it varies with gaze it is *incomitant*. With a cranial nerve palsy the degree of visual axis misalignment increases when gaze is directed into the field of the paretic extraocular muscle. An incomitant deviation is unlikely with congenital strabismus. It does not, however, definitively diagnose ophthalmoplegia, because muscular and neuromuscular deficits, as well as restrictive disease, also produce an incomitant deviation. With time, "spread of comitance" reduces this gaze-induced variability (Fig. 7.1). Therefore, old, incomplete cranial nerve deficits may be difficult to separate from childhood strabismus. By identifying the paretic muscle, the field of maximal separation provides a clue to the malfunctioning cranial nerve. Small degrees of visual axis misalignment are often encountered. These are seldom symptomatic because of the brain's ability to adjust for deviations up to several degrees horizontally (far fewer vertically). This adjustment is called *fusional vergence*.

7.1 | *A:* This 66-year-old man had closed head trauma after falling down a flight of stairs. He complained of vertical diplopia increasing on right gaze and tilt. He had 5° of excyclotorsion on double Maddox rod. *B:* Hess screen confirmed the presence of a left hyper. *C,D:* Fundus photographs revealed excyclotorsion in the left eye. Closed head trauma, often insignificant, is the most common cause of acquired IV nerve paresis. Although many clear spontaneously, some do persist. Treated with Fresnel prisms, this patient complained of visual blurring but had satisfactory resolution of his diplopia with prism ground into his glasses.

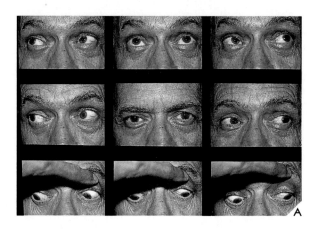

A

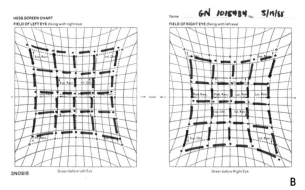

B

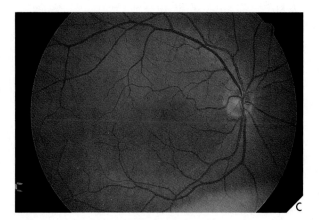

C

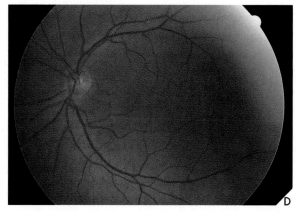

D

The tendency towards misalignment is referred to as a *phoria*. When fusional vergence can no longer compensate, the deviation becomes manifest and is termed a *tropia*. Subtle ophthalmoplegia may produce only an incomitant phoria. Because fusional vergence may mask a tendency to deviation, the afferent input should be dissociated by removing fusional clues. There are several means of assessing ocular misalignment (Fig. 7.2). A Maddox rod is particularly helpful as it delivers rapid assessment and breaks up the deviation into horizontal and vertical components. When viewing a light through a red Maddox rod held closely in front of one eye, the patient will see a white light and a red line oriented perpendicular to the ridges in the glass. If the light is not on the line there is a misalignment of the visual axes. If the light is seen as under the line, then the eye without the rod is higher. Similarly, if the light and line are seen as crossed (with the rod in front of the right eye the patient describes seeing the light to the right), then the eyes have a relative exodeviation. A cyclotorsional component to misalignment may be detected with a double Maddox rod test (a Maddox rod is placed over each eye and set parallel).

DIAGNOSIS

The misalignment induced by an ocular motor palsy fits classic patterns. Palsy of the VI cranial nerve results in an isolated unilateral abduction deficit. Dysfunction of the IV cranial nerve produces a hypertropia which increases on contralateral gaze and with ipsilateral head tilt. Head posturing may raise the suspicion of a IV, VI, or even a III nerve palsy.[1] A III nerve palsy involves relative impairment in elevation, depression, and adduction. Because the III nerve also innervates the pupillary sphincter, levator palpebrae, and ciliary body, an oculomotor palsy usually results in mydriasis, ptosis, and loss of accommodation as well as the motility disturbance. These "fellow travelers" are important concomitant and confirming evidence of a III nerve palsy. Sympathetic dysfunction can affect both lid position and pupil size through its innervation of Müller's muscle and the pupillary dilator muscles. As the sympathetics leave the carotid sheath initially in company with the VI nerve, an abducens palsy associated with miosis and mild ptosis suggests localization within the posterior cavernous sinus.[2,3] Another

Figure 7.2. Assessment of Ocular Axis Deviation

QUALITATIVE
Red glass test
Maddox rod

QUANTITATIVE
Maddox wing
Amblyoscope
Prism cross-cover test
Lancaster red/green test
Hess screen

"fellow traveler," facial sensory loss related to trigeminal involvement, usually indicates orbital apex or cavernous sinus localization. The presence of pain is also helpful, in that it excludes myasthenia. Facial weakness may accompany ophthalmoplegia when pathology at the level of the pontine brainstem affects both the VI and VII cranial nerves. This may be extra-axial or, more commonly, associated with intra-axial pathology affecting the VII nerve fascicular fibers at the loop around the VI nerve nucleus. Similarly, decreased hearing may accompany abducens palsy when the petrous bone and its auditory structures are involved (Fig. 7.3). Intra-axial pathology may simultaneously produce both a cranial nerve palsy and long tract signs (e.g., weakness, numbness, incoordination, abnormal reflexes, positive Babinski sign, etc.). Local orbital signs (proptosis, enophthalmos, globe dystopia, arterialization of the episcleral vessels) may suggest a mechanical cause for a motility disturbance (Fig. 7.4).

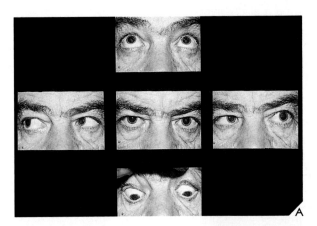

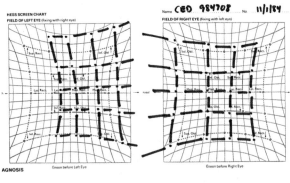

7.3 | *A:* This 58-year-old man complained of double vision on left gaze associated with left periauricular pain and decreased left hearing. This combination suggests the possibility of Gradenigo syndrome. Review of the patient's medical history revealed problems with mastoiditis treated with a tympanomastoidectomy. *B:* Hess screen confirmed the presence of an abduction deficit. *C, D,:* CT scans revealed a soft tissue mass within the nasopharynx invading the skull base. Nasopharyngeal carcinoma may frequently masquerade as Gradenigo syndrome in elderly patients.

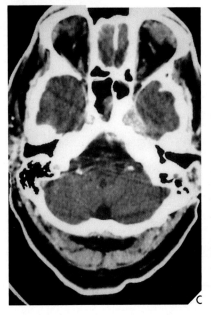

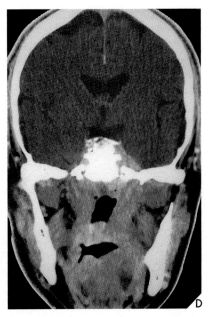

Accompanying signs are particularly helpful in revealing the location of ocular motor pathology. Although the cranial nerves may be affected anywhere from their origin within the brainstem to their insertion into the extraocular muscles (Fig. 7.5), the least frequent location is intraorbital. Here, local mass effect blurs the distinction between cranial nerve palsy and a local myopathic process. Decreased visual acuity is an additional clue to optic nerve compression seen with orbital apex involvement. When the pathology is posterior to the orbit, local orbital signs and decreased acuity are usually absent. Involvement within the cavernous sinus cannot be distinguished from pathology at the superior orbital fissure. Anatomically, the superior orbital fissure represents the anterior extent of the cavernous sinus. Features suggesting cavernous sinus involvement include multiplicity of cranial nerve palsies and facial sensory loss. Before entering the cavernous sinus the ocular motor nerves may be affected within the substance of the brainstem or within the subarachnoid space. Long tract signs, gaze palsy, and other local bulbar signs suggest brainstem nuclear or fascicular pathology. Within the subarachnoid space, inflammatory (basilar meningitis), vascular (subarachnoid hemorrhage from an aneurysm or arteriovenous malformation), traumatic, or neoplastic (frequently arising from the clivus) processes may affect the III, IV, and VI cranial nerves.

Misalignment due to weakness must be distinguished from poor ocular motility due to restriction. Restriction implies local orbital pathology. Although this is most often related to trauma or thyroid orbitopathy, inflammation and infiltration may also prevent normal relaxation. Local orbital signs (proptosis, enophthalmos) and a prior history of trauma or thyroid disease should raise the suspicion of restriction (Fig. 7.6). Diagnosis of a restrictive syndrome is traditionally made by testing forced ductions. This is performed by anesthetizing the globe at the limbus or over the insertion of the presumptively restricted muscle with cocaine, proparacaine, tetracaine, or 4% lidocaine applied topically. The eye is then grasped with toothed forceps while the patient is instructed to look in the direction of the impaired movement. Care must be taken with the forceps to avoid pushing the globe back

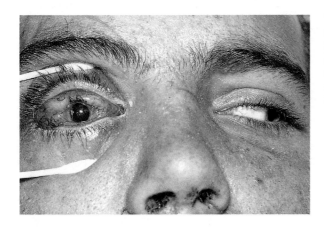

7.4 | This 19-year-old-man was involved in a motor vehicle accident with severe closed head trauma. There was complete ophthalmoplegia on the right. A loud bruit was heard over the orbit secondary to his traumatic carotid artery-cavernous sinus fistula. Ocular motility returned after treatment with balloon occlusion, but there was no recovery of vision.

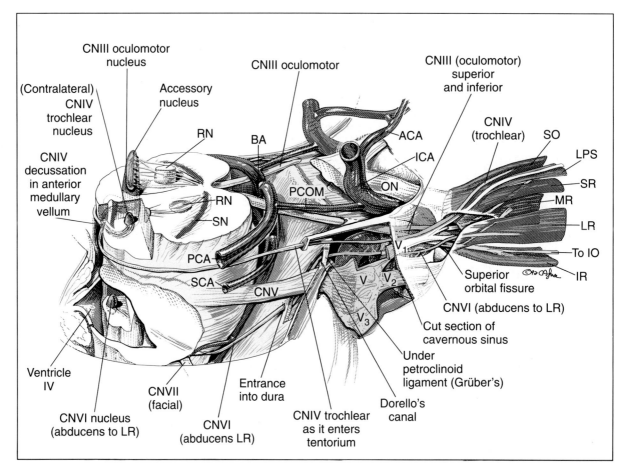

7.5 | The most common cause of acquired ocular devia-
tion (and thus of diplopia) is pathology affecting the
three ocular motor cranial nerves. The trochlear and oculomotor nerves arise in the midbrain while the abducens
nerve originates in the pons, as seen in this cut away diagram of the brainstem, middle cranial fossa, parasellar
area, and orbit. Pathology may involve these cranial
nerves at any point in their course. Clinically these may
be grouped, as indicated by the color blocks, into 1)
intraxial (within the brainstem); 2) subarachnoid; 3) cavernous sinus and superior orbital fissure; 4) intraorbital.
Suspicion is raised by fellow travelers and confirmation is
provided by neuroimaging studies (MRI) or angiography.
The anatomic relationship with the vessels of the circle of
Willis and the petrous and sphenoidal bones is obvious.
Thus pathology arising from these vessels (aneurysm,
AVM) or from the bone and brain coverings (meninges)

over the petrous ridge or medial sphenoid may easily
result in dysfunction of one of the three ocular motor
cranial nerves. Involvement of the optic nerve is more
suggestive of anteriorly located pathology, within the
orbit, or with a lesion above and secondarily affecting
the cavernous sinus.

ACA=anterior cerebral artery; BA=basilar artery;
CNV=trigeminal nerve; ICA=internal carotid artery;
IO=inferior oblique muscle; IR=inferior rectus muscle;
LPS=levator palpabrae superioris; LR=lateral rectus mus-
cle; MR=medial rectus muscle; ON=optic nerve;
PCA=posterior cerebral artery; PCOM=posterior commu-
nicating artery; RN=red nucleus; SCA=superior cerebellar
artery; SN=substantia nigra; SO=superior oblique muscle;
SR=superior rectus muscle; V_1=orbital branch; V_2=maxil-
lary branch; V_3=mandibular branch.

into the orbit and thereby producing a false-negative test. Severe restriction is easy to detect. Mild or incomplete restriction may be difficult to assess. One alternative is to measure intraocular pressure in primary position, then in the eccentric gaze producing diplopia.[4] Elevation of pressure of more than 4 mm or asymmetric elevation suggests restriction.

Also in the differential of ocular misalignment, primary muscle overaction is uncommon. Primary overaction of the inferior oblique and dissociated vertical deviation, both typically associated with congenital strabismus, are not rare. Spontaneous firing within the IV cranial nerve (superior oblique myokymia) may produce shimmering oscillopsia, torsion, and diplopia. Carbamazepine offers symptomatic relief. Unfortunately, this is not effective in all patients,[5] particularly in early-onset or congenital superior oblique myokymia. Recently, beta blockers have been reported to relieve symptomatic myokymia.[6] Still less common, ocular neuromyotonia is characterized by intermittent spontaneous firing of the III or VI cranial nerve.[7] This is usually induced by gaze in the direction of the nerve function and results in intermittent diplopia. Most of the reported cases have been associated with prior radiation to the area of the cavernous sinus.[8]

The most common vascular cause of cranial nerve palsies is secondary to small-vessel disease, often related to diabetes or hypertension. This has been assumed to cause isolated ophthalmoplegia within the subarachnoid space. Recent studies suggest that infarctions may also be intra-axial.[9] Other causes of vascular cranial nerve palsies are far less common (Fig. 7.7). These may be

PATHOPHYSIOLOGY OF CRANIAL NERVE PALSIES

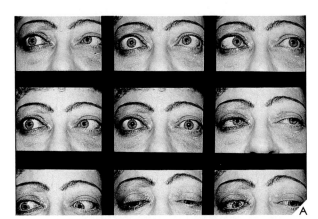

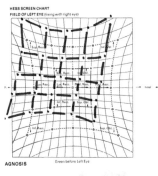

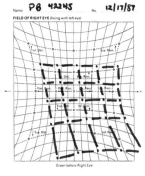

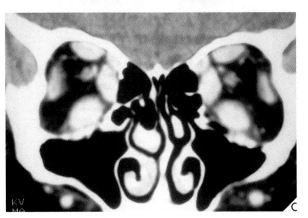

7.6 | *A:* A 45-year-old woman presented wearing an occluder over one eye to avoid diplopia. She had a history of thyroid hyperactivity 6 months earlier. *B:* Diplopia increased and she was treated with oral steroids, but her double vision worsened and she began to lose vision in both eyes. Her motility pattern revealed substantial restriction in upgaze bilaterally. *C:* The CT scan confirmed the presence of enlarged extraocular muscles compressing the optic nerve at its apex. She subsequently underwent bilateral transantral decompression for her thyroid orbitopathy with recovery of visual acuity from 20/100 to 20/30 bilaterally.

related to giant cell arteritis;[10,11] collagen vascular disease,[12] or vasospasm. Dissection within the wall of the carotid or vertebrobasilar arteries often causes pain but is an unusual cause of ophthalmoplegia. Abnormal communication between arterial branches and the venous system within and around the cavernous sinus (carotid-cavernous fistula) may cause ophthalmoplegia by compression or focal ischemia. The VI nerve is particularly sensitive in a dural cavernous sinus fistula.[13]

Inflammatory causes of ophthalmoplegia are frequent in younger patients (Fig. 7.8). The cranial nerves may be affected directly, as in postviral syndromes[14] or demyelinating disease. Ophthalmoplegia may be related to immune reaction to a viral illness. The C. Miller Fisher variant of the Guillain–Barré syndrome may produce variable motility deficits associated with ataxia and hyporeflexivity.[15] There usually is bilateral involvement of the facial musculature. Cerebrospinal fluid protein is characteristically elevated

Figure 7.7. Vascular Causes of Ophthalmoplegia

SMALL VESSELS
Diabetes
Hypertension
Collagen vascular disease: systemic lupus

MEDIUM-SIZED VESSELS
Giant-cell arteritis
Polyarteritis nodosa
Vasospasm

LARGE VESSELS
Atherosclerosis
Dissection
Arteriovenous malformation
Aneurysm formation

Figure 7.8. Inflammatory Causes of Ophthalmoplegia

Postviral
  Herpes zoster
Demyelinating
Sarcoidosis
Autoimmune
  C. Miller Fisher variant of Guillain–Barré
Infectious
  Bacterial
    Mycobacterial (TB)

Fungal
  Mucor
  Aspergillosis
Parasitic
  Toxoplasmosis
  Cysticercosis

Figure 7.9. Neoplastic Causes of Ophthalmoplegia

Meningioma
Craniopharyngioma
Pituitary adenoma
Neurilemoma
Chordoma
Chondrosarcoma
Epidermoid
Metastasis
  Lung
  Breast
  Prostate
Squamous cell carcinoma

Melanoma
Lymphoproliferative disorders
Glioma
Ependymoma
Medulloblastoma
Nasopharyngeal carcinoma
Adenoid cystic carcinoma
Adenocarcinoma
Esthesioneuroblastoma

without pleocytosis (cells in the CSF). Vertical gaze palsies[16,17] suggest that the brainstem is directly affected. Severe involvement may require intensive neurologic support, mainly respiratory. Fortunately, recovery is the rule, although it may take months. Basilar meningitis, usually tuberculous,[18] cryptococcal, fungal, or luetic,[19] has a propensity for involvement of the ocular motor nerves within the subarachnoid space. Sarcoidosis[20] is a presumably noninfectious inflammatory syndrome that may affect the ocular motor nerves in the subarachnoid space. Within the cavernous sinus septic thrombosis, usually bacterial[21] and arising from the orbit or paranasal sinuses, may produce ophthalmoplegia. Fungal infection related to *Mucor* or *Aspergillus* frequently involves the orbital apex or cavernous sinus. Parasitic infections of the CNS are rare in most states, but cysticercosis is an increasingly common cause of posterior fossa pathology in the southwestern United States. In the setting of acquired immune deficiency syndrome (AIDS), intracranial toxoplasmosis involving the brainstem[22] and cryptococcal meningitis are common causes of ophthalmoplegia.[23]

Neoplastic processes (Fig. 7.9) may mechanically compromise the ocular motor nerves. Alternatively, a neoplasm may secondarily affect their blood supply. Tumors may affect the ocular motor nerves in the parasellar region (meningiomas, craniopharyngiomas, pituitary adenomas, neurilemoma[24]), along the clivus (chordomas[25], metastases) or within the brainstem (gliomas,[26] metastases, ependymomas, medulloblastoma). Tumors may also arise from the paranasal sinuses secondarily invading the cranium. These include adenoid cystic carcinoma, nasopharyngeal carcinoma,[27] and esthesioneuroblastoma.

Congenital cranial nerve palsies may be hereditary or may represent embryologic developmental anomalies. Congenital abducens palsies are uncommon except for Duane syndrome (Fig. 7.10), in which maldevelopment of the VI nerve is associated with innervation of the lateral rectus muscle by branches of the oculomotor nerve.[28,29] Clinically, limited horizontal movement (most impressively abduction) is accompanied by narrowing of the palpebral fissure on adduction. Because of the horizontal co-contraction there is frequent associated ocular upshoot (and, less commonly, downshoot). Bilateral congenital absence of abduction may be associated with

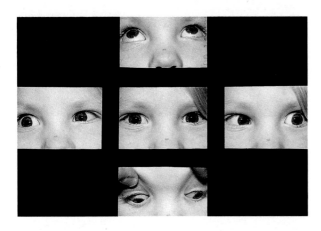

7.10 | This 6-year-old girl was noted to develop problems with "cross eyes" when she looked to either side. On examination she was found to have bilateral limitation in abduction associated with narrowing of her palpebral fissures on attempted adduction. Duane syndrome, here bilateral, is often overlooked for years because the patients seldom complain of diplopia.

facial diplegia and other bulbar abnormalities (Möbius syndrome).[30–33] Apparently congenital III nerve palsies are often perinatal, possibly related to birth trauma.[34] Pupillary involvement is variable, with the pupil occasionally miotic.[35] True congenital oculomotor paresis is uncommon and may be associated with cyclic episodes of overaction within the distribution of the III nerve (cyclic oculomotor paresis).[36] Congenital IV nerve palsies are common. Along with trauma they are the most frequent cause of trochlear nerve dysfunction in the nonelderly population.[24]

Trauma may mechanically disrupt the ocular motor nerves, particularly the VI nerve associated with basilar skull fractures (Fig. 7.11). Mechanical disruption of the abducens nerve may also be associated with increased intracranial pressure. This is presumably related to shifts in position of the brainstem and may also occur after lumbar puncture.[37] Less commonly, other ocular motor nerve palsies have also been reported with increased intracranial pressure.[38] An intracranial mass lesion may force the medial aspect of the temporal lobe through the incisura created by the tentorium.[39] In herniating downward, the III nerve may be stretched against the posterior cerebral and superior cerebellar arteries. The trochlear nerve is the most frequently affected ocular motor nerve with closed head trauma, although the pathophysiology remains unclear.

DIFFERENTIAL DIAGNOSIS

In considering the potential pathophysiologies of ophthalmoplegia,[24] the age of the patient[40,41] and the onset and course of the paralysis are most important (Fig. 7.12). This may be misleading, as even mass lesions may present "suddenly." The patient may have been previously unaware of a slowly progressive deviation because of compensation by fusional vergence. Sudden increase in tumor size (pituitary apoplexy) may lead to the rapid onset of symptoms. The presence of "fellow travelers" plays a major role in the diagnosis. Other associated cranial nerve palsies, especially the V (trigeminal), may rapidly point the astute clinician in the proper direction (Fig. 7.13). Eyelid position and pupil size and reaction are probably the most important

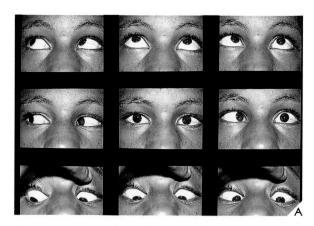

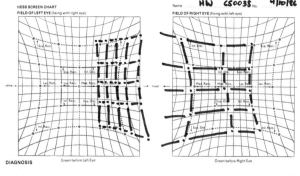

7.11 | *A:* A 15-year-old patient was struck in the head with an ax resulting in a severe depressed left parietal skull fracture. With recovery of mentation following neurosurgical intervention he noted horizontal diplopia which failed to clear, leading to a slowly progressive head turn. *B:* His complete abduction deficit relates to a traumatically induced left VI nerve palsy. He was subsequently treated with eye muscle surgery in which the superior and inferior rectus muscles were transposed to the lateral rectus insertion.

Figure 7.12. Important Factors in Differential Diagnosis

AGE

Perinatal
  Congenital
  Birth trauma
Childhood
  Postviral
  Posterior fossa mass lesion
    Cerebellar astrocytoma
    Medulloblastoma
    Pontine glioma
  Gradenigo syndrome
    (petrositis post-otitis media)

Young adults
  Demyelinating
  Trauma
  Arteriovenous
    malformation
  Aneurysm
Older adults
  Diabetes
  Hypertension
  Atherosclerosis
Elderly
  Giant-cell arteritis

ONSET AND COURSE

Acute
  Vascular
  Inflammatory
  Trauma
  Pituitary apoplexy
Slowly progressive
  Mass lesion
    Neoplastic
    Aneurysm
    Inflammatory mass
Fluctuating
  Myasthenia
  Inflammatory

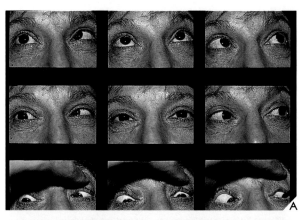
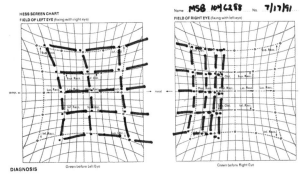
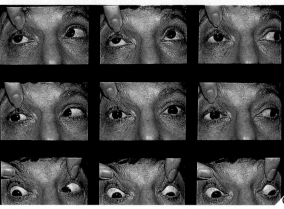
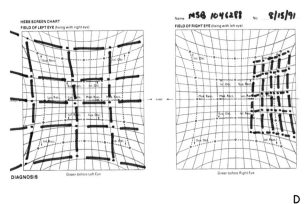

7.13 | *A:* A 56-year-old woman with a meningioma involving the right cavernous sinus presented with a progressive right VI nerve palsy resulting in an increasing esodeviation. There was decreased corneal sensation on the right side. *B:* The presence of an abduction deficit was further con-firmed on Hess screen. *C:* Following botulinum toxin injection into the medial rectus muscle on the right side, transient weakness in the medial rectus muscle reduced the head turn and progressive esodeviation. *D:* The Hess screen confirmed the change in pattern.

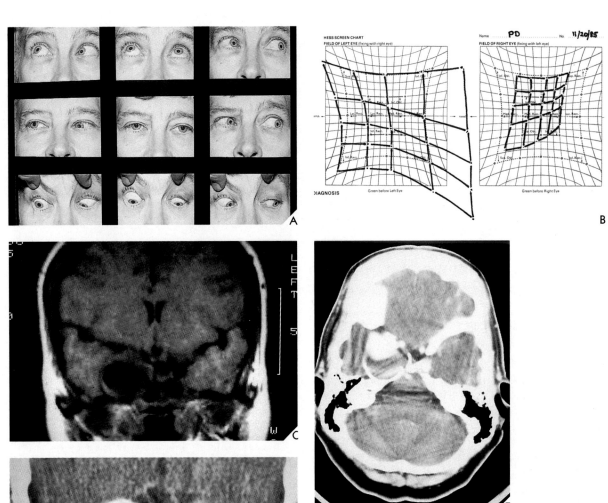

7.14 | *A:* This woman was bothered by double vision, particularly on down-right gaze. *B:* Hess screen confirmed a partial abduction deficit as well as problems with vertical gaze, particularly downgaze. The presence of a combined partial III and VI cranial nerve palsy localized pathology to the cavernous sinus. *C, D, E:* CT and MRI scans confirmed the presence of a giant cavernous sinus aneurysm.

concomitants to a motility disturbance. Their presence or absence may markedly alter the differential diagnosis. Multiplicity of cranial nerve involvement suggests cavernous sinus localization (Fig. 7.14). Long tract signs (focal motor weakness or sensory loss) increase the likelihood of intrinsic brainstem pathology.

Abducens palsies are the most common form of ophthalmoplegia. Involvement within the brainstem may cause a horizontal gaze palsy if the VI nerve nucleus is involved.[42] The VII nerve may be involved as it loops around the VI nerve nucleus, producing facial weakness. Hemiparesis, or other long tract signs, suggests intra-axial involvement. Extension to involve the laterally located sympathetic fibers can produce a first-order Horner syndrome (mild ptosis and miosis).[43] Inflammatory plaques may be related to demyelinating disease, a possibly underestimated cause of VI nerve palsy in the young adult population. Intrinsic brainstem glioma, small metastatic lesions, and arteriovenous malformations are other causes of a nuclear VI nerve palsy.[44] Other tumors within the posterior fossa, often arising from the cerebellum, may secondarily produce abducens paresis.

Within the subarachnoid space, especially as the VI nerve crosses over the petrous apex and under the petroclinoid ligament, the abducens nerve is subject to trauma and inflammation. Traumatic VI nerve palsies may be associated with basilar skull fractures, which often involve the clivus or petrous bone (see Fig. 7.11). This may be accompanied by CSF otorrhea (fluid in the middle ear) or mastoid ecchymosis (Battle's sign). Gradenigo[45] described the association of a VI nerve palsy with decreased hearing and facial pain secondary to petrositis. This may originate as otitis media in children. Apparent Gradenigo syndrome in adults is usually not inflammatory but may be due to nasopharyngeal carcinoma[27] (see Fig. 7.3). Microvascular disease associated with diabetes and hypertension most frequently produces an isolated palsy presumably involving the nerve in the subarachnoid space. The presence of other neurologic signs on a detailed examination changes the differential diagnosis and mandates a complete imaging workup.[46] Mechanical damage to the VI nerve may be associated with increased intracranial pressure, presumably related to a shift in the position of the brainstem. In children, acute VI nerve palsies may be post-viral,[47] although slow progression raises the possibility of a brainstem or cerebellar tumor. Congenital VI nerve palsies are unusual. These may be associated with aberrant innervation of the lateral rectus muscle (Duane syndrome) or may be bilateral, with other maldevelopment of brainstem nuclei (Möbius syndrome) with associated facial diplegia. Often a specific diagnosis remains elusive. This is less common with bilateral than unilateral VI nerve palsies.[44] Aneurysms may affect the VI nerve[48] although much less commonly than the III nerve.

Other conditions can simulate a VI nerve palsy. Medial rectus restriction, especially when mild, may be mistaken for ophthalmoplegia (Fig. 7.15). This may be related to trauma, thyroid orbitopathy, or orbital inflammatory disease (myositis).[49] Overaction of the medial rectus muscles, as seen in dor-

VI NERVE PALSY

sal midbrain syndrome (retraction-convergence nystagmus) or thalamic hemorrhage, may be mistaken for bilateral abduction deficits. A comitant esotropia greater at distance than near has been referred to as *divergence insufficiency.* Although prior studies have emphasized the lack of associated neurologic signs and symptoms,[50] with increasing use of MRI it is possible that more of these cases will be found to be associated with subtle brainstem lesions[51] and actually represent minimal abducens weakness with associated spread of comitance. Myasthenia gravis can cause any form of motility disturbance.

IV NERVE PALSY

Trochlear nerve palsy (innervating the superior oblique muscle) is the most common paretic cause of vertical or oblique diplopia (see Fig. 7.1). Classically, there is a hyperdeviation which increases with contralateral gaze and ipsilateral head tilt. With time, the deviation may become increasingly comi-

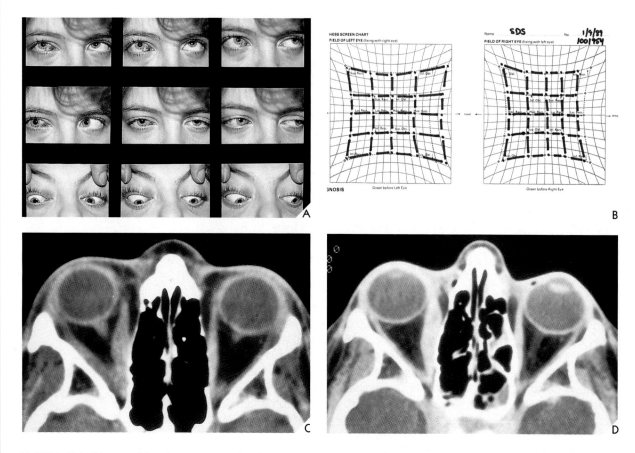

7.15 | *A:* This 15-year-old patient presented with a complaint of horizontal diplopia. The presence of injection over the medial rectus muscle suggested a local problem within the orbit. *B:* The Hess screen confirmed the presence of an abduction deficit but did not distinguish a paretic from restrictive cause. She responded to oral steroids with improvement in her motility. CT scans done initially without *(C)* and then with *(D)* contrast revealed enlargement of the medial rectus muscle on the right with marked enhancement, particularly at the insertion following injection of contrast.

tant. Maddox rod testing demonstrates excyclotorsion. If more than 10 degrees of excyclotorsion are present, bilateral IV nerve palsies are likely. Cyclotorsion may be less common with other causes of vertical deviation.[52] Myasthenia may also produce a vertical deviation. Mild thyroid orbitopathy or other restriction involving the inferior rectus muscle may masquerade as a IV nerve palsy. A skew deviation should be considered when a vertical strabismus does not fit a IV pattern and is not due to a local orbital problem or myasthenia. Asymmetric supranuclear dysfunction is frequently associated with involvement of the vestibular pathways.[53]

   Head trauma, often relatively trivial, is the most common cause of acquired IV nerve palsy.[54] In older patients microvascular disease is also common. Although most of these patients have diabetes or hypertension, the absence of either does not preclude a microvascular cause. A long-standing but previously undetected congenital IV nerve palsy may present at any age due to breakdown of a previously compensated phoria. The finding of increased fusional range or a head tilt on old photos (Fig. 7.16) is very helpful in establishing the diagnosis. Less common causes of IV nerve palsy include pineal tumors, demyelinating disease, and metastatic disease. Nuclear or fascicular IV nerve palsies are rare.[44] When present, they result in a contralateral hypertropia due to the crossing of fibers in the anterior medullary vellum. This is not infrequently associated with an ipsilateral Horner syndrome.[55] Bilateral involvement may be caused by hydrocephalus.[56] When a IV nerve palsy is isolated, workup is seldom revealing.

Because the III nerve innervates four of the six extraocular muscles, profound motility disturbances accompany involvement of the oculomotor nerve. With a complete III nerve palsy the eye may be significantly deviated in primary position, assuming a down and out direction. Because of the accompanying ptosis, patients with an oculomotor palsy may be unaware of their motility disturbance and may not complain of diplopia. Pathologic involvement within the midbrain can produce classical brainstem syndromes.[57]

III NERVE PALSY

7.16 | A 16-year-old patient was referred for intermittent vertical diplopia and hypertropia. On examination he had evidence of a left IV nerve palsy and left hypertropia increasing on right gaze. One of the more common causes of a hyperdeviation is a decompensated congenital IV nerve palsy. In this case examination of childhood pictures demonstrated a persistent right head tilt compatible with a long-standing left IV nerve palsy. He was treated with vertical eye muscle surgery.

Focal involvement of the III nerve nucleus[58] (usually related to metastasis, infarct related to vertebrobasilar insufficiency, or demyelinating plaque) produces bilateral incomplete ptosis and contralateral (usually bilateral) paresis of upgaze. The superior rectus muscle is innervated contralaterally, but the crossing of fibers at the level of the nucleus makes it difficult to see unilateral involvement. Simultaneous involvement of the fascicle of the III nerve within the midbrain tegmentum and the superior cerebellar peduncle (Nothnagel syndrome) can produce ipsilateral ataxia as well as ophthalmoplegia. Dysfunction involving the red nucleus and III nerve fascicle (Benedikt's) may produce a contralateral rubral tremor. More ventral involvement of the midbrain affecting the cerebral peduncle (Weber's) results in ipsilateral III nerve palsy associated with contralateral hemiparesis.

Third nerve involvement within the subarachnoid space may be microvascular or related to hemorrhage. This is most often due to an aneurysm located at the origin of the posterior communicating artery. Because recurrent hemorrhage from an aneurysm may have devastating neurologic consequence, making this diagnosis in a timely fashion is essential. The most useful means of distinguishing between these two common causes is the status of the pupil (Fig. 7.17). Although rare exceptions have been described, the sudden onset of a complete III nerve palsy with sparing of the pupil would be rare with an aneurysm.[59] In the majority of those reported exceptions, the pupil became involved within days of onset of the motility disturbance and ptosis.[60] That is not the case with a *slowly progressive* III nerve palsy related to a cavernous sinus mass (e.g., meningioma, giant cavernous aneurysm,[61] etc.), which may spare the pupil in up to 50% of cases (see Fig. 7.14). In essentially all compressive lesions that spare the pupil the ophthalmoplegia is not complete.[62,63] With microvascular disease (often associated with diabetes) the pupil is spared in 80–85% of most series. Traditionally, it is felt that the peripheral location of the pupillary fibers may be responsible for its lack of involvement by a local microvascular infarct. It is likely that the rapidity of onset plays at least as important a role. A more difficult diagnostic situation is presented by the patient with "relative sparing" of the pupil or the incomplete III nerve palsy with pupillary sparing.[59] In the latter situation, careful follow-up for late pupillary involvement may suffice.

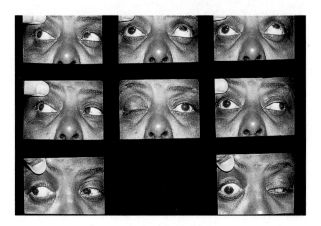

7.17 | This 49-year-old hypertensive woman complained of 5 days of periocular pain, ptosis, and double vision. When her lid was elevated she was noted to have difficulties with upgaze, downgaze, and adduction on the right. Her pupil, however, was not enlarged and reacted normally. In the setting of acute III nerve palsy the status of the pupil remains paramount. With complete pupil sparing the cause is almost always microvascular. Her III nerve palsy cleared over the next 10 weeks without residual.

In the former, the decreased morbidity of angiography suggests complete workup to exclude the possibility of an aneurysm.[64] MRI with MRA (magnetic resonance angiography) may pick up larger lesions but both are inadequate to exclude completely the presence of an aneurysm. Imaging studies (CT or, better, MRI with gadolinium) should precede angiography. A mass lesion on MRI or CT may preclude the need for angiography. Neurilemomas of the III nerve are an uncommon cause of subarachnoid oculomotor palsy.[65]

A significant clinical challenge arises with partial involvement of the oculomotor nerve. The III nerve divides into a superior (innervating the levator and superior rectus) and inferior (innervating the medial and inferior rectus, the inferior oblique, and the ciliary body and iris) division within the cavernous sinus. Traditionally, divisional palsies are felt to represent pathology at or anterior to the cavernous sinus. Although a superior divisional palsy may be a clue to ophthalmic artery aneurysm, it is not always localizing. Divisional III nerve palsies have been reported related to selective involvement of the fascicles exiting the brainstem or even within the nucleus itself.[66,67] Divisional palsies may also have a microvascular origin.[68] All divisional palsy should be worked up.

Aberrant regeneration of the III nerve occurs from presumed misdirection during regrowth after damage to the axons.[69] Clinically, these patients demonstrate variable degrees of miosis and lid retraction (or hang-up) on adduction or depression[70] (Fig. 7.18). Co-contraction within the vertical rectus muscles causes persistent vertical movement limitation and globe retraction. It occurs most frequently after trauma, surgery, or tumor compression. Congenital III nerve palsies may also be associated with aberrant regeneration. An unusual syndrome, primary aberrant regeneration, occurs without an antecedent III nerve palsy, usually related to a slowly progressive lesion in the cavernous sinus such as a meningioma[71] or a cavernous carotid aneurysm.[61] Therefore, the finding of aberrant regeneration without a preceding history of an oculomotor palsy demands further evaluation. Aberrant regeneration has never been reported after a microvas-

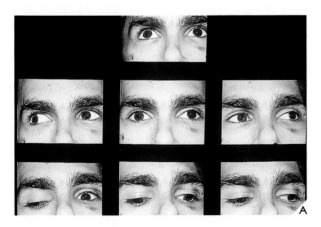
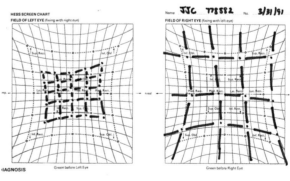

7.18 | *A, B:* This 30-year-old man developed double vision following a motor vehicle accident 12 years before. Although he had substantial improvement in his eye movements, he was left with a residual exodeviation and experienced problems with downgaze. With attempted down- and right gaze he developed lid eleva-

tion on the left. Abnormal lid hang-up or elevation with attempted adduction or downgaze as well as miosis marks the presence of aberrant regeneration. This misdirection syndrome does not occur following a microvascular III nerve palsy.

cular III nerve lesion. Therefore, the diagnosis of a microvascular etiology is not tenable if the oculomotor palsy clears with evidence of aberrant regeneration.

A microvascular cranial nerve palsy spontaneously recovers, usually within 3 months. As the deviation clears it tends to become increasingly comitant, possibly leaving a permanent strabismus. Although a microvascular III nerve palsy may leave a persistent deviation, failure to resolve completely requires investigation if a workup has not already been undertaken.

MULTIPLE CRANIAL NERVE PALSIES

Because involvement of multiple cranial nerves has localizing importance, detection of nonisolated ophthalmoplegia is essential. The combination of an abduction deficit with ptosis, or a limitation in adduction or vertical movement, immediately suggests multiplicity. When the III nerve is paretic, assessment of the IV nerve function is important. Loss of intorsion with attempted downgaze (notation of the movement of a conjunctival vessel) implies coexisting involvement of the IV nerve.

When more than a single cranial nerve palsy occurs simultaneously, the cavernous sinus is frequently the location of the pathology (Fig. 7.19 and see Fig. 7.14). This is particularly true when the palsy is associated with pain or facial sensory loss. Because the fibers of the trigeminal nerve are located just below the III and IV cranial nerves in the lateral wall of the cavernous sinus and the first division (ophthalmic) of the V nerve passes through the superior orbital fissure, it is not surprising that lesions of the cavernous sinus, superior orbital fissure, and the parasellar area often result in multiple cranial nerve palsies including the trigeminal nerve.[25] The VI nerve, which is deeper within the cavernous sinus, and the sympathetic fibers that leave the carotid artery in company with the VI nerve before joining fibers of the V may also be involved, producing a combination of abduction deficit, mild ptosis, and miosis. If the parasellar lesion is extensive, the optic nerve, chiasm, and optic tract may also be simultaneously involved, leading to decreased acuity, an afferent pupillary defect, and visual field defects. Pathology within the orbital apex does not have to be large to involve the optic nerve and be associated with poor acuity. Pathologic processes in the parasellar region[25] are outlined in Figure 7.20. Unusual pathology can include myeloma.[72] A sphe-

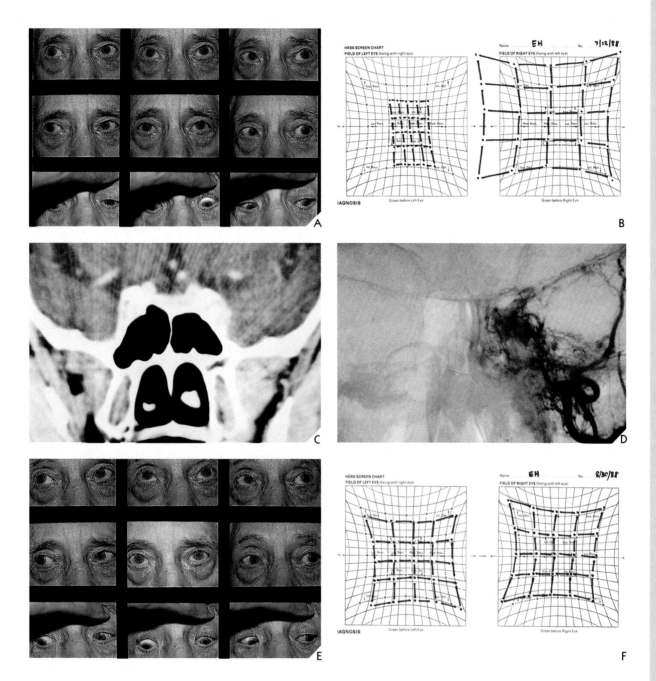

7.19 | *A:* This 79-year-old woman presented with a 3-month history of increasing left periorbital pain and a 6-week history of focusing difficulty. *B:* On examination she had evidence of problems with elevation, abduction, and adduction on the left side. *C:* A CT scan was initially interpreted as normal, but closer observation showed a fullness in the left cavernous sinus. *D:* An angiogram revealed a left dural cavernous fistula. She was treated with embolization, with marked improvement. *E, F:* Ocular motility improved and periorbital pain decreased. The differential diagnosis of painful ophthalmoplegia in the older population includes not only neoplastic and inflammatory pathology within the cavernous sinus, but also giant cell arteritis and dural cavernous sinus fistulae which may not show substantial external signs.

noid sinus mucocele[73,74] may expand into the cavernous sinus producing ophthalmoplegia. Squamous cell and adenoid cystic carcinoma reach the cavernous sinus perineurally from a peripheral primary.[75] Simultaneous involvement of more than one cranial nerve due to microvascular disease is uncommon[76] and requires a complete imaging workup to exclude other pathology.

PSEUDOPALSIES AND MYOPATHIES

Involvement of the individual extraocular muscles may masquerade as ophthalmoplegia. These patients may have diffuse slowing of saccades and limitation in ductions. In myotonic dystrophy, abnormalities in the extraocular muscles[77] are accompanied by other muscle involvement. Involvement of the levator results in bilateral ptosis, and there is frequent involvement of the

Figure 7.20. Differential Diagnosis by Location

ORBIT
Idiopathic orbital inflammatory disease
Thyroid orbitopathy
Trauma
Myasthenia

SUPERIOR ORBITAL FISSURE/CAVERNOUS SINUS (PARASELLAR)
Meningioma
Neurilemoma
Pituitary tumor
Cavernous aneurysm
Craniopharyngioma
Cavernoma (cavernous hemangioma)
Chordoma
Chondrosarcoma
Carotid-cavernous fistula
Myeloma
Metastases
Direct extension from the paranasal
  sinuses
  Sphenoid sinus mucocele
  Adenoid cystic carcinoma
  Squamous cell carcinoma
  Lymphoma
  Fungal infection
  Bacterial infection

SUBARACHNOID SPACE
Trauma
Microvascular
Nasopharyngeal carcinoma
Sarcoid
Aneurysm
Chordoma
Meningioma

INTRA-AXIAL BRAINSTEM
Infarction
Hemorrhage
Glioma
Medulloblastoma
Metastases
Arteriovenous malformation
Toxoplasmosis
Lymphoma

muscles of the head and neck.[78] Other ocular signs include cataractous changes.[79] In oropharyngeal dystrophy, a familial syndrome of French Canadians, bulbar musculature is affected, with characteristic temporalis wasting.[80]

The most common cause of primary muscle dysfunction is inflammation. This may be infectious (related to trichinosis[81]), but more commonly the causative agent is unknown. Orbital pseudotumor or idiopathic orbital inflammatory disease is often associated with a significant component of extraocular muscle involvement.[49,82] The myositis of idiopathic orbital inflammatory disease may be isolated to a single muscle, but more frequently it affects several. The disease process is often bilateral, even though symptoms are more frequently reported unilaterally. Local orbital signs (proptosis, injection) are common, and essentially all patients have some degree of discomfort. The involved extraocular muscle is usually enlarged on CT or MRI. Enhancement of the muscle, and particularly its insertion into the globe, may help to separate myositis from thyroid orbitopathy[83] (see Fig. 7.15). High-dose daily steroids are usually effective in reversing the disease process and eliminating the pain. Nonsteroidal anti-inflammatory drugs are less effective than steroids but have fewer side effects. In those few who do not respond or who become steroid dependent, low-dose radiation therapy (20 Gy) may be effective in inducing a remission.

Chronic progressive ophthalmoplegia (CPEO) is caused by a mitochondrial abnormality in the metabolic oxidative chain.[84] Patients with CPEO often present with bilateral ptosis, limitation in all eye movements, and markedly slowed saccades. Interestingly, in spite of ocular misalignment these patients seldom complain of diplopia. Clinically, there is often a significant weakness in the facial muscles, and overly aggressive attempts at treating the ptosis may lead to exposure keratopathy and corneal ulceration. Biopsy of systemic muscles reveals "ragged red fibers," with the mitochondria of the involved muscle fibers concentrated peripherally. CPEO may be associated with a number of other abnormalities affecting the central nervous system,[85] abnormalities in cardiac conduction,[86] and pigmentary retinopathy.[87]

MYASTHENIA GRAVIS

The "great masquerader" when the extraocular muscle system is evaluated is myasthenia gravis. This autoimmune syndrome is related to antibodies formed against the acetylcholine receptors on muscle fibers responsible for initiating muscle contraction.[88] Clinically, spontaneous remissions and exacerbations are common. Although any muscle in the body may be affected, the extraocular muscles are particularly at risk, probably related to their extremely high metabolic rate. Between 50%[89] and 70%[90] of patients with ocular symptoms eventually develop systemic involvement. The chance of systemic involvement declines substantially if involvement remains restricted to the extraocular muscles for more than 2 years.[89] Patients with ocular myasthenia most frequently present with ptosis and diplopia. All ages can be affected, although the incidence peaks in middle-aged adults. Any pattern of dysfunction is possible. The hallmarks of myasthenia are variability and fatigability. Repetitive muscle exertion leads to increasing weakness as the compromised receptors are exhausted. Symptoms, therefore, are more common in the afternoon. Cogan noted lid overshoot with occasional flutter when a patient looked from down to straight ahead (Cogan lid twitch sign).[91] A diagnosis of myasthenia can be definitively established by identifying a decrease in the acetylcholine receptors on a motor end-plate assay after biopsy.[92] This is rarely, if ever, necessary. Antibodies to the acetylcholine receptor can be assayed commercially.[93] When myasthenia is restricted to the extraocular muscles, however, levels are undetectable in 25% or more of cases.[94] Electromyography may reveal a decremental response with repeated stimulation. This can be seen even more impressively with single fiber studies.[95] The simplest clinical test for myasthenia (Fig. 7.21) is the administration of Tensilon® (edrophonium)[96] or Prostigmin® (neostigmine). By decreasing the turnover of acetylcholine, an increased transmission may produce a transient improvement in the muscular activity. This is most obvious when there is ptosis. When ocular muscle weakness alone is present, a Maddox rod may pick up a subtle change in muscle activity. With Prostigmin a longer duration is obtained, long enough to repeat motility measurements including a Hess screen or Lancaster red/green test.[97]

The presence of myasthenia does not preclude the coexistence of intracranial pathology. Without other neurologic findings, however, workup is likely to be unrevealing. There is an increased incidence of thyroid dysfunction in patients with myasthenia. Although thyroid levels may be abnormal in only approximately 5%, up to 15% of myasthenics may have some evidence of thyroid dysfunction.[98] Ocular involvement in myasthenia often does not respond to Mestinon® (pyridostigmine). Steroid therapy may be effective,[89] but questions regarding the potential side effects of long-term high-dose steroids must be raised even when they are used every other day. Some advocate gradually building up a steroid dose,[99] while others recommend initiating therapy at a high daily dose with gradual taper to alternate

Figure 7.21. Tensilon Test

INDICATIONS
Suspicion of myasthenia
Presence of ptosis
Extraocular muscle dysfunction

PREPARATION
Reclinable chair
Venous access
Atropine (0.4 mg) drawn up
Tensilon (10 mg/1 ml)
Saline for flush

ADMINISTRATION
Monitor pulse (ECG or radial pulse
  monitor)
Administer 0.2 cc (2 mg) Tensilon
Observe for 2 minutes
If no response, administer remainder
  (possibly in increments)

OBSERVATION
Systemic effects
  Lacrimation
  Stomach grumbling
  Bradycardia

Positive effects
  Reduction of ptosis
  Improvement in motility
  Increase in saccadic
  velocity
  Change in misalignment

days. For safety, high-dose therapy can be administrated initially while the patient is hospitalized, as there may be transient worsening. In young patients and in those with evidence of thymus enlargement, a thymectomy may lead to remission.[100] All patients who are suspected of having myasthenia should have a baseline neurologic examination and should be warned of the potential for respiratory and bulbar muscle involvement leading to swallowing and breathing difficulties. Immediate relief of diplopia may be afforded by occlusion therapy. Although Fresnel prisms may occasionally be of benefit, the variability of the process makes correction difficult. Strabismus surgery is seldom, if ever, indicated.

TOXIC INVOLVEMENT

Toxic involvement at the neuromuscular junction is rare.[101] *Botulinum* toxin, one of the most potent toxins known, inhibits calcium-mediated release of acetylcholine at the presynaptic terminal. The effect is irreversible, leading to muscle weakness lasting up to one to three months. With systemic botulism, ophthalmoplegia is associated with mydriasis.[102] There may be rapid quivering movements of the eyes. When the muscles of respiration are involved, mechanical support becomes critical. Although botulism is usually associated with ingestion of home-canned products, clostridial infection of a wound can also produce systemic poisoning.[104] Ticks may produce a toxin that results in presynaptic neuromuscular blockade,[105] leading to flaccid paralysis with associated mydriasis. Diphtheria toxin may produce a profound impairment in accommodation.

RESTRICTIVE SYNDROMES
TRAUMA

A restrictive syndrome related to prior trauma is usually appropriately diagnosed by history, although local signs (enophthalmos, numbness in the V2 distribution, facial scars) may help to raise the issue (Fig. 7.22). The inferior rectus muscle is most frequently involved, leading to a variable hypertropia that usually increases on upgaze. Traditionally, this has been ascribed to "entrapment" of the inferior rectus associated with a blowout fracture.[106] It is

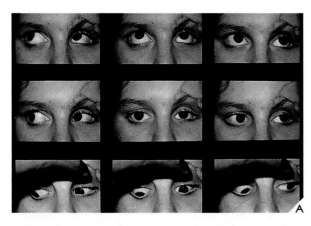

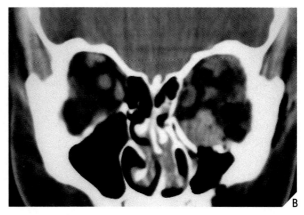

7.22 | *A:* This 18-year-old woman was involved in motor vehicle accident with trauma to the left brow and orbit. She complained of double vision both on up- and downgaze. *B:* Hemorrhage around and within the infe-

rior rectus muscle likely accounted for both the focal weakness as well as the restrictive component, which improved but did not entirely resolve.

possible that most of these cases are related to scarring around the muscle due to hemorrhage, or to actual fibrosis within the muscle secondary to prior intramuscular hemorrhage and/or edema.[107] Trauma may also result in persistent weakness within the muscle itself. The medial rectus is involved less commonly than the inferior but may be associated with a medial wall fracture. Forced ductions may reveal the restriction, but subtle defects are often better picked up on tonometry in primary and eccentric gaze.

THYROID ORBITOPATHY

Restrictive syndromes are most commonly associated with thyroid orbitopathy (see Fig. 7.6), an apparent autoimmune phenomenon associated with enlargement of the extraocular muscles.[108] Unlike orbital inflammatory disease and its accompanying myositis, this condition is almost always bilateral (although it may be quite asymmetric) and the muscle tendons are relatively spared on CT scanning. Thyroid hormone levels may be elevated, normal, or even low.[109] Treatment of hyperthyroidism with radioactive iodine often precedes or even precipitates orbital involvement. When accompanied by other prominent orbital signs (proptosis, lid retraction, lid and globe lag, prominence of the episcleral vessels over the horizontal rectus muscles, and lid edema), there is little question about the diagnosis (Fig. 7.23). When these are not present, arriving at the correct diagnosis may be more difficult. The diagnostic study of choice is a direct coronal CT scan of the orbits to assess the size of the extraocular muscles.[83,108] Bilateral enlargement is strongly suggestive of thyroid orbitopathy, even when the endocrine studies are unremarkable. Measurement of T_3, T_4, and TSH should be done. This is not necessary to make the diagnosis, but abnormal levels must be recognized and the patient referred to an endocrinologist for appropriate treatment.

Because the inferior rectus muscle is most frequently involved, the most common clinical complaint is vertical or oblique diplopia. Restriction of the inferior rectus, coupled with increased orbital volume, often leads to intraocular pressure elevation, especially on upgaze.[4] The medial rectus is the second most commonly affected muscle, followed by the superior rectus. Recession of the restricted muscle may be performed but should be deferred until the deviation is stable. Fresnel prisms may play an interim role, although occlusion is often necessary to avoid incapacitating diplopia. Use of

7.23 | This 40-year-old woman complained of diplopia. The presence of marked lid retraction immediately suggested that her double vision was related to restriction secondary to thyroid orbitopathy. Other causes of lid retraction include Collier's sign seen with dorsal midbrain syndrome.

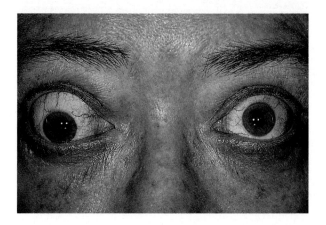

adjustable sutures is advised, as it is often difficult to predict the amount of surgery necessary. Under- and overcorrections, unfortunately, are common. When orbital surgery is necessary for compressive optic neuropathy or exposure keratopathy, it should be undertaken before muscle surgery, because decompression will probably increase or change the amount of restriction.

CONGENITAL SYNDROMES

Restrictive syndromes are rarely congenital. Congenital fibrosis of the inferior rectus muscle may be familial.[109] This can be distinguished from a double elevator palsy related to abnormal function in the superior rectus and inferior oblique. Patients with a double elevator palsy often have an associated ptosis, making the diagnosis easier. Studies suggest that at least some cases diagnosed as supranuclear palsy may have a restrictive component.[110] Congenital abnormality in the development of the extraocular muscles includes anomalies of insertion and even complete absence.[111] This has most frequently been reported in connection with craniofacial anomalies.[112] Even when the muscles are present, abnormal innervation may lead to misalignment. In Duane syndrome there is secondary fibrosis of significant portions of the lateral rectus. Brown syndrome (congenital short superior oblique tendon) may resemble inferior oblique paresis and thus raise the possibility of myasthenia. Because of the inability of the congenitally short tendon to relax, the involved eye is limited in elevation when adducted.[113]

OTHER SYNDROMES

Fibrosis and scarring within an extraocular muscle can also be acquired. In addition to trauma and thyroid orbitopathy, inflammation can lead to loss of muscle fibers and secondary fibrosis. This may be related to the primary destructive process of the inflammation alone or to secondary ischemia related to swelling (tissue compartment syndrome). Other inflammatory syndromes such as Wegener's granulomatosis[114] and giant-cell arteritis[115] may directly affect the extraocular muscles. In acquired Brown syndrome, inflammation affects the trochlea and limits the relaxation of the superior oblique. This may be associated with rheumatoid arthritis[116] or with idiopathic orbital inflammatory disease.[117] Other infiltrative processes (amyloidosis[118], carotid cavernous fistula,[83] and lymphoma) may also limit extraocular muscle relaxation. Neoplasia may affect the muscle from local orbital extension but also may grow directly within a muscle from a metastatic source.[119] These processes are best evaluated with direct enhanced coronal CT images of the orbit. Fat suppression sequences on MRI may provide additional soft-tissue data. Orbital congestive syndromes can cause a restrictive component. Carotid-cavernous fistula, cavernous sinus thrombosis, inflammation, or infection may prevent involved muscles from relaxing. Orbital cellulitis may be bacterial (usually from a paranasal sinus source) or fungal (often associated with the metabolic acidosis of diabetes mellitus). These patients are extremely ill, and appropriate antibiotic therapy possibly combined with surgical drainage is essential.[120]

PAINFUL OPHTHALMOPLEGIA

One commonly encountered special syndrome involving diplopia is "painful ophthalmoplegia." Acute microvascular III, IV, or VI cranial nerve palsies are often accompanied by discomfort. This is usually retrobulbar and is presumably related to concomitant dural ischemia that produces referred pain, as the dura is innervated by recurrent branches of the trigeminal nerve. Specific ischemic syndromes, including giant-cell arteritis[11] and ocular ischemic syndrome related to carotid compromise, are often associated with pain referred to the face and retrobulbar area. Pain may also occur related to vasospasm. These variants of migraine are often unassociated with ophthalmoplegia. In the Raeder paratrigeminal syndrome, dysfunction of the sympathetic fibers causes unilateral ptosis and miosis.[121] Ophthalmoplegic migraine is uncommon after childhood. It is often accompanied by pain and can be associated with sparing of the pupil.[122] Carotid dissection may also produce a painful Horner syndrome, although ophthalmoplegia is uncommon.

Inflammation of *Herpes zoster* infection affecting the ophthalmic division of the trigeminal nerve may spread contiguously to involve the III, VI, and most frequently IV[123] cranial nerves in the area of the cavernous sinus.[124] Although usually ipsilateral, contralateral and even bilateral cases are seen. Associated pain is frequent. Corneal, uveitic, and optic nerve involvement may reduce acuity. Ophthalmoplegia usually follows involvement by several weeks but may occur earlier. Aggressive therapy with acyclovir may modify the course of zoster ophthalmicus but there are little data on its effect on ophthalmoplegia. Fortunately, the prognosis for recovery is very good, although residual deficits may persist.[125] The possibility of an underlying HIV (human immunodeficiency virus) should be considered in patients who present with zoster ophthalmoplegia.[126]

Nonspecific inflammation affecting the cavernous sinus can produce painful ophthalmoplegia (Tolosa–Hunt syndrome).[127,128] Pathologic specimens have shown granulomatous inflammation.[129] Any pattern of cranial nerve palsy is possible.[130] Extension through the superior orbital fissure suggests a possible association with idiopathic orbital inflammatory disease and may lead to decreased vision. The association with orbital inflammatory disease is further supported by the common embryologic origin of the orbit and cavernous sinus. Steroid therapy in low doses results in resolution of the pain and improvement in the ophthalmoplegia. Tolosa–Hunt syndrome is a diagnosis of exclusion. Neoplastic processes, especially lymphoma, may mimic Tolosa–Hunt syndrome and improve with initiation of steroid therapy.[25] Although Tolosa–Hunt syndrome may recur, continued pain or recurrence while the patient is receiving steroids suggests the possibility of an alternative diagnosis.

Ophthalmoplegia secondary to more common causes, including compression, subarachnoid hemorrhage, and microvascular disease, may also be painful. Vascular pathology in the parasellar region including carotid-cavernous fistulae[131,132] (see Fig. 7.19), cavernous sinus thrombosis,[21] and carotid dissection are often uncomfortable.

DIAGNOSTIC AIDS

Before engaging in an expensive workup, it is important to tailor the testing to the particular clinical circumstance. Because imaging studies in cases of isolated ocular motor palsies are often negative, the most important initial study is a thorough neurologic exam for evidence of more extensive involvement. Although hypertension and diabetes predispose to microvascular infarction, their presence does not exclude other possible causes.

The course of the ocular motor nerves is best evaluated anatomically with neuroimaging studies. MRI is the study of first choice. The VI nerve at the level of the pons is best seen in axial section, whereas the cavernous sinus may be better evaluated in coronal section. MRI offers the advantage of multiplanar capability without uncomfortable patient positioning. MRI can identify the course of large and medium-sized vessels by the presence of a flow void, and may be even more sensitive to vessel wall involvement than angiography. Soft-issue detail is better shown on MRI, and this technique is particularly sensitive to hemorrhage. Because the signal characteristics change with blood metabolism, the age of the hemorrhage may be estimated. MRI can be repeated without cumulative radiation effects. Paramagnetic contrast agents (gadolinium) enhance the image of some tumors (meningiomas in particular) that are often isointense with brain. Its use also permits some separation between tumor and surrounding edema. Because basilar skull tumors are a frequent cause of cryptic progressive cranial nerve palsies, MRI should be directed to the parasellar region and the floor of the middle cranial fossa.[133]

The role of magnetic resonance angiography (MRA), which uses special sequencing to obtain an outline of the vascular system, is less clear at this time. Large and medium-sized vessels are imaged but detail is lacking, and the technique is not a substitute for angiography in excluding an aneurysm. It does, however, offer a noninvasive means of assessing the integrity of the major vessels.

Computerized tomography, the gold standard of the last two decades, still plays an important role in assessment. Calcium is not imaged on MRI, and tumors containing calcium (e.g., meningioma, craniopharyngioma), as well as calcified aneurysms, may be easier to detect with CT. Cortical bone is also not imaged on MRI and subtle evidence of bone erosion may only be seen on CT. Suspected fractures are also better imaged with CT. Although MRI is our current assessment mode of choice, CT plays a complementary adjunctive role. CT should be done with contrast unless acute hemorrhage is suspected (pituitary apoplexy) or there is a history of contrast allergy. Direct coronal sections best delineate the cavernous sinus. Axial scans are better for assessing the midbrain and pons. Bone-hardening artifacts off the petrous pyramids limit the resolution of CT in posterior fossa pathology. With progressive improvement in the quality of imaging studies, repeat studies should be performed even in the face of a previously negative workup.[134]

Exclusion of a possible aneurysm requires cerebral angiography. In good hands, there has been a substantial decrease in the morbidity of this procedure. Direct carotid puncture has been replaced in the majority of cases by catheterization of the carotid and vertebral arteries from a femoral or brachial entry site. Although not always required, multiple vessel studies are advisable because multiple lesions are not atypical and may be missed if only a single vessel is studied.

CSF analysis may indicate an underlying inflammatory or infectious process, or a prior subarachnoid hemorrhage. Oligoclonal bands or elevated myelin basic protein support the diagnosis of demyelination. Millipore filtration or cytospin of CSF combined with a cytologic study may reveal evidence of carcinoma or other neoplasia.[135] Blood studies, including ANA, RA latex, protein immunoelectrophoresis, and acetylcholine receptor antibody levels, help to assess the status of the immune system. A simple screening test for inflammation, the sedimentation rate, is particularly useful in suspected giant-cell arteritis. Evoked potential studies (visual, auditory, somatosensory) may provide evidence of demyelination (increased latency) in a patient with suspected multiple sclerosis, as well as defining other focal evidence of brainstem dysfunction. Invasive studies include meningeal biopsy to exclude meningeal carcinomatosis[135] and stereotactic biopsy or open craniotomy to evaluate an intracranial mass lesion. A Tensilon test should always be considered.

THERAPY

Symptomatic diplopia is most commonly dealt with acutely with occlusion. As there is spread of comitance, prisms may permit binocular single vision, at least in primary position. Fresnel prisms are a less expensive alternative to having them ground into the patient's glasses (Fig. 7.24). They also offer a substantial increase in prism dioptric power. Oculinum injection into the opposing muscle can prevent progressive deviation and contralateral contracture[136,137] (see Fig. 7.13). Acutely, this may provide a larger area of binocular single vision. Once a residual deficit is stable, extraocular muscle surgery may be appropriate.[138,139] Adjustable sutures are particularly useful.

CONCLUSION

Abnormalities of ocular motility are common. Although some are related to primary orbital pathology and secondary restriction, most are paretic. Ophthalmoplegia may have multiple causes. A detailed rigorous approach to the history and physical findings will usually lead to the appropriate diagnosis. Attention to the presence of "fellow travelers" is particularly important. The course and age of onset are also critical in establishing a differential diagnosis. Newer imaging studies available are extremely helpful but should be used in a directed fashion by an informed clinician.

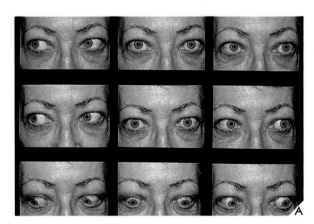

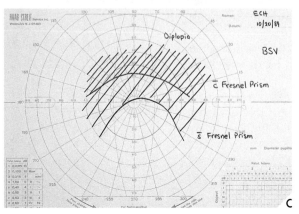

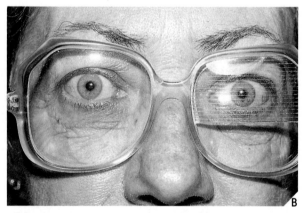

7.24 | *A:* A 56-year-old woman was referred for 4 months of vertical diplopia. She had also noted periorbital edema and workup revealed a goiter. Neither eye would rise substantially above midline but the left was restricted more than the right, leading to 5 diopters of right hyperdeviation increasing with attempted upgaze. She was still able to fuse in downgaze. *B:* Her diplopia in primary position was relieved by placing a Fresnel prism over the upper segment of her glasses. *C:* Binocular single-vision fields quantitate diplopia in upgaze. With the Fresnel prism over her glasses, the diplopia is now present only in far upgaze.

8 | SUPRANUCLEAR DISORDERS

Joseph M.R. Furman

For the ocular motor system, the term "supranuclear" properly refers to central nervous system structures that are important for the control of eye movements, not to structures that are above (rostral in the neuroanatomical sense) the ocular motor nuclei. Motility disturbances are not supranuclear if they affect the III, IV, and VI cranial nerves or nuclei, the neuromuscular junction, the extraocular muscles, or the globe. Typically, supranuclear disorders do not affect the conjugacy of eye movements; each eye is affected similarly. Therefore, diplopia is an unusual symptom of supranuclear disorders.

SUBSYSTEMS OF EYE MOVEMENT CONTROL

The eye movement control subsystems can be divided into those that produce conjugate movements, called versions, and those that produce disconjugate movements, called vergences (divergence and convergence). The subsystems controlling versions produce binocular eye movements that are equal in terms of position, speed, and direction. The vergence system causes the eyes to move in opposite (convergent or divergent) directions to produce binocular vision.

Conjugate eye movements can be slow or fast (rapid). Ocular pursuit and the slow component of optokinetic and vestibular nystagmus are examples of slow conjugate eye movements. Volitional rapid conjugate eye movements are called saccades. The purpose of slow eye movement is to maintain the visual image on the fovea and to minimize "retinal slip," i.e., motion of an image across the retina. Saccades are used to rapidly reposition the eyes so that a new visual target can be seen as quickly as possible.

SLOW EYE MOVEMENTS

Ocular pursuit, also called "smooth pursuit," is a visuo-ocular reflex that requires a small foveal target moving slowly. The smooth pursuit system can accurately follow a target moving predictably if its velocity is less than about 40° per second. A quickly moving or quickly accelerating target cannot be followed accurately by the smooth pursuit system. The optokinetic reflex causes ocular following, much like the pursuit system, except that the requisite visual stimulus is a full-field visual surround rather than a foveal target. Simplistically, smooth pursuit can be considered a foveally mediated visuo-ocular reflex, whereas the optokinetic response can be regarded as dependent upon extra-foveal vision. Because optokinetic tapes used at the bedside stimulate so little of the peripheral retina, they actually assess the pursuit rather than the optokinetic system. Accurate assessment of the optokinetic reflex can be achieved only in a laboratory environment using a full-field visual surround. Because abnormalities in the optokinetic reflex are usually accompanied by abnormalities in the smooth pursuit system, bedside evaluation of smooth pursuit is usually sufficient for an evaluation of optokinetics.

Visual fixation can be thought of as pursuit at zero velocity. With this idea, fixation instabilities associated with slow drifts, which often result in nystagmus, can be regarded as manifestations of abnormal pursuit.

The cerebral regions thought to be important for smooth pursuit and the slow component of optokinetic nystagmus are thought to include the peristriate cortex and adjacent association areas of the cerebral cortex (Fig. 8.1), the posterior limb of the internal capsule, the brainstem, including the dorsolateral pontine nuclei and vestibular nuclei, and the cerebellar flocculus.

The vestibulo-ocular reflex also produces a slow eye movement with velocities of up to 100°/sec. Depending on the vestibular stimulus, fast cor-

8.1 | Cortical areas important for the control of eye movements. Note that the frontal eye fields are particularly important for the generation of saccadic eye movements and that the medial superior temporal visual area and the middle temporal visual area are particularly important for smooth pursuit and optokinetic nystagmus. (Adapted from Leigh RJ, Zee DS: Synthesis of the command for conjugate eye movements, in *The Neurology of Eye Movements*, ed 2. Philadelphia: FA Davis, 1991.)

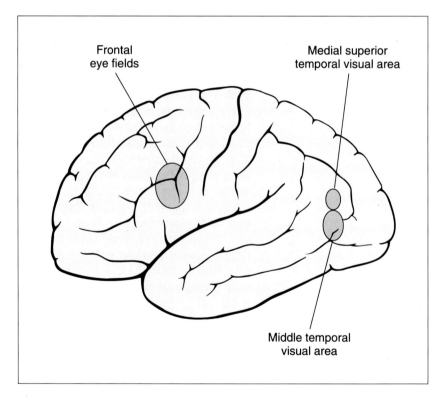

Frontal eye fields

Medial superior temporal visual area

Middle temporal visual area

rective movements are produced, resulting in nystagmus (400–700°/sec). Structures important for the horizontal vestibulo-ocular reflex include the vestibular labyrinth, the VIII cranial nerve, the vestibular nuclei, the medial longitudinal fasciculus, and the ascending tract of Deiters (tractus vestibulo-tegmentalis lateralis).[1] Vertical and torsional vestibular responses are carried from the vestibular nuclei to the midbrain by the medial longitudinal fasciculus. The supranuclear structures important for the optokinetic and vestibular systems are thought to be shared to some extent. Specifically, nucleus propositus hypoglossi and the vestibulocerebellum are sensorimotor integration centers for visual, vestibular, and combined visual–vestibular stimuli.

RAPID EYE MOVEMENTS

Fast or saccadic eye movements are the only purely volitional eye movements. The frontal eye fields, which are important for the initiation of volitional saccades, are located in the premotor frontal cortex (see Fig. 8.1). The superior colliculus is also important for generating saccades, especially to unexpected visual targets. The supranuclear command signal for a saccade, which can arise from the frontal eye fields or the superior colliculus, triggers a premotor circuit that includes the so-called "burst" cells and "pause" cells in the brainstem. The burst cells that are important for the horizontal eye movement system are found in the paramedian pontine reticular formation; those for vertical eye movements are found in the rostral interstitial nucleus of the medial longitudinal fasciculus (Fig. 8.2). Pause neurons are believed to have a high tonic firing rate that inhibits the burst neuron activity. To accomplish a ballistic eye movement (saccade) in which the eye moves rapidly to acquire a target and to hold a new position as well, a neural firing of a so-called "pulse–step" is required.[2] The pulse is required to overcome the inertia of the globe and the step is required to overcome the elastic (spring-like) restoring forces exerted by the tissues surrounding the eye. An inade-

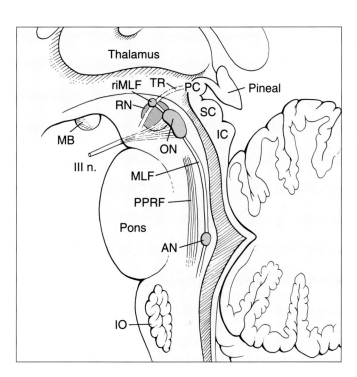

8.2 | The brainstem in sagittal section, illustrating structures important for the control of eye movements. TR = tractus retroflexus; riMLF = rostral interstitial nucleus of the MLF; PC = posterior commissure; RN = red nucleus; ON = oculomotor nucleus; MB = mamillary body; SC = superior colliculus; IC = inferior colliculus; MLF = medial longitudinal fasciculus; AN = abducens nucleus; PPRF = paramedian pontine reticular formation; IO = inferior olive. (Adapted from Baloh RW, Furman JMR, Yee RD: Dorsal midbrain syndrome: Clinical and oculographic findings. *Neurology 1985; 35(1):54–60.*)

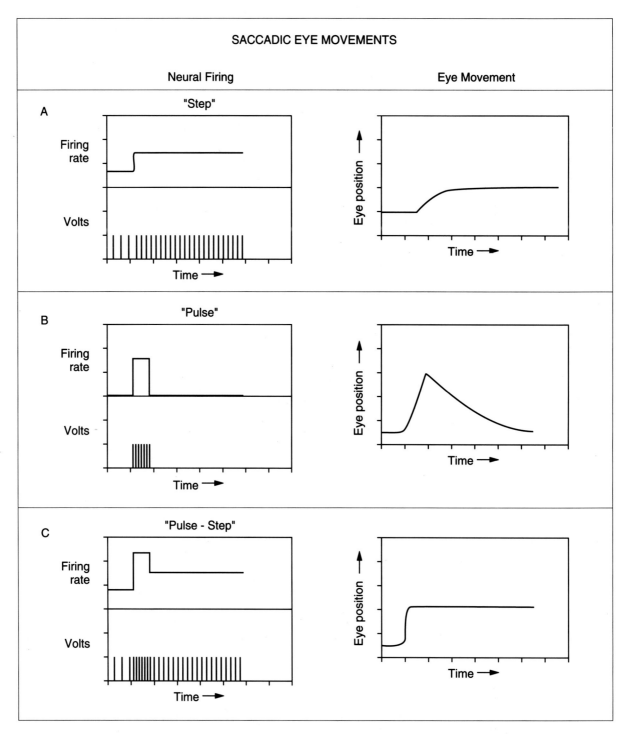

8.3 | Neural activity underlying saccadic eye movements. Illustrated are a step change of firing rate that causes an exponential movement to a new eye position *(A)*, an impulsive change in firing rate that leads to a rapid change in eye position followed by a slow drift *(B)*, and a pulse-step change of firing rate that is thought to underlie saccadic eye movements *(C)*.

quate pulse results in slow saccades. An inadequate step results in postsaccadic drift (Fig. 8.3). The pulse of the neural firing rate is probably caused by burst neurons and the step change in firing rate is probably the result of integration (in the mathematical sense) of the pulse; added together, they form a pulse–step. Abnormalities of saccadic eye movements include prolonged latency between the appearance of a visual target and the initiation of a saccade, inaccuracy (dysmetria), and abnormalities in speed (e.g., low velocity). Several of the supranuclear disorders to be discussed below result in abnormal timing, accuracy, and/or velocity of saccades.

Physiologic disconjugate eye movements include convergence and divergence. The vergence eye movement system is composed of premotor neurons in the midbrain, which provide neural input to the medial rectus subnuclei of the oculomotor nucleus and probably to the abducens nucleus. The vergence eye movement system is known to play a role in the vestibulo-ocular reflex, in that the amount of eye movement appropriate for a given head movement depends on the viewing distance.

Wallenberg syndrome, also known as the lateral medullary syndrome, is characterized by the combination of dizziness, ipsilateral limb dysmetria, contralateral dissociated sensory loss, dysphagia, and Horner syndrome. The region of the lateral medulla is commonly damaged as a result of infarction in the region supplied by the posterior inferior cerebellar artery (Fig. 8.4). Damage to the vestibular nuclei results in several eye movement abnormalities[3]: a central vestibular nystagmus that beats away from the side of the lesion when gaze is directed ahead or away from the side of the lesion; a gaze-evoked nystagmus when the patient looks to the side of the lesion; asymmetrically impaired pursuit and optokinetic movements with greater difficulty pursuing a target or following optokinetic stripes moving away from the side

SELECTED SUPRANUCLEAR DISORDERS IMPAIRING EYE MOVEMENT CONTROL
WALLENBERG SYNDROME

8.4 | Drawing of the medulla oblongata indicating the specific neural structures that are commonly damaged in Wallenberg syndrome. Note involvement of the vestibular nuclei. (Adapted from Miller NR: Topical diagnosis of neuropathic ocular motility disorders, in Walsh, Hoyt (eds): *Clinical Neuro-Ophthalmology.* Vol 2, ed 4. Baltimore: Williams & Wilkins, 1985, 743.)

of the lesion; saccadic lateropulsion in which the eyes are driven towards the side of the lesion and saccades are hypermetric towards the side of the lesion and hypometric away from the side of the lesion; oblique vertical saccades; and skew deviation with hypertropia contralateral to the side of lesion, presumably on the basis of an otolith–ocular abnormality. Damage to the anterior inferior cerebellar artery can produce a similar syndrome, including a central vestibular imbalance and abnormal eye movements that may include lateral gaze palsies. Cerebellopontine angle tumors, when large, can result in a combination of peripheral vestibular and ipsilateral cerebellar abnormalities quite similar to those seen in Wallenberg syndrome.

WERNICKE'S ENCEPHALOPATHY

Wernicke's encephalopathy is a disease caused by hypovitaminosis B_1 and is frequently, but not exclusively, associated with alcoholism. It is characterized by a combination of ocular motor abnormalities, cognitive loss, and gait ataxia. Ocular motor abnormalities include cranial nerve and lateral gaze palsies, nystagmus that is often vertical, abnormal ocular pursuit and saccades, and abnormal vestibulo-ocular responses. Neuropathologically, Wernicke's encephalopathy is known to include damage to the mammillary bodies, the brainstem, and the cerebellum. Two of the eye movement abnormalities associated with Wernicke's encephalopathy, vertical nystagmus and abnormal vestibulo-ocular reflexes, are noteworthy because they illustrate particular aspects of loss of supranuclear ocular motor control. The type of vertical nystagmus seen in Wernicke's encephalopathy (Fig. 8.5) is somewhat unusual in that it violates Alexander's law. Specifically, it is the decrease of the upbeating nystagmus on upgaze that violates Alexander's law, which states that nystagmus should increase when the subject looks in the direction of the quick component. This unusual feature of the vertical nystagmus in Wernicke's encephalopathy suggests that the nystagmus is not simply the result of a vestibular imbalance. Another unusual feature of vertical nystagmus in Wernicke's encephalopathy is that convergence not only may diminish the magnitude of the nystagmus but may reverse its direction, possibly as the result of a complex interaction between vergence and the vestibulo-ocular reflex.[4,5]

An important sign of Wernicke's encephalopathy is the marked diminution or absence of vestibulo-ocular responses. Although some vestibular responsiveness may be recovered after treatment with thiamine, patients with Wernicke's encephalopathy typically suffer lasting damage to the vestibulo-ocular reflex, presumably on the basis of damage to velocity storage (see above), which is thought to depend in part on the nucleus prepositus hypoglossi, an area known to be damaged in Wernicke's encephalopathy.

Other diseases with similar manifestations as Wernicke's encephalopathy include poorly localized metabolic abnormalities such as Leigh's disease, hepatic encephalopathy, and maple syrup urine disease. As noted above, treatment of Wernicke's encephalopathy with thiamine is often helpful, although a lasting deficit in neurologic function may remain.

The Arnold–Chiari malformation, which can be congenital or acquired, is characterized by extension of the cerebellar tonsils below the level of the foramen magnum. It is associated with ocular motor abnormalities, long tract signs, and lower cranial nerve findings, including dysphagia. The eye movement abnormalities in Arnold–Chiari malformation include downbeating nystagmus, abnormal smooth pursuit and optokinetic movements, abnormal vestibular function and, rarely, periodic alternating nystagmus. These abnormalities are thought to result from damage to the vestibulocerebellum, i.e., the flocculonodular lobe. Because of its frequent association with Arnold–Chiari malformation, the finding of downbeating vertical nystagmus warrants appropriate imaging to rule out low-lying cerebellar tonsils

ARNOLD–CHIARI
MALFORMATION

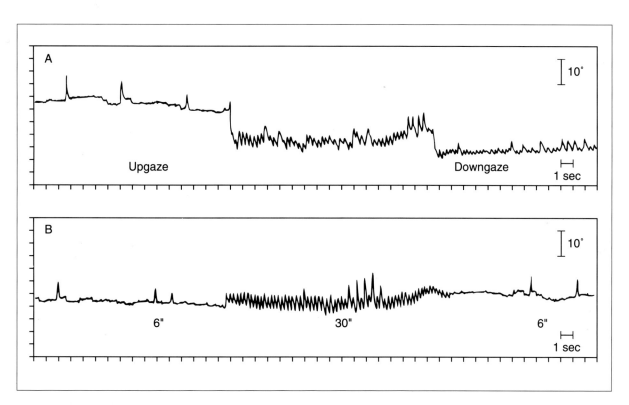

8.5 | Vertical electro-oculographic recording of the effect of gaze position on upbeating nystagmus in a patient with Wernicke's encephalopathy. *A:* Effect of vertical gaze deviation. Note that nystagmus is essentially absent on upward gaze and is diminished by downgaze. *B:* Effect of convergence on upbeating nystagmus. Note that with near fixation, at about 6 inches, nystagmus is virtually abolished and that there may be some downbeating nystagmus. (Adapted from Furman JMR, Becker JT: Vestibular responses in Wernicke's encephalopathy. *Ann Neurol 1979;26(5):669–674.*)

(Fig. 8.6). The abnormal pursuit and optokinetic movements in Arnold–Chiari malformation presumably are caused by damage to the cerebellar flocculus, a structure known to be important for both ocular pursuit and vestibular function. Other lesions may damage the vestibulocerebellum and thus produce ocular motor abnormalities indistinguishable from those associated with the Arnold–Chiari malformation. These include foramen magnum meningiomas, arachnoid cysts appropriately located in the posterior fossa, cerebellar degeneration, platybasia, multiple sclerosis, and stroke. Patients with Arnold–Chiari malformation should be considered for suboccipital craniectomy and decompression of the posterior fossa. Patients who manifest periodic alternating nystagmus may benefit from treatment with baclofen.

FRIEDREICH'S ATAXIA

Friedreich's ataxia is an autosomal recessive inherited condition characterized by spinocerebellar degeneration. The condition presents in the third decade and is characterized neurologically by the combination of cerebellar dysmetria and ataxia, dorsal root ganglion degeneration leading to sensory loss and absent deep tendon reflexes, and corticospinal tract involvement leading to weakness and extensor plantar responses. In addition, many patients have a mild dementia. The ocular motor abnormalities observed in Friedreich's ataxia result from a combination of cerebellar degeneration and degeneration of the vestibular nerve. Although no single ocular motor abnormality is pathognomonic for Friedreich's ataxia, there is a characteristic constellation of abnormalities including square-wave jerks, saccadic dysmetria, symmetrically impaired pursuit and optokinetic nystagmus, and decreased vestibular responses.[6] Cerebellar degeneration syndromes other than Friedreich's ataxia also impair ocular motor function on a supranuclear basis but are usually characterized by preserved vestibulo-ocular responses and sometimes even hyperactive vestibular responses, presumably on the basis of a loss of inhibition from the cerebellum as a result of degeneration. Olivopontocerebellar atrophies result in the abnormalities seen with parenchymal cerebellar degeneration, such as saccadic dysmetria and, in addition, slow saccades, presumably on the basis of damage to the paramedian pontine reticular formation, which contains the burst cells (described earlier) known to be important for saccade velocity.

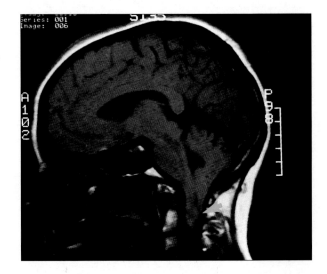

8.6 | Sagittal MRI of a patient with Arnold–Chiari malformation. Note that the cerebellar tonsils descend to the level of C2 (arrow). (Reprinted from Furman JMR, Wall III C, Pang D: Vestibular function in periodic alternating nystagmus. *Brain* 1990;113:1425–1429, by permission of Oxford University Press.)

Paraneoplastic syndromes are neurologic abnormalities that result from neoplasm remote from the nervous system. Common examples of paraneoplastic syndromes include limbic encephalitis, pure sensory neuropathy, and saccadic oscillations. The tumors most commonly associated with paraneoplastic syndromes include oat-cell carcinoma of the lung and breast carcinoma. The most common ocular motor abnormality associated with paraneoplastic syndrome is the occurrence of involuntary saccades during fixation. Patients with such unwanted saccades during fixation typically have otherwise normal eye movements. Many conditions have been associated with the minor abnormality of square-wave jerks, in which the eyes are taken off target briefly by small horizontal saccades that displace the eyes less than four degrees.[7] However, opsoclonus, in which involuntary saccades occur wildly in all directions (horizontal, vertical, and torsional), warrants a thorough search for an occult carcinoma. Occasionally, opsoclonus has resolved spontaneously before the manifestation of a remote carcinoma, suggesting that even if a malignancy is not found initially, patients with opsoclonus should be followed closely.[8] Steroid treatment of opsoclonus associated both with paraneoplastic disease and with postviral encephalitis, such as dancing eyes–dancing feet syndrome, has occasionally proven helpful.

PARANEOPLASTIC SACCADIC OSCILLATIONS

Multiple sclerosis, because of its ability to damage white matter anywhere in the central nervous system, has a variety of patterns of ocular motor abnormality, none of which is pathognomonic or characteristic. The ocular motor abnormalities in multiple sclerosis are often internuclear, i.e., internuclear ophthalmoplegia, or supranuclear (e.g., abnormal ocular pursuit and acquired pendular nystagmus). Infrequently, intraparenchymal infranuclear (fascicular) lesions in multiple sclerosis cause limitation of eye movement. Although no single eye movement abnormality is pathognomonic for multiple sclerosis, bilateral internuclear ophthalmoplegia in a young adult is highly suggestive of the condition. Acquired pendular nystagmus is of unknown pathophysiology and, unfortunately, often produces oscillopsia. Because other conditions can cause the same eye movement abnormalities as multiple sclerosis (e.g., vascular lesions, metastases, or myasthenia gravis), diagnosis rests on the finding of additional neurological abnormalities and on imaging studies suggestive of demyelination. There is no specific treatment for multiple sclerosis, but steroids and antimetabolites have been used with some success. Eye movement abnormalities can be treated symptomatically (e.g., with patching for diplopia). Acquired pendular nystagmus can be treated with high-minus contact lenses but these are frequently not tolerated.

MULTIPLE SCLEROSIS

Progressive supranuclear palsy is a syndrome characterized by limitation of voluntary vertical eye movements, dementia, and abnormal gait. Neuropathologically, patients with progressive supranuclear palsy have extensive neuronal loss in the mesencephalon, although other structures, including the remainder of the brainstem, the cerebellum, and the cerebral hemispheres, are also involved. Despite the limitation of vertical gaze, which is more often downward than upward, the condition is appropriately labeled

PROGRESSIVE SUPRANUCLEAR PALSY

supranuclear because nuclear and infranuclear structures are relatively preserved early in the disease process, as evidenced by intact or even hyperactive vestibulo-ocular responses, including the oculocephalic reflex. Other abnormalities include square-wave jerks,[9] impaired vergence eye movements leading to difficulty aligning the eyes and focusing on near targets, and abnormal ocular pursuit. Although spared in the early stages of the disease, horizontal saccades also eventually become hypometric and slow. Very late in the course of progressive supranuclear palsy, the ocular motor abnormality may become nuclear, with limitation of both volitional and reflexive eye movements. Progressive supranuclear palsy typically afflicts persons in their sixth decade of life and is characterized by a gradual decline of function. Because of the bradykinesia and rigidity associated with progressive supranuclear palsy, the condition is often confused with Parkinson's disease, especially early in its course. Unfortunately, progressive supranuclear palsy does not respond favorably to anti-Parkinsonian agents, although in the early stages of the disease medications such as bromocriptine may provide some benefit. Whipple's disease, like progressive supranuclear palsy, causes vertical eye movement abnormalities. In addition, Whipple's disease has been associated with slow saccades, pendular vertical oscillations, and oculomasticatory myorhythmia.[10,11]

PARINAUD SYNDROME

Another supranuclear ocular motor disorder caused by a lesion of the mesencephalon is Parinaud syndrome, also known as the dorsal midbrain syndrome or as Elschnig–Koerber–Salus syndrome. Parinaud syndrome is characterized by impairment of upward eye movements including saccades, pursuit, and vestibulo-ocular movements.[12,13] Associated findings include square-wave jerks, lid retraction, some disturbance of downward eye movements, disturbances of vergence including convergence–retraction nystagmus, and light–near dissociation. Parinaud syndrome is thought to be caused by damage to upward gaze pathways traveling in the posterior commissures. These pathways may be affected by extrinsic compression (e.g., tumors and hydrocephalus) and intrinsic disease (e.g., infiltrative tumors, inflammation, infections, and cerebrovascular disease). Treatment is aimed at alleviating the underlying condition.

PARKINSON'S DISEASE

Parkinson's disease is characterized by the triad of tremor, rigidity, and bradykinesia and is caused by abnormalities in the extrapyramidal motor system, specifically, degeneration in the substantia nigra of the midbrain with a concomitant loss of dopaminergic activity in the corpus striatum. The ocular motor abnormalities seen in Parkinson's disease include impaired pursuit and saccadic hypometria with a moderate increase in saccadic latency.[14] The velocity of saccades is relatively preserved, indicating that the premotor structures in the pons and the ocular motor nuclei are relatively spared. In addition to difficulty with the initiation of saccades, patients with Parkinson's disease may display oculogyric crises in which the eyes are tonically elevated for brief periods of time. Treatment for Parkinson's disease is aimed at rebalancing the loss of dopaminergic activity with either dopaminergic agents such as L-dopa or anticholinergic agents such as benztropine.

Huntington's disease, an autosomal dominant condition, is characterized by adventitious movements, notably chorea, dementia, dysarthria, and gait instability. Neuropathologically, degeneration is seen most severely in the striatum (caudate and putamen) of the basal ganglia. Ocular motor abnormalities include increased saccadic latency with moderate reduction of saccadic velocity.[15-19] In addition, patients with Huntington's disease display fixation instability, i.e., square-wave jerks. They also have increased distractibility of saccades, i.e., they have difficulty maintaining fixation when a novel stimulus is presented. The basis for this distractibility is unknown. As with so many other nervous system diseases, patients with Huntington's disease have impaired ocular pursuit. Treatment with haloperidol often provides improvements initially but usually loses effectiveness as the disease progresses.

HUNTINGTON'S DISEASE

As illustrated in Figure 8.1, the frontal lobes are important for the initiation of volitional saccades whereas the occipital and parieto-occipital association areas are important for ocular pursuit.[10,20] As a result, cerebral infarction may selectively impair saccades or pursuit eye movements, depending on the location of the lesion. Because the frontal lobes (the "frontal eye fields") tonically drive the eyes contralaterally, patients with acute frontal lobe lesions have a gaze deviation towards the side of the lesion, with relative difficulty in making volitional saccades contralateral to the lesion. Typically, the gaze deviation seen with frontal lobe lesions can be overcome with suitably intense vestibular stimulation, such as caloric irrigation. This contrasts with lesions of the abducens nucleus, in which vestibular stimulation cannot overcome the gaze deviation. After unilateral frontal lobe lesions, patients eventually lose their gaze deviation and regain their ability to make volitional saccades in all directions. Lesions involving the parietal and parieto-occipital association areas are known to impair ocular pursuit and optokinetic responses in both directions, but more so when the visual target is moving towards the side of the lesion. Another abnormality reported with cerebral hemisphere lesions is spontaneous nystagmus, but this has been reported only with massive lesions such as hemidecortication.[21]

CEREBRAL INFARCTION

9 | Nystagmus and the Vestibular System

Joseph M.R. Furman

CLASSIFICATION OF NYSTAGMUS

Broadly speaking, nystagmus can be divided into *jerk* nystagmus and *pendular* nystagmus (Figs. 9.1A and 9.1B). Jerk nystagmus refers to a rhythmic back and forth movement of the eyes (horizontal, vertical, torsional, or any combination thereof) in which one of the two movements is clearly of higher velocity than the other. By definition, the direction of jerk nystagmus corresponds to the direction of the faster of the two nystagmus components (i.e., if the direction of the quick component is to the right, there is *right beating nystagmus*). This nomenclature originated from clinical observation, because the quick component is the more obvious to the bedside examiner. Generally speaking, jerk nystagmus is pathologic, except for the following forms of physiologic jerk nystagmus: vestibular nystagmus (e.g., that induced by caloric irrigation or head rotation); optokinetic nystagmus induced by movement of a full-field visual surround; and end-gaze nystagmus, a horizontal nystagmus beating in the direction of gaze brought out by maximal horizontal right and left gaze. Moreover, abnormalities may occur in each type of physiologic jerk nystagmus that render them pathologic. For example, some patients with congenital nystagmus (see below) display inverted optokinetic nystagmus in which quick components are in the same direction as that of the stimulus.

Pendular nystagmus refers to a rhythmic back and forth movement of the eyes without a clearly discernible quick component, i.e., the to-and-fro movements appear to have equal velocities. When eye position is plotted versus time, some forms of pendular nystagmus are sinusoidal and others have more irregular waveforms.

Pendular nystagmus can be acquired or congenital. The distinction between the two appears to be obvious (based on clinical history), but on occasion, with an inadequate history of abnormal eye movements since birth, the distinction can be difficult. However, there are certain characteristics of congenital nystagmus that enable it to be recognized in most cases (see below).

A rhythmic back-and-forth movement of the eyes often confused with nystagmus is that of saccadic oscillations wherein each of the movements is of high velocity (i.e., saccadic) (Fig. 9.1C). Saccadic oscillations include square-wave jerks, square-wave oscillations, macro-square-wave jerks, macro-saccadic oscillations, ocular flutter, and opsoclonus. These instabilities in eye movement are thought to be caused by saccadic abnormalities. Jerk nystagmus, pendular nystagmus, and saccadic oscillations can usually be distinguished at the bedside by an experienced observer. However, laboratory measurement of eye movements is sometimes necessary to make such a distinction.

The subject of nystagmus often brings to mind the vestibular system, given that the normal response to vestibular stimulation is a nystagmoid eye movement. A discussion of the vestibular system follows.

9.1 | Nystagmus and nystagmus-like waveforms. All traces show horizontal eye position versus time. *A:* Typical jerk nystagmus with a clearly defined quick and slow movement. *B:* An example of pendular nystagmus, in this case congenital, in which there is no clearly defined quick and slow component. *C:* An example of saccadic fixation instability with a combination of square-wave jerks and ocular flutter. (*B,* adapted from Carl JR, et al: Head shaking and vestibulo-ocular reflex in congenital nystagmus. *Invest Ophthalmol Vis Sci 1985; 26(8):1046.*)

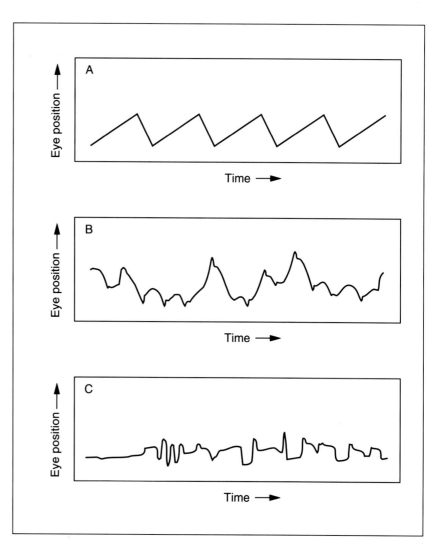

The peripheral vestibular system is illustrated in Figure 9.2. The vestibular end-organs sense motion of the head along and about each of the three spatial axes. The semicircular canals respond to angular acceleration, whereas the otolith organs sense linear acceleration, including changes in orientation with respect to gravity. The vestibular system is made up of a paired structure with the left and right sides being mirror images of one another. Stimulation of the vestibular end-organs causes a change in the firing rate of the VIII cranial nerve, which enters the brainstem at the pontomedullary junction after traversing the internal auditory canal.

The vestibular end-organs are spatially arranged to be somewhat selective in their ability to sense motion. Specifically, the horizontal semicircular canals sense rotation about the rostral–caudal body axis (so-called "yaw" rotation) such that rotation towards an ear excites and rotation away from inhibits the end-organ. The vertical semicircular canals (i.e., the anterior and posterior canals) sense a combination of roll and pitch rotations such that tipping the head back and towards the left ear excites the left posterior canal and inhibits the right anterior canal. Tipping the head back and to the right excites the right posterior canal and inhibits the left anterior canal. The otolith organs sense linear acceleration, by the utricle in the horizontal plane and by the saccule in the vertical plane.

Vestibular afferent information is relayed by way of the VIII cranial nerve fibers that terminate, in large part, in the vestibular nuclei in the medulla oblongata. The vestibular nuclei, which receive input from the vestibular, visual, somatosensory, and auditory systems, serve as a sensory integration center for spatial orientation. The vestibular nuclei project to and receive projections from many structures in the nervous system. The vestibulospinal tracts are important for head and body movement; rostral projections are important for the vestibulo-ocular reflex. Connections between the vestibular nuclei and the cerebellum are important for adaptive modification

THE VESTIBULAR SYSTEM

9.2 | Diagram of the vestibular labyrinth, indicating the three semicircular canals, which sense angular motion, and the two otolith organs, the utricle and saccule, which sense linear motion.

of vestibular reflexes. Like the vestibular end-organs, the vestibular nuclei are paired. They project to one another in a crossed inhibitory fashion. Excitation of one vestibular nucleus causes decreased neural activity contralaterally, thereby increasing the effect of unequal activity in the left versus the right labyrinth, such as that which occurs during head movement.

The vestibulo-ocular reflex refers to the involuntary eye movements induced by vestibular stimulation. Figure 9.3 illustrates diagrammatically the connections between the labyrinth and the extraocular muscles for the horizontal vestibulo-ocular reflex. This diagram is limited to the three- (and

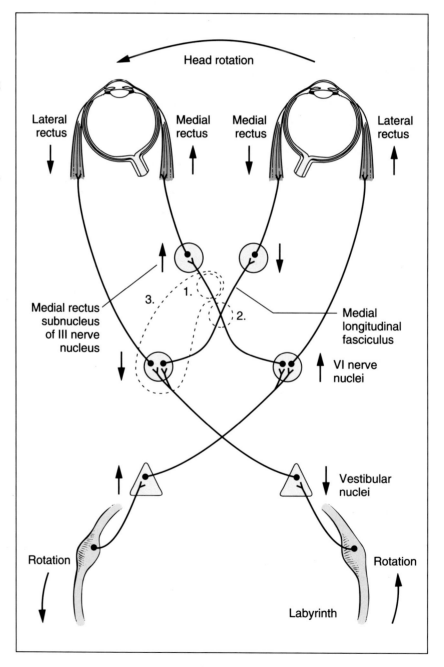

9.3 | Schematic of the vestibulo-ocular reflex showing excitatory connections in a simplified way. Note that head rotation to the left induces a compensatory eye movement to the right by causing an imbalance in neural activity in the vestibular nuclei. Fibers exiting the VI nerve nuclei assure yoking of the two eyes through interneurons that reach the contralateral III nerve nucleus. The shaded regions indicate the locations of lesions causing unilateral internuclear ophthalmoplegia (1), bilateral internuclear ophthalmoplegia (2), and the one and one-half syndrome (3).

four)-neuron arc that is the most rudimentary portion of the vestibulo-ocular reflex. Not shown are inhibitory and polysynaptic pathways and connections between the cerebellum and the brainstem that are important for horizontal eye movements. As shown in Figure 9.3, a head rotation to the left results in activation of the right lateral rectus and left medial rectus muscles accompanied by decreased activity in the antagonist muscles, i.e., the left lateral rectus and the right medial rectus muscles. During head rotation the eyes can move to the right only a limited number of degrees because of the physical constraints of the globe. Subsequently, a quick eye movement will bring the eyes back to near the primary position. As a head rotation to the left continues, slow eye movements to the right will be followed by quick movements to the left, thereby inducing a left beating vestibular nystagmus. This type of nystagmus is physiologic. It should be noted that any imbalance in the activity of the vestibular nuclei, whether physiologic or pathologic, will cause a *vestibular nystagmus* in the absence of visual fixation. Thus, vestibular nystagmus can be caused by head rotation, caloric irrigation, and peripheral vestibular lesions.

Typically, vestibular nystagmus caused by a loss of peripheral vestibular function is a jerk, horizontal–torsional nystagmus that obeys Alexander's law (nystagmus increases when looking in the direction of the quick component) and can be markedly diminished or suppressed entirely by visual fixation (Fig. 9.4). Vestibular nystagmus does not change direction with eccentric gaze.

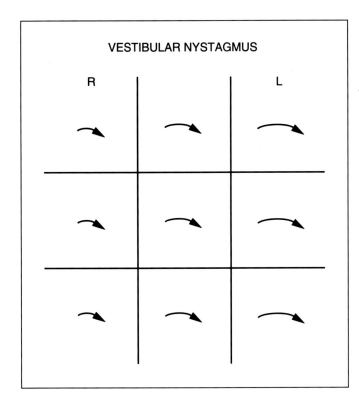

9.4 | Chart shows the direction of the quick component and the magnitude of the slow component velocity of vestibular nystagmus (third degree), in which the nystagmus is horizontal–torsional and beats in the same direction regardless of the direction of gaze. The nystagmus velocity increases when gaze is directed in the direction of the quick component.

Another type of vestibular nystagmus, called positional nystagmus, denotes a nystagmus that is absent when a patient is seated or standing but is manifest with changes in head position, such as lying in the right or left lateral position. Positional nystagmus can be divided into two broad categories: *static* positional and *paroxysmal* positional nystagmus. Static positional nystagmus persists for as long as the individual remains in the provoking position. Clinically, the most important feature of positional nystagmus, in terms of its likelihood of reflecting a peripheral versus a central vestibular abnormality, relates to the ability to use visual fixation to suppress the nystagmus. Positional nystagmus that cannot be suppressed with visual fixation is much more likely to represent a CNS abnormality.

Paroxysmal positional nystagmus refers to a nystagmus that is present for only a limited time after movement into a provoking position. Paroxysmal positional nystagmus can be elicited by placing an individual quickly into a right or left head-hanging position (Hallpike's maneuvers). The most common type of paroxysmal positional nystagmus is benign paroxysmal positional nystagmus with vertigo, the characteristics of which are: (1) a predominately torsional and vertical eye movement with the top of each eye beating towards the dependent ear and the vertical component upbeating (towards the forehead); (2) fatigability (i.e., with repeated positioning the nystagmus and vertigo are no longer present); (3) a latency of about 5 to 10 seconds; (4) a duration of 10 to 30 seconds; and (5) the association with true rotational vertigo. The cause of benign paroxysmal positional nystagmus and vertigo is thought to be "cupulolithiasis," in which debris from the utricular macula becomes attached to the cupula of the posterior semicircular canal. As a result, the cupula and the endolymph no longer have the same specific gravity, which causes the cupula to become gravity sensitive.

9.5 | Downbeating nystagmus. Note that the nystagmus is oblique–torsional on down and lateral gaze, and that it is abolished by upgaze.

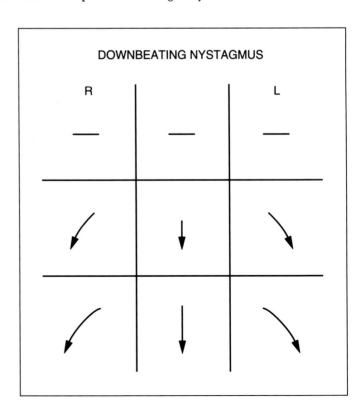

Posterior fossa lesions are more likely to cause pathologic nystagmus than lesions in any other location in the nervous system.[1] Because the medulla oblongata contains the vestibular nuclei, lesions in this location often cause a *central vestibular nystagmus*. The lateral medullary (Wallenberg) syndrome causes central vestibular nystagmus,[2] which is practically indistinguishable from the nystagmus of a peripheral vestibular lesion (see above) except for certain characteristic features, including a change in direction when looking away from the quick component and, occasionally, a reversal in direction with eye closure or with loss of visual fixation. In addition, patients with Wallenberg syndrome have abnormalities of neurologic function including lower cranial nerve abnormalities, dissociated sensory loss, and hemiataxia, all of which are absent with peripheral vestibular lesions. Wallenberg syndrome is usually caused by infarction in the region supplied by the posterior inferior cerebellar artery, often resulting from an occlusion of the vertebral artery ipsilaterally. Treatment is aimed at preventing future cerebrovascular accidents. No specific therapy for the nystagmus is warranted because it typically resolves spontaneously.

Abnormalities at the cervicomedullary junction region often produce *downbeating nystagmus*[3] (Fig. 9.5). The term "downbeating" is somewhat of a misnomer, because the nystagmus is actually an oblique–torsional nystagmus that may be present only during down and lateral gaze. Downbeating nystagmus is typically unaffected by attempts at visual fixation. Downbeating nystagmus should always be considered pathologic and warrants a thorough neurologic evaluation and magnetic resonance imaging, including views of the craniocervical junction. Downbeating nystagmus is often "idiopathic." The differential diagnosis of downbeating nystagmus includes cerebellar degeneration, multiple sclerosis, Arnold–Chiari malformation, Wernicke encephalopathy, and lithium intoxication, among others. The pathophysiology of downbeating nystagmus may relate to abnormal tonic activity in the up versus down vertical vestibulo-ocular reflex pathways, possibly by involvement of vestibular pathways to the vertical eye movement centers in the midbrain rather than involvement of the vestibular nuclei directly.[3] If this mechanism is accurate, downbeating nystagmus, like the horizontal–rotatory nystagmus of Wallenberg syndrome, represents a pathologic nystagmus caused by a central vestibular imbalance. Alternatively, downbeating nystagmus may represent an imbalance in vertical ocular pursuit pathways.[4,5] Treatment for downbeating nystagmus should be aimed at the underlying condition, if treatable. Idiopathic downbeating nystagmus has been treated with medications (e.g., clonazepam) with variable success.

Cerebellar disorders are known to cause a variety of ocular motor abnormalities, including several types of nystagmus. With the exception of rebound nystagmus, most forms of cerebellar nystagmus can also be attributed to brainstem disease, either on the basis of direct involvement of brainstem structures or because of involvement of pathways linking the brainstem to the cerebellum. *Gaze-evoked nystagmus* (Fig. 9.6) is characterized by an abnormality of gaze-holding while attempting to look away from the primary position. Gaze-evoked nystagmus is usually horizontal, is present only when looking laterally, and always beats in the direction of gaze (i.e., a right beat-

PATHOLOGIC NYSTAGMUS CAUSED BY CNS LESIONS

MEDULLA-CRANIOCERVICAL JUNCTION

CEREBELLUM

ing gaze-evoked nystagmus is induced by right lateral gaze and a left beating gaze-evoked nystagmus is induced by left lateral gaze). In addition, gaze-evoked nystagmus may also be present on upward gaze, in which case it is upbeating. It is important to distinguish between the upbeating nystagmus associated with gaze-evoked nystagmus, in which the upbeating nystagmus is present only when looking up, from primary position upbeating nystagmus (to be described below), which has much different implications clinically. Upbeating nystagmus elicited by looking up has the same implications as horizontal gaze evoked nystagmus and, like horizontal end-gaze nystagmus, may be physiologic. There is no physiologic downbeating nystagmus; whether seen in the primary position or elicited by downgaze, downbeating nystagmus is always pathologic.

The pathophysiology of gaze-evoked nystagmus relates to an abnormality of the so-called neural integrator, a neural processing center that integrates, in the mathematical sense, an eye velocity signal into the eye position signal necessary to hold the eyes away from the primary position against the elastic restoring forces of the globe.[6] Abnormalities of the neural integrator allow the eyes to drift back towards the primary position, accounting for the slow component of gaze-evoked nystagmus. Refixations account for the quick components of gaze-evoked nystagmus such that the (gaze-evoked) nystagmus is always in the direction of gaze. The central nervous system structures that correspond to the neural integrator probably include the nucleus propositus hypoglossi.[7] However, the cerebellum, specifically the vestibulocerebellum, is also required for proper gaze holding.[8,9] Gaze-evoked nystagmus is most commonly caused by medications such as sedatives and

9.6 | In gaze-evoked nystagmus the direction of the nystagmus is in the direction of gaze. Note that there is no downbeating component.

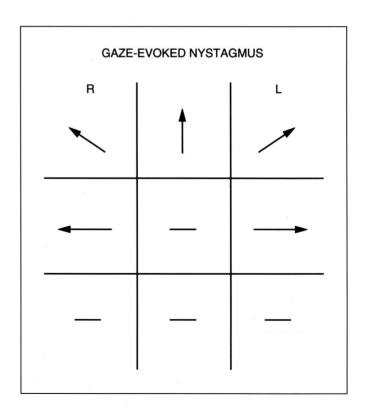

anticonvulsants. Other conditions that should be considered include many types of intrinsic cerebellar or brainstem disease.

Rebound nystagmus is pathognomonic for a cerebellar abnormality and is characterized by a horizontal gaze-evoked nystagmus that fatigues or even reverses direction after prolonged (about 30 seconds) maintenance of eccentric gaze.[10] Immediately after this gaze-holding maneuver, if the patient makes a saccade back to the primary position, a nystagmus can be observed (in the primary position) that beats in the same direction as the saccade just made. For example, if a patient with rebound nystagmus looks to the right, a right beating nystagmus can be seen that fatigues, and immediately after return to the primary position a brief left beating nystagmus is observed. Patients with rebound nystagmus have been shown to have hyperactive vestibular responses,[10] suggesting an involvement of the vestibulocerebellum (i.e., the flocculonodular lobe of the cerebellum). Intrinsic cerebellar diseases that should be considered in patients with rebound nystagmus include many of the same cerebellar lesions that also cause gaze-evoked nystagmus.

Another type of nystagmus associated with cerebellar lesions is that of *periodic alternating nystagmus*, characterized by a horizontal jerk nystagmus whose slow component velocity changes periodically in amplitude and direction.[11] The periodicity of this nystagmus is often about 4 minutes, 2 minutes of right beating nystagmus and 2 minutes of left beating nystagmus. Periodic alternating nystagmus can be congenital or acquired. Bedside diagnosis can be difficult because of the slow time course of the nystagmus, which therefore requires several minutes of observation. Moreover, some patients are able to use visual fixation mechanisms to diminish the nystagmus so that it may only be present intermittently. The pathophysiology of periodic alternating nystagmus probably relates to a hyperresponsiveness of the vestibulo-ocular reflex with a relative instability in the so-called velocity storage element,[12] a hypothetical neural circuit that perseverates the eye movement response to both vestibular and optokinetic stimulation. Although the neurologic localization of periodic alternating nystagmus is uncertain, recent data suggest that it may be caused by lesions of the cerebellar uvula and nodulus or their connections with the brainstem vestibular nuclei.[13] Many conditions have been reported to cause periodic alternating nystagmus, including Arnold–Chiari malformation, multiple sclerosis, and cerebellar degeneration. Some patients with periodic alternating nystagmus have been successfully treated with baclofen, which may provide its benefit by influencing the activity of gamma-aminobutyric acid (GABA), the inhibitory neurotransmitter used by the Purkinje cells, which are the output neurons of the cerebellar cortex.

PONS

Lesions of the pons cause a variety of ocular motor abnormalities that may include nystagmus. The yoking of horizontal movements of the left and right eyes depends on the integrity of the medial longitudinal fasciculus, a fiber tract that carries the axons of interneurons whose cell bodies reside in the nucleus abducens and that synapse in the contralateral medial rectus subnucleus of the oculomotor nucleus (see Fig. 9.3). A unilateral lesion of the medial longitudinal fasciculus causes a unilateral internuclear ophthalmoplegia, which leads to ipsilateral limitation or slowing of adduction and typically contralateral abduction nystagmus. *Dissociated nystagmus*, often seen in patients with internuclear ophthalmoplegia, is characterized by asymmetric or unilateral nystagmus: with a left medial longitudinal fasciculus lesion, patients when looking to the right often manifest an abducting (i.e., right beating) nystagmus in the right eye, whereas no nystagmus or a nystagmus of lower velocity and lower amplitude is observed in the left eye. When convergence is preserved, it can be assumed that the medial rectus subnucleus of the oculomotor nucleus is intact, implying that the lesion is caudal to the oculomotor nuclei. Skew deviation is often seen in patients with unilateral internuclear ophthalmoplegia. The most common causes of internuclear ophthalmoplegia are multiple sclerosis and brainstem infarction. Other less common causes of internuclear ophthalmoplegia include brainstem tumors, metastases, Arnold–Chiari malformation, trauma, and encephalitis.

Bilateral internuclear ophthalmoplegia, caused either by a single lesion that involves the interneurons at their decussation or by involvement of the left and right medial longitudinal fasciculus separately, is characterized by bilateral adduction impairment, bilateral abduction nystagmus, vertical gaze-evoked nystagmus, and abnormal vertical pursuit and vertical vestibular-induced eye movements.

When both the abducens nucleus (or the paramedian pontine reticular formation, the cellular area responsible for horizontal saccades) and the medial longitudinal fasciculus on the same side are damaged, the patient is unable to look ipsilaterally with either eye or to adduct the ipsilateral eye, a condition called the one and one-half syndrome (see Fig. 9.3).

MIDBRAIN

The mesencephalon (midbrain) is responsible for the control of vertical and torsional eye movements. In addition, the midbrain is important for the control of vergence eye movements. Two types of nystagmus associated with midbrain lesions include *convergence–retraction nystagmus* and *upbeating nystagmus*. Convergence–retraction nystagmus is most commonly seen as a component of the dorsal midbrain syndrome (Parinaud syndrome), i.e., a supranuclear paralysis of vertical gaze resulting from damage to the mesodiencephalic region.[14] Convergence–retraction nystagmus is characterized by opposed horizontal saccadic movements towards the midline, most commonly elicited with a downward optokinetic stimulus such that the eyes move obliquely up and in during quick components. Ochs et al[15] were unable to observe retraction of the globe in their case report of so-called "convergence–retraction nystagmus." The causes of dorsal midbrain syndrome include tumors in the pineal region with compression of the midbrain and intrinsic midbrain lesions such as infarction, infection, and demyelination.

Upbeating nystagmus, like downbeating nystagmus, can be based upon an imbalance of central vestibular pathways.[16] Unlike downbeating nystagmus, however, upbeating nystagmus, which is diagrammed in Figure 9.7, does not increase on lateral gaze. Typically, upbeating nystagmus follows Alexander's law: the nystagmus amplitude increases on upward gaze and decreases on downward gaze, although this pattern may be violated (e.g., in Wernicke encephalopathy). Convergence has a variable effect on upbeating nystagmus; nystagmus may increase, decrease, or even reverse direction. Upbeating nystagmus can be associated with cerebellar lesions and other localizations, including the medulla and the pontomesencephalic junction. Many causes are associated with upbeating nystagmus, including degeneration syndromes, infarction, tumors, Wernicke encephalopathy, and encephalitis.

Abnormalities of the cerebrum typically do not cause nystagmus. However, a small-amplitude nystagmus, possibly appreciated only during ophthalmoscopy, may be seen after hemidecortication. Another unusual circumstance in which a cerebral lesion causes nystagmus is epileptic nystagmus. Both of these forms of nystagmus may be caused by pursuit system imbalance.

Congenital nystagmus is present from birth and is usually pendular, although it may have a jerk-like character in some cases. Congenital nystagmus is typically conjugate, horizontal, is inhibited by convergence, and is diminished markedly by eye closure. It may worsen with fixation. It also may have an unusual waveform in the sense of a complicated repeating pattern of eye position versus time (see Fig. 9.1B). It remains horizontal in all fields of gaze, although it may become jerk nystagmus with the quick component in the direction of gaze, similar to gaze-evoked nystagmus. One or more of these characteristics may be absent. Curiously, with eyes open in the dark as opposed to eyes closed, congenital nystagmus is often present, presumably as a result of the intent to view. Although congenital nystagmus is of uncertain etiology, it is known to be associated with strabismus, albinism, and other forms of visual impairment. Treatment is usually not needed because of brief foveation periods that allow normal or nearly normal visual acuity. However, successful treatment with medications (e.g., baclofen) has been reported.

CEREBRAL HEMISPHERES

PATHOLOGIC NYSTAGMUS CAUSED BY CNS LESIONS IN MULTIPLE OR UNCERTAIN LOCATION

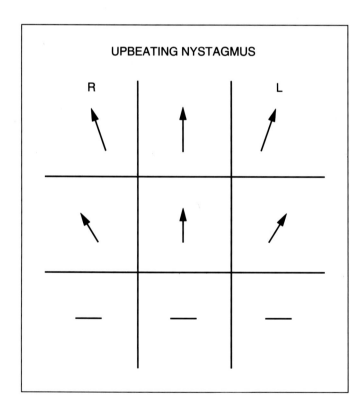

UPBEATING NYSTAGMUS

9.7 | Upbeating nystagmus. In this example the nystagmus is abolished by downgaze.

Another type of nystagmus thought to begin in childhood is that of *latent nystagmus,* wherein a jerk nystagmus, not present during binocular viewing, becomes evident during monocular viewing. Latent nystagmus is typically horizontal, beating in the direction of the viewing eye, and is often present bilaterally. For example, a right beating latent nystagmus will be noted when only the right eye is viewing and a left beating latent nystagmus will be noted when only the left eye is viewing. Latent nystagmus is always associated with strabismus and may be seen in combination with congenital nystagmus, resulting in a complicated pattern of eye movement abnormalities. Occasionally, a unilateral visual impairment in adulthood leads to a loss of binocularity and the appearance of a latent nystagmus that was previously unknown, a so-called *manifest latent nystagmus.*

Pendular nystagmus also may be acquired. This condition, often seen in the setting of multiple sclerosis, is of uncertain pathophysiology, although an interruption of connections between the inferior olive and the cerebellar dentate nucleus may be involved (see below). Unlike congenital nystagmus, acquired pendular nystagmus may be disconjugate, is often both horizontal and vertical, and is variably affected by eye closure. Unlike those with congenital nystagmus, patients with acquired pendular nystagmus often complain of oscillopsia. Unfortunately, it is often very difficult to treat these patients. However, some patients have benefitted from such drugs as baclofen, trihexyphenidyl, valproic acid, and clonazepam.

See-saw nystagmus is an unusual type of nystagmus that is characterized by upward and intorsional movement of one eye coupled with downward and extorsional movement of the other eye in a repetitive (i.e., nystagmoid) manner. See-saw nystagmus can be congenital or acquired; in the latter case it is often associated with mass lesions in the parasellar and chiasmal region, such as craniopharyngioma. The pathophysiology of this condition may relate to damage to the interstitial nucleus of Cajal or its connections, given this structure's role in the ocular tilt reaction.

A rare type of nystagmus is *monocular nystagmus* in the primary position, wherein only one eye is moving back and forth. Typically, monocular nystagmus is vertical. This condition may be seen with intracranial lesions such as multiple sclerosis and brainstem infarction, and in the setting of monocular visual loss, the so-called Heimann–Bielschowsky phenomenon. Vertical monocular oscillations may also be seen as part of spasmus nutans, a self-limited condition affecting children which consists of nystagmus, head nodding, and abnormal head position. Another eye movement abnormality that includes monocular oscillations is superior oblique myokymia, characterized by high-frequency, small-amplitude vertical and torsional movements that occur intermittently.

NYSTAGMUS-LIKE OSCILLATIONS

Saccadic oscillations differ from nystagmus in that they are rapid conjugate eye movements of high velocity in both directions.[17] With saccadic oscillation, there is no clearly defined slow and quick component and both movements are fast. Figure 9.1C shows an example of a purely horizontal saccadic oscillation, i.e., *ocular flutter.* Note that each of the movements of the eyes is fast (i.e., saccadic). Moreover, the normal time interval between successive saccades, 200 milliseconds, is shortened, sometimes to as low as 50 milliseconds. Another type of saccadic oscillation, the most florid saccadic oscillation, is that of *opsoclonus*, which has also been called "saccadomania." As with ocular flutter, the intersaccadic interval in opsoclonus is often short as compared with the normal interval. Moreover, unlike ocular flutter, in which conjugate eye movements are restricted to the horizontal plane, with opsoclonus the eye movements may be in all directions. A patient improving from opsoclonus often manifests ocular flutter before recovery. Although the precise pathogenesis and neurologic localization for saccadic oscillations are unknown, it is likely that the abnormality involves the premotor circuits for saccades, including the so-called burst neurons found in the paramedian pontine reticular formation and the so-called pause neurons in the brainstem.[18] Just before and during a saccadic eye movement, the pause neurons, whose tonic firing rate is high, pause, allowing the burst neurons to discharge a burst of neural activity and thereby generate a saccade. During saccadic oscillations, it is presumed that either the pause cells are pausing inappropriately, the burst cells are no longer inhibited by the pause cells, or a trigger external to the pause-cell–burst-cell circuitry is causing the pause cells to pause inappropriately. Saccadic oscillations may be seen in several circumstances: as a paraneoplastic syndrome with neuroblastoma in children and in adults with carcinoma of the lung, breast, or ovaries; in association with viral encephalitis, one type being the so-called "dancing eyes and dancing feet" syndrome; as the result of toxic exposure (e.g., to chlordecone or toluene); and, less commonly, with other conditions including hydrocephalus, multiple sclerosis, and hyperosmolar coma. How these conditions cause saccadic oscillations is not known. Theories include direct damage to the pause cells or burst cells or damage to cerebellar Purkinje cells, which has been demonstrated neuropathologically.

With *ocular bobbing*, a rapid downward movement of the eyes is followed by a slow return to the primary position. It is often associated with severe pontine lesions, coma, and marked impairment or absence of horizontal eye movement. Two other nystagmus-like oscillations are similar to ocular bobbing, i.e., inverse bobbing (ocular dipping), in which the downward movement is slow and the upward movement is fast, and reverse bobbing, in which the eyes deviate rapidly upward with a slow return to the primary position. Inverse and reverse bobbing do not provide the same localizing information as ocular bobbing, and have been seen with anoxic coma and metabolic encephalopathy.

Oculopalatal myoclonus is a term used to describe a simultaneous movement of the soft palate and the eyes in a rhythmic (usually 1–5 cycles/second) continuous manner. Often there are associated movements of other muscles, including the tongue and diaphragm. When eye movements of this type are seen in isolation, they are denoted as pendular nystagmus (see above). However, this terminology is misleading, in the sense that true myoclonus refers to a jerk of limb muscles very different from the rhythmic movements of oculopalatal myoclonus. The pathophysiology of oculopalatal myoclonus relates to interruption of the connections between the cerebellar dentate nucleus, the inferior olive, and the red nucleus, the so-called Mollaret triangle. Oculopalatal myoclonus is usually observed months after brainstem or cerebellar infarction and is associated neuropathologically with hypertrophy of the inferior olive.

VISUAL LOSS, DIPLOPIA, AND OSCILLOPSIA AS NEURO-OPHTHALMIC CLUES TO SYSTEMIC DISEASE

Jacqueline M.S. Winterkorn
Jeffrey G. Odel

The eye is a window to the pathophysiology not only of the brain but also of the entire body. Systemic disease is often signaled by visual symptoms and can be confirmed by signs noted on neuro-ophthalmic examination. This chapter describes selected visual symptoms of visual loss, diplopia, and oscillopsia, and discusses certain accompanying signs that can suggest the diagnosis of underlying systemic disease, with special emphasis on unusual syndromes that often might be overlooked.

TRANSIENT VISUAL LOSS

Transient visual loss is a common neuro-ophthalmic symptom. Typically, the patient describes an episode of visual obscuration on one side, usually perceived as loss of vision in one eye. The physician must try to determine whether the patient describes true monocular visual loss or binocular, homonymous visual field loss. Monocular blurring often is not appreciated by a patient when both eyes are open. A horizontal line descending like a curtain, especially if appreciated in only one eye by alternately covering the eyes, represents monocular pathology. A patient who sees a vertical edge, a fixed shadow, or a blur with both eyes open more often than not has suffered homonymous visual field loss rather than monocular loss.

When the visual loss is homonymous, further evaluation of the postchiasmal pathway is in order. When the loss is monocular, further history and examination should seek clues to distinguish between localized ocular disease and underlying systemic pathology affecting one eye.

Although amaurosis fugax (Latin: fleeting blindness) most often results from systemic disease such as intravascular embolization or carotid hypoperfusion, local ocular causes must also be seriously considered.

LOCAL CAUSES   Examples of ocular conditions that cause transient visual loss are listed in Figure 10.1.

Patients with blepharospasm who cannot keep their eyes open may experience moments of visual loss. Blurred vision is commonly caused by irregularity of the corneal tear film. In such cases, a blink or application of a tear supplement usually improves visual clarity. On examination with the slit lamp, the tear film and cornea may appear abnormal, with rapid tear break-up time and punctate keratopathy suggestive of keratitis sicca. A Schirmer test may confirm inadequate tear production.

Transient obscuration of vision resulting from opacities in the media of the anterior chamber or the vitreous can mimic amaurosis fugax. For example, recurrent hyphema may occasionally cause transient monocular blindness in patients with anterior chamber lenses who develop UGH (uveitis–glaucoma–hyphema) syndrome.[1] Large vitreous debris sometimes can also obscure vision.

All patients with amaurosis fugax should have the anterior chamber angle examined gonioscopically for angle-closure glaucoma, episodes of which are almost always accompanied by pain. The anterior lens should be inspected for glaukomflecken, indicating prior episodes of angle closure.

Delayed visual recovery after exposure to bright light indicates that the patient has macular disease, such as sensory detachment or age-related macular degeneration. This phenomenon is utilized in the photostress test, in which return of normal central acuity is abnormally prolonged in an eye with macular disease after exposure for 10 seconds to a bright light. Patients suffering from ocular ischemia and patients with intraocular lenses report temporary loss of vision after exposure to a bright light (such as sunlight), which causes retinal bleaching.

FIGURE 10.1. Causes of Transient Visual Loss

LOCAL CAUSES	SYSTEMIC CAUSES
Ocular causes	Emboli
Blepharospasm	Cardiac
Tear film/corneal abnormalities	Valvular disease (rheumatic heart disease, prosthetic valve)
Recurrent hyphema	Endocarditis
Vitreous debris	Mural thrombi
Angle-closure glaucoma	Atrial myxoma
Photostress with ocular ischemia	Great vessels
	Carotid atheroma
Photostress with macular disease	
Optic disc edema	Vasculitis
	Giant-cell arteritis
Disc anomalies	Hypoperfusion
Drusen	
Coloboma	Vasospasm–migraine
Orbital mass	Hyperviscosity
Parasellar tumor	Hypercoagulability
	Functional

Disc anomalies, such as optic nerve head drusen,[2] high myopia, and colobomas,[3] are identified in patients who experience brief, 10–30 second episodes of visual loss (Fig. 10.2). Patients with orbital masses, such as hemangioma or meningioma, and especially those with an intraconal mass accompanied by disc swelling, may experience transient obscurations of vision in certain fields of gaze, especially downgaze.[4] These obscurations presumably result from positional vascular obstruction.

In rare cases, intrasellar or parasellar tumors may present with a history of transient visual loss. For example, patients with a craniopharyngioma may report experiencing visual blackouts of undetermined origin.[5]

SYSTEMIC CAUSES

After local ocular causes of transient monocular visual loss have been ruled out, retinovascular and cerebrovascular bases of the problem must be considered. In the 1950s, C. Miller Fisher called attention to retinal emboli as a significant cause of transient monocular visual loss (amaurosis fugax).[6] His observation proved of paramount importance in establishing embolism as a frequent cause of cerebrovascular and retinovascular disease. Although emboli are a major systemic cause of amaurosis fugax, other systemic causes must also be considered. Amaurosis fugax may result not only from emboli but also from hypoperfusion, vasospasm, vasculitis, hypercoagulable states, or local venous stasis.

EMBOLISM

In retinal vascular obstruction, the patient typically reports that a curtain of darkness descends over one eye, resulting in a loss of vision lasting from seconds to minutes.[7] In cases when some residual intact circulation persists in a retinal or cilioretinal artery, the curtain may descend only partially. At resolution, the curtain may either ascend or dissolve like a clearing fog. Some patients with amaurosis fugax of embolic origin report brief photopic phenomena, such as swirling points of light that perhaps represent entoptic stimulation of the retina as emboli pass through its circulation.

Inspection of the retina during the episode of visual loss may reveal an embolus in the retinal circulation. Within days, a cotton-wool spot marking the area of infarcted retina may be observed distal to the embolus (Fig. 10.3).

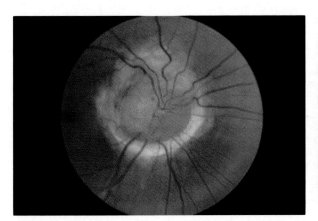

10.2 | Disc coloboma in 23-year-old woman who suffers from frequent transient obscurations of vision.

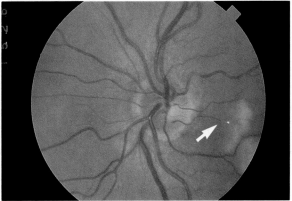

10.3 | Cotton wool infarct just distal to retinal embolus (arrow), seen after endarterectomy in a 65-year-old man who had presented with frequent episodes of amaurosis fugax.

The source of an embolus can be inferred from its appearance (Fig. 10.4). Cholesterol crystals, usually representing embolization from the carotid arteries or great vessels, appear as golden, birefringent, glistening shards called Hollenhorst plaques.[8] Hollenhorst plaques are found lodged at vascular bifurcations in the retina, and often seem larger than the retinal vessel occupied (Fig. 10.5). Typically, the blood column appears normal distal to the embolus. When gentle pressure is applied to the eye during ophthalmoscopic examination and retinal arterial pulsations are produced, the cholesterol embolus can often be seen to rock with the pulse and occasionally to move, thus confirming its embolic origin. After a retinal embolus has resolved, a focal narrowing or sheathing of the involved retinal arterioles may be observed in some patients (Fig. 10.6).

Fibrin–platelet emboli are thought to originate as accumulations of thrombotic material on ulcerated arterial plaques or on damaged heart valves. These emboli appear as cream-colored elongated plugs of material

FIGURE 10.4. Characteristics of Emboli

	FIBRIN-PLATELET	CHOLESTEROL (HOLLENHORST PLAQUE)	CALCIFIC
Color	Creamy white	Shiny; metallic gold, orange, yellow	Gray-white, dull
Mobility	Highly mobile	Jiggles when eye is pressed; moves on or breaks up over days to weeks	Fixed, permanent
Shape	Conforms to vessel, long smooth segments	Rectangular shards or crystals	Ovoid blobs
Location	Usually in motion	In medium and small vessels; often at bifurcations	In unbranched segments of main or medium-sized retinal vessels
Apparent caliber	Fills lumen	Larger than blood column	Same or slightly larger than proximal blood column
Ischemic changes	Transient slowing of blood flow, rarely infarction	Dilation of vein may be present; may produce retinal infarction	Usually produces dense, sharply delimited retinal infarction; small ischemic hemorrhages
Vessel change	No damage seen	Gray-white segmental mural opacity; sheathing after embolus resolved	Segmental narrowing; collateral shunts develop
Source	Heart and great vessels, thrombus or atheroma	Carotid bifurcation, plaque	Cardiac valves (e.g., with rheumatic heart disease)

(Modified from Hoyt WF: Ocular symptoms and signs, in Wylie ES, Ehrenfeld WK (eds): *Extracranial Occlusive Cerebrovascular Disease: Diagnosis and Management*. Philadelphia: WB Saunders, 1970, 69–75.)

conforming to the shape of a blood vessel, filling and occluding it. These accumulations have been seen to move slowly through a vessel and eventually to break up distally as they approach the periphery.

Calcific emboli from the cardiac valves are solitary white blobs which occlude the blood flow and are found lodged at or near the disc. Calcific emboli may remain in place for years, and more often result in permanent rather than transient visual loss, whereas cholesterol emboli and fibrin-platelet emboli are less permanent and may disappear in time. Compensatory vascular shunts or collaterals may be present years after an occlusion by a calcific embolus (Fig. 10.7).

The work-up of a patient with suspected embolism must include evaluation of the heart and the great vessels. The most likely source of a suspected embolus depends on the medical history (e.g., rheumatic heart disease) and

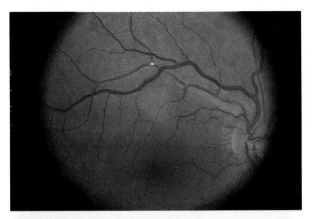

10.5 | Hollenhorst emboli at bifurcations of retinal arterioles in 62-year-old man.

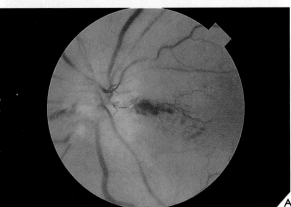

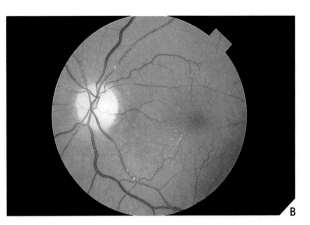

10.6 | *A:* Disc infarction after central retinal artery occlusion by embolus from carotid artery (note embolic shard in macular branch). *B:* Same patient one month later shows disc atrophy, narrowed vessels, and embolic fragments in retinal arterioles.

also in part on the age of the patient. Younger patients—those under 40—typically have healthy carotid arteries and are more likely to have emboli of cardiac origin, and, therefore, require echocardiography as part of the diagnostic work-up. Because older patients more often have carotid artery disease, they should also be evaluated with carotid duplex scan, magnetic resonance angiography, or traditional cerebral angiography. Less common causes of retinal emboli include atrial myxomas, contaminants in radiographic materials, talc from illicit intravenous drug preparations, fat emboli after trauma, and leukoembolization. Acute pancreatitis has been associated with embolic infarction of the retina (Fig. 10.8), owing either to fat embolization[9] or to leukoembolization.[10] Leukoembolization occurs in response to complement-induced aggregation of white blood cells,[10] and, therefore, may constitute an early diagnostic clue to autoimmune or hematologic disease.

10.7 | Fundus of patient with history of rheumatic heart disease shows collateral formation around old calcium embolus present since first valve replacement 20 years ago as well as new cotton-wool spot distal to embolization from artificial valve just before its recent replacement.

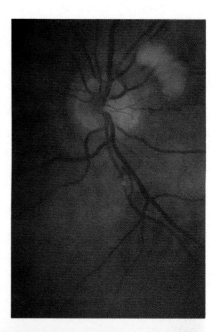

10.8 | Macular infarction and hemorrhage in patient with acute pancreatitis reflects an autoimmune process, in which complement induces aggregation of white blood cells that circulate as emboli.

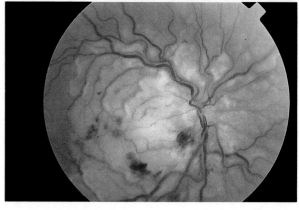

HYPOPERFUSION

Patients reporting progressive restriction of vision from the periphery (i.e., an iris–diaphragm pattern of visual loss) may be suffering from hypoperfusion. Amaurosis fugax produced by an embolus tends to last longer than that resulting from hypoperfusion, the latter lasting only seconds to 1–2 minutes. They may be affected by position or posture, and occur when the patient stands up from sitting or sits up from reclining. Hypoperfusion can be caused by cardiac arrhythmia or by critical stenosis of the great vessels. The transient obscurations of vision experienced by patients with increased intracranial pressure or elevated intraocular pressure may also result from hypoperfusion.

Amaurosis fugax in elderly patients (those over age 65) can also be caused by temporal arteritis. Therefore, the diagnostic work-up must include a Westergren erythrocyte sedimentation rate, and the patient must be questioned about symptoms of temporal arteritis or polymyalgia rheumatica, including headache, scalp tenderness, jaw claudication, weight loss, depressed appetite, proximal joint pain, muscle aches, myalgias, and malaise. Unless treated immediately with high-dose corticosteroids, temporal arteritis heralded by amaurosis fugax may lead to permanent blindness in one or both eyes, which sometimes—but not always—can be averted or reversed by immediate treatment with high-dose intravenous steroids.[11]

VASOSPASM OF RETINAL, CHOROIDAL, OR OPHTHALMIC VESSELS

Vasospasm is the presumed cause of transient monocular visual loss in two clinical circumstances. The young patient who experiences stereotyped monocular episodes of severe visual loss and whose evaluation reveals no evidence of abnormality in the heart or great vessels or of intraluminal clotting diathesis may have migraine or autoimmune diathesis.

Another group of patients in whom vasospasm is suspected to underlie transient visual loss is more elderly, with no history of prior migraine symptoms and an equally negative work-up of heart and great vessels. Some of these patients have been examined during the attack and found to have constriction of the retinal arteries.[12-15] To support the likelihood of vasospasm, work-up must rule out other causes of transient visual loss and should include complete blood count, Westergren erythrocyte sedimentation rate, cardiac and carotid evaluation, and tests for hyperviscosity and hypercoagulability (anticardiolipin antibody, antiphosphotidyl choline and serine, antinuclear antibody, serum protein electrophoresis, PTT, VDRL, protein S, and protein C). Hayreh has recently questioned the conclusion that vasospasm is the causative mechanism.[16] Nevertheless, calcium channel blockers that prevent vasospasm seem to provide relief from attacks of amaurosis in some cases.[13,14]

MIGRAINE

The most frequently encountered transient visual loss is the binocular, homonymous hemianopic defect caused by cortical migraine.[15] In classic migraine, or migraine with aura, the patient may notice a premonitory feeling of vague uneasiness or a sense of distance from the environment. This is followed by positive visual phenomena including scintillations, photopsias, colors, zig-zag lines, or fortification figures (Fig. 10.9), which occur simultaneously in both eyes and can be appreciated with eyes open or closed. The classic, characteristic visual aura is the migrainous teichopsia, a binocular, homonymous illusion that begins paracentrally as a small C-shaped form, with the concave side of the "C" directed medially. Over a period of about 20 minutes, the C-shaped figure expands and migrates away from the midline in the direction of the convex border of the "C," until it eventually disappears into the periphery.

An observant patient will report that the C-shaped figure is composed of fortified zig-zag figures, which may appear to change colors continuously. After the positive phenomenon passes through an area of visual field, that portion of the field may be depressed and the patient may note a negative scotoma, even progressing to complete homonymous hemianopia. In classic migraine or migraine with aura, the resolution of the visual phenomena typically is followed by the onset of contralateral hemicrania, a throbbing headache aggravated by light and noise which may be accompanied by nausea and vomiting. The headache may last for hours or even days, and in many instances is relieved only by sleep.

10.9 | Phases of migrainous teichopsia.

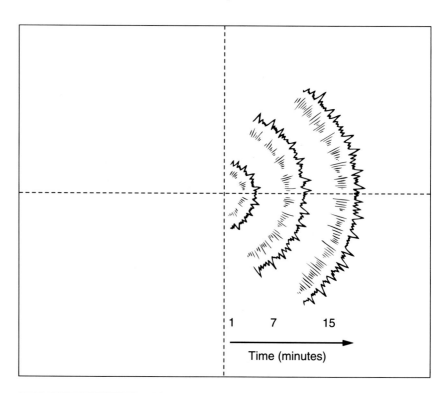

1   7   15

Time (minutes)

FIGURE 10.10. Suspicious "Migraines"

Symptoms and headache never switch sides
Scotoma does not expand and migrate
Visual field defect is fixed
Headache precedes aura

In classic migraine with aura, episodes may occur on either side, and even if they predominate on one side they occasionally will occur on the other side. A patient whose unilateral attacks take place persistently on the same side must be investigated for the presence of a structural lesion with symptoms mimicking migraine, such as an occipital arteriovenous malformation[17] or a tumor (Fig. 10.10). Patients with classic migraine occasionally are found to have a fixed visual field deficit. This may be of cerebral, retinal, or optic nerve origin. The most common fixed deficit is the homonymous hemianopic scotoma of occipital origin, as illustrated by the famous case of Mallory.[18] Nevertheless, a full work-up is required to rule out more sinister causes of homonymous hemianopia in such a patient. Because patients with systemic lupus erythematosus may complain of migrainous teichopsia,[19] ANA testing is appropriate in patients with this symptom.

Migraines affect at least 20% of the population, women more frequently than men. Headaches may commence at any age but most typically appear during the teens or twenties. Migraine sufferers report having been susceptible to motion sickness in childhood.

As the patient with migraine becomes older the intensity of the headache may diminish, or the headache may not occur after the visual symptoms. A diagnostic dilemma is presented by the elderly patient who experiences a migraine-like aura for the first time, which is neither accompanied nor followed by headache. The diagnostic differentiation between migrainous vasospasm and vertebrobasilar insufficiency is difficult.[20] Treatable causes of cerebrovascular disease or a source of emboli should be ruled out. Some neurologists recommend carotid Doppler testing to exclude obstruction, and blood tests including complete blood count and erythrocyte sedimentation rate are appropriate. Magnetic resonance imaging (MRI) may demonstrate hyperintense areas indicative of vertebrobasilar insufficiency. The prognosis is usually good, especially with aspirin prophylaxis.

The relationship between visual loss and carotid insufficiency has received considerable attention. Two distinct clinical syndromes have been found to underlie venous stasis retinopathy, in which the retina contains engorged veins and midperipheral hemorrhage. The first clinical situation, described by Kearns,[21,22] is a hypotensive retinopathy consisting of ocular ischemia secondary to carotid occlusive disease that leads to low retinal artery pressure, poor perfusion, and a midperipheral retinopathy similar to that found in the diabetic retina. The second, described by Hayreh[23,24] and by Ellenberger and Epstein,[25] consists of a nonischemic retinal vein occlusion despite normal perfusion pressure in the central retinal artery. This causes both edema of the disc and diffuse hemorrhage.

The hypotensive form of venous stasis retinopathy caused by tight stenosis of the ophthalmic or carotid artery represents the "ocular ischemic syndrome." A patient with this syndrome may experience orbital ache or may describe pulsatile visual dimming, relieved by lying down to improve perfusion to the head. In addition, the patient may suffer pain or visual loss owing to corneal decompensation, neovascular glaucoma, or uveitis. This ischemic form of uveitis consists of anterior chamber inflammation poorly responsive to steroids. As a result of ischemia the pupil becomes dilated and fixed. A cataract often develops or progresses. Neovascularization may occur in the iris as well as in the disc and retina. Examination of the fundus may reveal spontaneous retinal arterial pulsations, indicating that the diastolic

OTHER FORMS OF VISUAL LOSS OF SYSTEMIC ORIGIN

HIGH-GRADE CAROTID STENOSIS—OCULAR ISCHEMIC SYNDROME

pressure falls below the intraocular pressure. The intraocular pressure is characteristically low; significantly, a unilaterally low intraocular pressure may be an indication of ocular ischemia.

The prognosis for recovery is poor after significant ocular ischemia from carotid stenosis. More important, the risk of cerebral ischemia is high. If surgical risk can be minimized, carotid endarterectomy may be indicated in cases of high-grade (70%) stenosis, to avoid ophthalmic and neurologic sequelae.[26]

TOXIC AND NUTRITIONAL AMBLYOPIA

Bilateral central or cecocentral scotomas, experienced by the patient as slowly progressive blurring of vision and loss of color vision, may be the consequence of a nutritional deficiency, a toxic effect of a drug, or a manifestation of other systemic disease (Fig. 10.11).

Nutritional amblyopia typically is seen in alcoholics who do not follow a diet sufficient to meet the body's need for B-complex vitamins. Nutritional amblyopia develops after months to years of dietary deficiency. A central or cecocentral scotoma with prominent dyschromatopsia, particularly for red, is characteristic. Patients may complain, for example, of the inability to tell the difference between red and green traffic lights. Visual acuity may be mildly to markedly affected. The optic discs usually are pale temporally. Occasionally, retinal hemorrhages are seen. Experienced observers have noted peripapillary vascular changes, similar to the telangiectasia seen in Leber's hereditary optic neuropathy. Occasionally the two eyes may be asymmetrically involved.

Carroll[27] demonstrated that nutritional amblyopia does not result from toxic effects of alcohol and tobacco, but rather from a vitamin deficiency. Patients with nutritional amblyopia who continued to drink and smoke recovered their vision if they consumed diets complete in vitamins, especially vitamin B complex. If a patient with nutritional amblyopia eats a normal diet and takes vitamin B supplements, the visual field defect usually clears in a period of weeks to months. However, if optic atrophy is already present the condition may not be completely reversible, depending on the extent of the nerve damage.

DRUG-INDUCED VISUAL LOSS
Ethambutol

Patients receiving antituberculous medication may experience dimming of color vision and a decrease in visual acuity. In a patient on multidrug therapy, the antituberculous drug most likely responsible for visual loss is ethambutol,[28] although isoniazid may also produce an optic neuropathy. The

FIGURE 10.11. Causes of Progressive Cecocentral Visual Loss

Cancer-associated retinopathy
Drug toxicity
    Chloroquine
    Digoxin
    Ethambutol
    Mellaril
Leber's optic neuropathy

Nutritional amblyopia
    Thiamine
    B12 (pernicious anemia)
Optic nerve compression
    Thyroid eye disease
    Tumor
Optic nerve infiltration

visual field defect, although usually cecocentral, occasionally shows a bitemporal or hemianopic pattern of loss. This suggests that an optic neuropathy resulting from drug poisoning can be localized to the optic nerve, to the optic chiasm, or to the optic tract. Pathological findings on experimental animals and autopsied patients who had prior ethambutol toxicity have revealed demyelinating lesions centrally in the optic chiasm and in the optic nerve. Retinal damage apparently is rare.

The toxic effects of ethambutol are experienced by about 1% of patients taking the drug. This toxicity is thought to be dose related, with optic neuropathy in as many as 10% of those who receive 30 mg/kg daily but in only 5% of those receiving 25 mg/kg daily. When ethambutol is discontinued or when the dose is greatly reduced, vision gradually returns, usually over months.

Digoxin Toxicity

Patients who describe unusual photopsias, such as peripheral flickering lights, a dazzling glare, or the perception that objects are covered by snow, should be questioned about cardiac medication. Patients who take digitalis and its congeners frequently complain of such unusual visual symptoms. The first physician to note the beneficial effects of digitalis, Withering, also was the first to call attention to "xanthopsia," a yellow tint to vision experienced by patients with digoxin toxicity. Patients may experience not only yellow vision but also orange- or green-tinted vision.

In 80% of patients taking digoxin, disturbances of color vision may be elicited by careful testing, although most patients are unaware of this problem. Patients taking modern preparations of cardiac glycosides, such as digoxin, are likely to suffer photopsias, sometimes continuously throughout the day. These photopsias are unlike symptoms of migraine in that they may be present only in the light and disappear in the dark; they are diffusely distributed and not arranged in a hemianopic pattern, and they rarely obscure vision.

Development of central or paracentral scotomata is an uncommon but well-documented toxic reaction to cardiac glycoside administration. Toxic effects may be seen even at "therapeutic" levels of the drug, although they are clearly more common when drug levels are high, and they are usually reversible. Electroretinography typically reveals prolongation of the cone B-wave implicit time, which returns to normal when the drug is withdrawn and the patient becomes asymptomatic.

CANCER-ASSOCIATED RETINOPATHY

Complaints of painless, progressive loss of visual acuity and color vision over weeks to months, with selective night blindness, should arouse the suspicion of cancer-associated retinopathy (CAR). Photosensitivity, shimmering photopsias, and peripheral constriction of visual fields are early symptoms of CAR.[29-32] This syndrome of retinal degeneration has most often been reported in men with small-cell carcinoma of the lung,[29] but has also been seen in women with breast cancer and gynecologic tumors, or with malignant melanomas. The retinal degeneration may appear at the time of initial occurrence of a malignancy or may signal the recurrence of a previously treated cancer.

Visual loss may begin monocularly and become binocular. In asymmetric cases, a relative afferent pupillary defect can be demonstrated. The pattern of visual field loss is midzonal and central, and often produces a ring scotoma, reflecting the retinal origin of the defect.[33]

Inflammatory cells have been observed in the vitreous of patients with CAR, and examination of the fundus may reveal optic disc pallor, arteriolar narrowing, and a golden sheen to the light reflex of the retina.

Extensive loss of photoreceptor elements has been demonstrated in patients with CAR, and electroretinograms typically are extinguished for both rods and cones. Some patients also suffer loss of ganglion cells. Retinal cell loss is thought to result from antibodies to the tumor that attack the photoreceptors and ganglion cells.[29,30] Steroids may provide temporary benefit but the prognosis is grave.

DOUBLE VISION AND OSCILLOPSIA

Patients with defects in eye movement complain of blurred vision or frank double vision, which resolves when either eye is covered. Diagnosis of the movement abnormality is assisted by determining if the double images are side by side or vertically displaced. Patients may also complain that the world is shaking or moving, producing blurred vision and difficulty with reading. The subjective sense of movement of the visual world is called oscillopsia, and usually reflects the objective finding of nystagmus (Fig. 10.12). Eye movement abnormalities are associated with both drug ingestion and several systemic diseases that involve the nervous system, and examination of eye movements may allow specific diagnosis of disease as well as precise localization of lesions. Both common and rare systemic and neurologic disorders may present initially or be diagnosed early by recognition of associated eye movement abnormalities, especially ophthalmoplegia and nystagmus. For example, ophthalmoplegia is a prominent finding in myasthenia gravis, Miller Fisher syndrome, pituitary apoplexy, Wernicke–Korsakoff syndrome, botulism, Whipple's disease, and certain movement disorders.

FIGURE 10.12. Systemic Diseases and Conditions Causing Nystagmus

Drugs
    Alcohol
    Anticonvulsants
    Barbiturates
    Lithium
    Tobacco
    Tranquilizers

Encephalitis

Magnesium deficiency

Myasthenia gravis

Neuroblastoma

Subacute cerebellar degeneration (paraneoplastic)

Wernicke–Korsakoff syndrome

Whipple's disease

Supranuclear ophthalmoplegia can be caused by Whipple's disease. With Whipple's disease, vertical eye movements typically are affected more than horizontal eye movements.[34] The patient usually suffers from gastrointestinal complaints such as diarrhea and malabsorption, and less frequently from malaise, fever, lymphadenopathy, weight loss, anemia, and arthritis. A biopsy of the jejunal mucosa reveals foamy macrophages and PAS-positive granules in the lamina propria.

Whipple's disease is associated not only with supranuclear ophthalmoplegia but also with a pattern of nystagmus called "oculomasticatory myorhythmia," which is pathognomonic for Whipple's disease.[35] This consists of an unusual pendular convergent nystagmus accompanied by jaw movements that are in synchrony with the movements of the eye. On further ocular examination, Whipple's patients may have cells in the vitreous and edema of the optic disc. Whipple's disease is presumed to be caused by an infectious agent[36] and can be treated successfully with cephalosporin antibiotics.

Blurred vision from accommodative paresis, diplopia from lateral rectus palsy, and discomfort from dry eyes may prompt the patient with botulism to seek ophthalmic care.[37] Botulism is caused by a toxin produced by the gram-positive anaerobic bacillus *Clostridium botulinum*. The toxin is usually acquired by eating home-canned food in which the toxin has not been destroyed by adequate cooking (or sterilization). Adults who have abnormal gastrointestinal tracts or have recently taken antibiotics (producing abnormal gastrointestinal flora) may be especially susceptible to botulism. Wound botulism, a rare variety, is caused by frank infection of a wound with the bacillus, with in situ production of the toxin.

Another variety of botulism is seen in infants who have ingested botulinum spores. Those spores germinate in the GI tract and elaborate toxin, which is then systemically absorbed .

Botulinum toxin interferes with the calcium-mediated release of acetylcholine at nerve terminals in the peripheral, autonomic, and probably even central nervous system. Early diagnosis of botulism is critical so that supportive measures can be instituted.

Lateral rectus palsy, gaze palsies, and nystagmus in a patient who is alcoholic or thiamine deficient for any other reason may indicate the Wernicke–Korsakoff syndrome. Recognizing this syndrome is critical because it constitutes a medical emergency.[38]

Bilateral VI nerve palsies are seen in more than half the patients with Wernicke–Korsakoff syndrome, and conjugate gaze palsies are observed in slightly less than half. Nystagmus, usually horizontal and gaze evoked, occurs in as many as 85% of these patients. About half of the patients with Wernicke–Korsakoff syndrome have both vertical and horizontal nystagmus, but vertical or rotary nystagmus in isolation is not typically seen. Significant anisocoria is rarely attributable to Wernicke–Korsakoff syndrome.

The classic patient with Korsakoff psychosis presents in a "global confusional state," with disorientation and loss of memory. The patient may

WHIPPLE'S DISEASE

BOTULISM

WERNICKE–KORSAKOFF SYNDROME

exhibit delirium tremens, agitation, and hallucinations. Other signs of the Wernicke–Korsakoff syndrome include ataxia and polyneuropathy, with loss of reflexes, sensation, and hearing.

The oculomotor abnormalities of these patients usually respond rapidly to the administration of thiamine. Victor et al[38] suggest the rapid and simultaneous administration of thiamine 50 mg IV and 50 mg IM for any patient suspected of having the Wernicke–Korsakoff syndrome. However, even with adequate thiamine therapy the cognitive dysfunctions of these patients do not resolve quickly.

The Wernicke–Korsakoff syndrome can occur not only in alcoholics but also in patients who do not absorb sufficient thiamine, such as those on total parenteral nutrition. Unfortunately, administration of intravenous glucose may precipitate the symptom or worsen patients with this syndrome who have low storage reserves of thiamine. Glucose alone, without the simultaneous intravenous administration of thiamine, should never be administered to malnourished patients, especially those with decreased mentation or disordered oculomotor function.

PARANEOPLASTIC SYNDROMES
DOWNBEAT NYSTAGMUS

Downbeat nystagmus is associated with cerebellar malformations such as Arnold–Chiari syndrome, skull base abnormalities such as platybasia, posterior fossa tumors, cerebrovascular accidents, and cerebellar atrophy. When downbeat nystagmus occurs with ataxia of trunk and limbs and with dysarthria, developing rapidly over days to weeks in a middle-aged person, a paraneoplastic syndrome, subacute cerebellar degeneration (SCD), should be suspected.[39] The presence of cancer is frequently unsuspected at the onset of neurological dysfunction. However, these signs can develop at any time in the course of cancer. The associated occult tumor in women most often is ovarian or breast cancer and in men most often is lung cancer or Hodgkins lymphoma.[40-43]

An autoimmune basis for SCD is suspected but remains to be proven. In about half of the patients with SCD, antibodies to tumor antigens have been found that crossreact with cerebellar Purkinje cell cytoplasm.[40] On pathologic examination, loss of Purkinje cells is seen in the cerebellar cortex. Steroids may provide temporary relief but unfortunately treatment of the associated malignancy does not usually reverse the cerebellar degeneration.

FIGURE 10.13. Paraneoplastic Syndromes Involving the Visual System

Cancer-associated retinopathy

Eaton–Lambert myasthenic syndrome

Opsoclonus/myoclonus

Optic neuritis

Subacute cerebellar degeneration

Magnetic resonance imaging should be performed in a search for other diagnoses when patients present with primary-position downbeat nystagmus (Fig. 10.13). However, the MRI of patients with subacute cerebellar degeneration remains normal until very late stages, when mild cerebellar atrophy may be detected. If the MRI is normal or shows only mild cerebellar atrophy a spinal tap should be performed. Patients with SCD have either normal spinal fluid or a slight elevation of CSF protein and mild lymphocytosis. If the MRI and the spinal tap are normal, the diagnosis of SCD can be presumed when the onset of nystagmus, ataxia, and dysarthria is acute (or subacute) in a patient without family history of cerebellar degeneration. An aggressive search should be pursued for the site of an occult malignancy.[39-41]

OPSOCLONUS/FLUTTER

The patient who complains of sudden onset of oscillopsia may exhibit irregular bursts of involuntary conjugate saccadic jerks in all directions. This frenzy of saccades is called opsoclonus and may be accompanied by myoclonus or other evidence of cerebellar dysfunction.[44] It almost always signals underlying neurologic or systemic disease. A similar phenomenon, ocular flutter, consists of bursts of horizontal saccades without an intersaccadic interval and has the same implications as opsoclonus.

Opsoclonus may occur in youngsters with viral encephalitis or even in normal neonates.[45] However, the observation of opsoclonus in any infant or child should initiate an investigation for neuroblastoma, including neuroimaging, abdominal CT, and 24-hour urine collection for catecholamines. Prognosis for the affected child's life is improved by early diagnosis. The opsoclonus may respond to the removal of the tumor.

In both adults and children opsoclonus may accompany infectious or postinfectious encephalitis. In adults it can also be caused by metabolic abnormality, drug toxicity, or vertebrobasilar ischemia. Of greatest concern, however, is the possibility that opsoclonus heralds an occult malignancy. It has been reported in patients with cancer of the lung, breast, uterus, ovary, bladder, or thyroid. A work-up is mandatory to determine the presence and extent of disease. However, neuroimaging is usually unrevealing. Spinal tap may yield CSF containing elevated protein and lymphocytic pleocytosis.

The pathology underlying opsoclonus seems to be immune-mediated damage to Purkinje cells in the cerebellum. In addition, a lymphocytic infiltration throughout the central nervous system has been observed. An antineural antibody (anti-Ri) has been reported in opsoclonus patients with breast cancer.[41]·Physiologically, opsoclonus reflects disinhibition of brain stem burst cells, presumably owing to dysfunction of the pause cells. In adults, removal of the tumor rarely provides relief from opsoclonus.

SUMMARY

The neuro-ophthalmic examination enables the physician to locate precisely lesions in the central nervous system that produce visual symptoms and signs. Neuro-ophthalmic examination often will reveal an underlying systemic disease that otherwise might be missed, and this chapter has described several specific examples of systemic diseases that can be diagnosed by a careful neuro-ophthalmic examination if the disease is suspected on the basis of the patient's complaints. Some of the syndromes described, such as amaurosis fugax, are rather common, but the patient's history must be carefully evaluated to interpret correctly the meaning of the symptoms. Other diseases mentioned are quite rare, such as the paraneoplastic syndromes. Without a high suspicion for these syndromes the diagnosis is often missed or delayed.

REFERENCES

1. Østerberg G: Topography of the layer of rods and cones in the human retina. *Acta Ophthalmol 1935;(suppl 6):8.*
2. de Monasterio FM, Mc Crane EP, Newlander JK, Schein SJ: Density profile of blue-sensitive cones along the horizontal meridian of *Macaque* retina. *Invest Ophthalmol Vis Sci 1985;26:289–302.*
3. Hart WM Jr: Acquired dyschromatopsias. *Surv Ophthalmol 1987;32: 10–31.*
4. Cohen AI: The retina, in Moses RA, Hart WM Jr (eds): *Adler's Physiology of the Eye,* ed 8. St Louis: CV Mosby, 1987;458–490.
5. Weise EE, Yannuzzi LA: Ring maculopathies mimicking chloroquine retinopathy. *Am J Ophthalmol 1974;78:204–210.*
6. Arey LB, Bickel WH: The number of fibers in the human optic nerve (abstr 4). *Anat Rec 1935; (suppl 61):3.*
7. Balazsi AG, Rootman J, Drance SM, et al: The effect of age on the nerve fiber population of the human optic nerve. *Am J Ophthalmol 1984; 97:760–766.*
8. Harrington DO: Differential diagnosis of the arcuate scotoma. *Invest Ophthalmol 1969;8:96–105.*
9. Livingston MS, Hubel DH: Psychophysical evidence for separate channels for the perception of form, color, movement and depth. *J Neurosci 1987;7:3416–3468.*
10. Wilbrand H, Saenger A: *Neurologie des Auges,* Vol III, Part 1. Wiesbaden: JF Bergmann, 1904, 103.
11. Kearns TP, Rucker CW: Arcuate defects in the visual fields due to chromophobe adenoma of the pituitary gland. *Am J Ophthalmol 1958; 45:505–507.*
12. Marino R, Rasmussen T: Visual field changes after temporal lobectomy in man. *Neurology 1968;18:825–835.*
13. Horton J, Hoyt WF: The representation of the visual field in human striate cortex. A revision of the classic Holmes map. *Arch Ophthalmol 1991;109:816–824.*

CHAPTER 1
TOPOGRAPHIC DIAGNOSIS IN DISEASES OF THE AFFERENT VISUAL SYSTEM

1. Nikoskelainen E: Symptoms, signs and early course of optic neuritis. *Acta Ophthalmol 1975;53:254–272.*
2. Hutchinson WM: Acute optic neuritis and the prognosis for multiple sclerosis. *J Neurol Neurosurg Psychiatr 1976;39:283–289.*
3. Gass JDM: *Stereoscopic Atlas of Macular Diseases: Diagnosis and Treatment.* St. Louis: CV Mosby, 1987, 46–59.
4. Sptiznas M: Pathogenesis of central serous retinopathy: A new working hypothesis. *Graefes Arch Clin Exp Ophthalmol 1986;224:321–324.*
5. Ellis W, Little HL: Leukemic infiltration of the optic nerve head. *Am J Ophthalmol 1973;75:867–871.*
6. Early Treatment Diabetic Retinopathy Study Research Group: Photocoagulation for diabetic macular edema: Early Treatment Diabetic Retinopathy Study report number 1. *Arch Ophthalmol 1985;103:1796–1806.*
7. Holmes G: *Introduction to Clinical Neurology.* Edinburgh: E & S Livingstone, 1946.
8. Lepore FE: Visual obscurations: Evanescent and elementary. *Semin Neurol 1986;6:167–175.*
9. Perkins GD, Rose FC: *Optic Neuritis and Its Differential Diagnosis.* Oxford: Oxford University Press, 1979, 194–200.
10. Glaser JS: *Neuro Ophthalmology,* ed 2. Philadelphia: JB Lippincott, 1990, 115–117.
11. Sadun AA, Currie JN, Lessell S: Transient visual obscurations with elevated optic discs. *Ann Neurol 1984;16:489–494.*
12. Fine AM, Elman MJ, Ebert JE, et al: Earliest symptoms caused by neovascular membranes in the macula. *Arch Ophthalmol 1986;104:513–514.*
13. Folk JC: Aging macular degeneration: Clinical features of treatable disease. *Ophthalmology 1985;92:594–602.*
14. Fineberg E, Thompson HS: Quantitation of the afferent pupillary defect, in Smith JL (ed): *Neuro-ophthalmology Focus.* New York: Masson, 1979, 25–29.

CHAPTER 2
DISTINGUISHING OPTIC NERVE DISEASE FROM RETINAL/ MACULAR DISEASE

15. Cox TA, Thompson HS, Hayreh SS, et al: Visual evoked potential and pupillary signs: A comparison in optic nerve disease. *Arch Ophthalmol 1982;100:1603–1607.*

16. Hart WM Jr: Acquired dyschromatopsias. *Surv Ophthalmol 1987; 32:10–31.*

17. Mainster MA, Dieckert JP: A simple haploscopic method for quantitating color brightness comparison. *Am J Ophthalmol 1980;89:58–61.*

18. Fleishman JA, Beck RW, Linares OA, et al: Deficits in visual function after resolution of optic neuritis. *Ophthalmology 1987;94:1029–1035.*

19. Preston DS, Bernstein L, Sadun AA: Office techniques for detecting optic neuropathies: Brightness sense compared to traditional screening tests. *Neuro-Ophthalmology 1988;8:245–250.*

20. Sadun AA, Lessell S: Brightness-sense and optic nerve disease. *Arch Ophthalmol 1985;103:39–43.*

21. Glaser JS: *Neuro Ophthalmology,* ed 2. Philadelphia: JB Lippincott, 1990, 27–33.

22. Glaser JS: Clinical evaluation of optic nerve function. *Trans Ophthalmol Soc UK 1976;96:359–362.*

23. Sadun AA: Brightness sense testing, in Wall M, Sadun AA (eds): *New Methods of Sensory Visual Testing.* New York: Springer-Verlag, 1989, 14–28.

24. Mills RP: Automated perimetry: Theoretical and practical considerations, in Wall M, Sadun AA (eds): *New Methods of Sensory Visual Testing.* New York: Springer-Verlag, 1989, 112–131.

25. Younge BR: Computerized perimetry in neuro-ophthalmology, in Whalen WR, Spaeth GL (eds): *Computerized Visual Fields: What They Are and How to Use Them.* Thorofare, NJ: Slack, 1985, 239–276.

26. Johnson CA, Keltner JL, Lewis RA: Automated kinetic perimetry, an efficient method of evaluating peripheral visual field loss. *Appl Opt 1987;26:1409–1414.*

27. Amsler M: Earliest symptoms of diseases of the macula. *Br J Ophthalmol 1953;37:521–537.*

28. Wall M, Sadun AA: Threshold Amsler grid testing: Cross-polarizing lenses enhance yield. *Arch Ophthalmol 1986;104:520–523.*

29. Wall M, May DR: Threshold Amsler grid testing in maculopathies. *Ophthalmology 1987;94:1126–1133.*

30. Patterson VH, Heron JR: Visual field abnormalities in multiple sclerosis. *J Neurol Neurosurg Psychiatry 1980;43:205.*

31. Tagami Y: Correlations between atrophy of maculopapillar bundles and visual functions in cases of optic neuropathies. *Doc Ophthalmol Proc Ser 1979;19:17–26.*

32. Hayreh SS, Podhajsky P: Visual field defects in anterior ischemic optic neuropathy. *Doc Ophthalmol Proc Ser 1979;19:53–71.*

33. Aulhorn E, Tanzil M: Comparison of visual field defects in glaucoma and in acute anterior ischemic optic neuropathy. *Doc Ophthalmol Proc Ser 1979;19:73–79.*

34. Lonn LI, Hoyt WF: Papillophlebitis: A cause of protracted yet benign optic disc edema. *Ear Nose Throat J 1966;45(10):62–68.*

35. Minckler DS, Tso MOM, Zimmerman LE: A light microscopic, autoradiographic study of axoplasmic transport in the optic nerve head during ocular hypotony, increased intraocular pressure, and papilledema. *Am J Ophthalmol 1976;82:741–757.*

36. Hayreh SS: Optic disc edema in raised intracranial pressure. VI. Associated visual disturbances and their pathogenesis. *Arch Ophthalmol 1977;95:1566–1579.*

37. Stevens RA, Newman NM: Abnormal visual-evoked potentials from eyes with optic nerve head drusen. *Am J Ophthalmol 1981;92:857–862.*

38. Grehn F, Knorr–Held S, Kommerell G: Glaucomatouslike visual field defects in chronic papilledema. *Graefes Arch Clin Exp Ophthalmol 1981;217:99–109.*

39. Corbett JJ, Savino PJ, Thompson HS, et al: Visual loss in pseudotumor cerebri: Follow-up of 57 patients from five to 41 years and a profile of 14 patients with permanent severe visual loss. *Arch Neurol 1982; 39:461–474.*

40. Trobe JD, Glaser JS: Quantitative perimetry in compressive optic neuropathy and optic neuritis. *Arch Ophthalmol 1978;96:1210–1216.*

41. Salinas–Garcia RF, Smith JL: Binasal hemianopia. *Surg Neurol 1978; 10:187–194.*

42. Glaser JS: *Neuro Ophthalmology,* ed 2. Philadelphia: JB Lippincott, 1990, 18–20.

43. Glaser JS, Savino PJ, Sumers KD, et al: The photostress recovery test in the clinical assessment of visual function. *Am J Ophthalmol 1977; 83:255–260.*

44. Halliday AM: New developments in the clinical application of evoked potentials. *Contemp Clin Neurophysiol 1978;34:105.*

45. Halliday AM, McDonald WI, Mushin J: Delayed visual evoked response in optic neuritis. *Lancet 1972;1:982–985.*

46. Weinstein GW: Clinical aspects of the visually evoked potential. *Ophthalmic Surg 1978;9(1):56–65.*

47. Towle VL, Sutcliffe E, Sokol S: Diagnosing functional visual deficits with the P300 component of the visual evoked potential. *Arch Ophthalmol 1985;103:47–50.*

48. Regan D, Milner BA, Heron JR: Delayed visual perception and delayed visual evoked potentials in the spinal form of multiple sclerosis and in retrobulbar neuritis. *Brain 1976;99:43–66.*

49. Bodis–Wollner I, Camisa JM: Contrast sensitivity in clinical diagnosis, in Lessell S, Van Dalen JTW (eds): *Neuro Ophthalmology.* Amsterdam: Elsevier Science Publishers, 1980, 373–401.

50. Regan D, Silver R, Murray TJ: Visual acuity and contrast sensitivity in multiple sclerosis hidden visual loss: An auxiliary diagnostic test. *Brain 1977;100:563–579.*

51. Regan D, Neima D: Low-contrast letter charts as a test of visual function. *Ophthalmology 1983;90:1192–1200.*

52. Arden GB, Jacobson JJ: A simple grating test for contrast sensitivity: Preliminary results indicate value in screening for glaucoma. *Invest Ophthalmol Vis Sci 1978;17:23–32.*

53. Ginsburg AP, Cannon MW: Comparison of three methods for rapid determination of threshold contrast sensitivity. *Invest Ophthalmol Vis Sci 1983;24:798–802.*

54. Ginsburg AP: A new contrast sensitivity vision test chart. *Am J Optom Physiol Opt 1984;61:403–407.*

CHAPTER 3
THE OPTIC
NEUROPATHIES

1. Jaeger W: Hereditary optic atrophies in childhood. *J Genet Hum 1966; 15:312–321.*

2. Lodberg CV, Lund A: Hereditary optic atrophy with dominant transmission: Three Danish families. *Acta Ophthalmol 1950;28:437–468.*

3. Kjer P: Infantile optic atrophy with dominant mode of inheritance: A clinical and genetic study of nineteen Danish families. *Acta Ophthalmol (Copenh) 1959;(suppl 54).*

4. Kline LB, Glaser JS: Dominant optic atrophy: The clinical profile. *Arch Ophthalmol 1979;97:1680–1686.*

5. Hoyt CS: Autosomal dominant optic atrophy: A spectrum of disability *Ophthalmology 1980;87:245–251.*

6. Smith DP: Diagnostic criteria in dominantly inherited juvenile optic atrophy: A report of three new families. *Am J Optom 1972;49:183–200.*

7. Krill AE, Smith VC, Pokorny J: Similarities between congenital tritan defects and dominant optic-nerve atrophy: Coincidence or identity? *J Opt Soc Am [A] 1970;60:1132–1139.*

8. Miller NR: (Discussion of paper by Hoyt). *Ophthalmology 1980;87: 250–251.*

9. Grehn F, Kommerell G, Ropers H-H, et al: Dominant optic atrophy with sensory neural hearing loss. *Ophthalmic Paediatr Genet 1972;1:77.*

10. Johnston PB, Gaster RN, Smith VC, et al: A clinicopathologic study of autosomal dominant optic atrophy. *Am J Ophthalmol 1979;88:868–875.*

11. Kjer P, Jensen OA, Klinken L: Histopathology of the eye: Optic nerve and brain in a case of dominant optic atrophy. *Acta Ophthalmol 1983; 61:300–312.*

12. Waardenburg PJ: Different types of hereditary optic atrophy. *Acta Genet Statist Med 1957;7:287–298.*

13. Francois J: Mode d'hérédite des héredo-degénérescences du nerf optique. *J Genet Hum 1966;15:147–220.*

14. Behr C: Die komplizierte, hereditar-familiare Optikusatrophie des Kindesalters: Ein bisher nicht beschriebener Symptomkomplex. *Klin Monatsbl Augenheilk 1909;47:138–160.*

15. Horoupian DS, Zucker DK, Moshe S, et al: Behr syndrome: A clinicopathologic report. *Neurology 1979;29:323–327.*

16. Francois J: Hereditary degeneration of the optic nerve (hereditary optic atrophy). *Int Ophthalmol Clin 1968;8:999–1054.*

17. Wolfram DJ: Diabetes mellitus and simple optic atrophy among siblings. *Mayo Clin Proc 1938;13:715–717.*

18. Editorial. *Lancet 1986; May 10:1075–1076.*

19. Lessell S, Rossman NP: Juvenile diabetes mellitus and optic atrophy. *Arch Neurol 1977;34:759–765.*

20. Attardi G: The elucidation of the human mitochondrial genome: A historical perspective. *Bioessays 1987;5:34–39.*

21. Leber T: Über hereditare und congenital angelegte Sehenervenleiden. *Graefes Arch Ophthalmol 1871;17:249–291.*

22. Newman NJ, Lott MT, Wallace DC: The clinical characteristics of pedigrees of Leber's hereditary optic neuropathy with the 11778 mutation. *Am J Ophthalmol 1991;111:750–762.*

23. Smith JL, Hoyt WF, Susac JO: Ocular fundus in acute Leber's optic neuropathy. *Arch Ophthalmol 1973;90:349–354.*

24. Nikoskelainen E, Sogg RL, Rosenthal AR, et al: The early phase in Leber's hereditary optic atrophy. *Arch Ophthalmol 1977;95:969–978.*

25. Nikoskelainen E, Hoyt WF, Nummelin K: Ophthalmoscopic findings in Leber's hereditary optic neuropathy. II. The fundus findings in affected family members. *Arch Ophthalmol 1983;101:1059–1068.*

26. Lessell L, Gise RL, Krohel GB: Bilateral optic neuropathy with remission in young men: Variation on a theme by Leber? *Arch Neurol 1983;40:2–6.*

27. Taylor J, Holmes GM: Two families, with several members in each suffering from optic atrophy. *Trans Ophthalmol Soc UK 1913;33:95.*

28. Wallace DC: Leber's optic atrophy: A possible example of vertical transmission of a slow virus in man. *Aust Ann Med 1970;3:259–262.*

29. Foulds WS, Cant JS, Chisholm IA, et al: Hydroxy cobalamine in the treatment of Leber's hereditary optic atrophy. *Lancet 1968;1:896–897.*

30. Imachi J, Nishizaki K: The patients of Leber's optic atrophy should be treated brain-surgically. *Folia Ophthalmol Jpn 1970;21:209–217.*

31. Ford FR: *Diseases of the Nervous System in Infancy, Childhood and Adolescence,* ed 5. Springfield, IL: Charles C Thomas, 1966, 291–293.

32. Lees F, MacDonald A-ME, Aldren Turner JW: Leber's disease with symptoms resembling disseminated sclerosis. *J Neurol Neurosurg Psychol 1964;27:415–421.*

33. Bereday M, Cobb S: Relation of hereditary optic atrophy (Leber) to other familial diseases of the central nervous system. *Arch Ophthalmol 1952;48:669–680.*

34. Rose FC, Bowden AN, Bowden PMA: The heart in Leber's optic atrophy. *Br J Ophthalmol 1970;54:388–393.*

35. Nikoskelainen E: The clinical findings of Leber's hereditary optic neuropathy. *Trans Ophthalmol Soc UK 1985;104:845–852.*

36. Kermode AG, Mosley IF, Kendall BE, et al: Magnetic resonance imaging in Leber's optic neuropathy. *J Neurol Neurosurg Psychiatr 1989;52: 671–674.*

37. Wallace DC, Singh G, Lott MT, et al: Mitochondrial DNA mutation associated with Leber's hereditary optic neuropathy. *Science 1988; 242:1427–1430.*

38. Parker WC, Oley CA, Parks JK: A defect in mitochondrial electron-transport activity (NADH-coenzyme Q oxidoreductase) in Leber's hereditary optic neuropathy. *N Engl J Med 1989;320:1331–1333.*

39. Coppinger JN, Stone EM, Slavin ML, et al: Leber's hereditary optic neuropathy in a sixth generation pedigree with a wild-type ND-4 gene. *Invest Ophthalmol Vis Sci 1990;31(suppl 4): 1452.*

40. Lott NT, Voljavec AS, Wallace DC: Variable genotype of Leber's hereditary optic neuropathy patients. *Am J Ophthalmol 1990;109:625–631.*
41. Newman NJ, Wallace DC: Mitochondria and Leber's hereditary optic neuropathy. *Am J Ophthalmol 1990;109:726–730.*
42. Roberts SM: Review of the papers on the ocular toxicity of ethambutol hydrochloride: Myambutol and anti-tuberculosis drugs. *Am J Optom Physiol Opt 1974;51:987–992.*
43. DeVita EG, Miao M, Sadun AA: Optic neuropathy in ethambutol-treated renal tuberculosis. *J Clin Neuro Ophthalmol 1987;7:77–83.*
44. Carr RE, Henkind P: Ocular manifestions of ethambutol. *Arch Ophthalmol 1962;67:566–577.*
45. Salmon JF, Carmichael TR, Welsh NH: Use of contrasensitivity measurement in the detection of subclinical ethambutol toxic optic neuropathy. *Br J Ophthalmol 1987;71:192–196.*
46. Yiannikas C, Walsh JC, McLeod JG: Visual evoked potentials in the detection of subclinical optic toxic effects secondary to ethambutol. *Arch Neurol 1983;40:645–648.*
47. Kass I, Mandel W, Cohen H, et al: Isoniazid as a cause of optic neuritis and atrophy. *JAMA 1957;164:1740–1743.*
48. Godel V, Nemet P, Lazar M: Chloramphenicol optic neuropathy. *Arch Ophthalmol 1980;98:1417–1421.*
49. Adam JW, Bofenkamp TM, Kobrin J, et al: Recurrent acute toxic optic neuropathy secondary to 5-FU. *Cancer Treat Rev 1984;68:565–566.*
50. Pickrell L, Purvin V: Ischemic optic neuropathy secondary to intracarotid infusion of BCNU. *J Clin Neuro Ophthalmol 1987;7:87–91.*
51. Klingele TG, Burde RM: Optic neuropathy associated with penicillamine therapy in a patient with rheumatoid arthritis. *J Clin Neuro Ophthalmol 1984;4:75–78.*
52. Feiner LA, Younge BR, Kazmier FJ, et al: Optic neuropathy and amiodarone therapy. *Mayo Clin Proc 1987;62:702–705.*
53. Ricoy JR, Ortega A, Cabello A: Subacute myelo-optic neuropathy (SMON). *J Neurol Sci 1982;53:241–251.*
54. Haining WM, Beveridge GW: Toxic amblyopia in a patient receiving ethchlorvynol as a hypnotic. *Br J Ophthalmol 1964;48:598–600.*
55. Potts AM: Tobacco amblyopia. *Surv Ophthalmol 1973;17:313–331.*
56. Harrington DO: What is the etiology of alcohol and tobacco amblyopia?, in Brockhurst RJ, Boruchoff SA, Hutchinson BT, Lessell S (eds): *Controversies in Ophthalmology.* Philadelphia: WB Saunders, 1977, 866–872.
57. Carroll FD: Nutritional retrobulbar neuritis. *Am J Ophthalmol 1947;30: 172–176.*
58. Carroll FD: Etiology and treatment of tobacco alcohol amblyopia. *Am J Ophthalmol 1944;27:713–725;847–863.*
59. Dreyfus PM: Blood transketolase levels in tobacco alcohol amblyopia. *Arch Opthalmol 1965;74:617–620.*
60. Frisen L: Fundus changes in acute malnutritional optic neuropathy. *Arch Ophthalmol 1983;101:577–579.*
61. Rodieck RW, Brening RK: Retinal ganglion cells: Properties, types, general pathways and transpecies comparisons. *Brain Behav Evol 1963; 23:121–164.*
62. Smiddy WE, Green WR: Nutritional amblyopia: A histopathologic study with retrospective clinical correlation. *Graefes Arch Ophthalmol 1987;225:321–324.*
63. Benton CD, Calhoun FP: The ocular effects of methyl alcohol poisoning. Report of a catastrosphe involving 320 persons. *Trans Am Acad Ophthalmol Otolaryngol 1952;56:875–885.*
64. Lessell S: Indirect optic nerve trauma. *Arch Ophthalmol 1989;107: 382–386.*
65. Kline LB, Morawetz RB, Swaid NS: Indirect injury of the optic nerve. *Neurosurgery 1984;14:756–764.*
66. Katz B, Herchler J, Brick D: Orbital haemorrhage and prolonged blindness: A treatable posterior optic neuropathy. *Br J Ophthalmol 1983; 67:549–553.*

67. Hollenhorst RW, Svien HJ, Benoit CF: Unilateral blindness occurring during anesthesia for neurosurgical operations. *Arch Ophthalmol 1954; 52:819–830.*

68. Guyer DR, Miller NR, Long DM, et al: Visual function following optic nerve decompression. *J Neurosurg 1985;62:631–638.*

69. Anderson RL, Panje WR, Gross CE: Optic nerve blindness following blunt forehead trauma. *Ophthalmology 1982;89:445–455.*

70. Joseph MP, Lessell S, Rizzo J, Momose J: Extracranial optic nerve decompression for traumatic optic neuropathy. *Arch Ophthalmol 1990; 108:1091–1093.*

71. Fukado Y: Results in 400 cases of surgical decompression of the optic nerve. *Mod Probl Ophthalmol 1975;14:474–481.*

72. Spoor TC, Mathog RH: Restoration of vision after optic canal decompression. *Arch Ophthalmol 1986;104:804–806.*

73. Seiff SR: High dose corticosteroids for treatment of vision loss due to indirect injury of the optic nerve. *Ophthalmic Surg 1990;21:389–395.*

74. Boghen DR, Glaser JS: Ischemic optic neuropathy: The clinical profile and natural history. *Brain 1975;98:689–708.*

75. Kurz O: Vascular opticopathy. *Doc Ophthalmol 1969;26:582–591.*

76. Ellenberger C, Netsky MD: Infarction of the optic nerve. *J Neurol Neurosurg Psychiatr 1968;31:606–611.*

77. Hayreh SS: Anterior ischemic optic neuropathy. I. Terminology and pathogenesis. *Br J Ophthalmol 1974;58:955–963.*

78. Hayreh, SS: *Anterior Ischemic Optic Neuropathy.* Berlin: Springer-Verlag, 1975.

79. Feit RH, Tomsak RL, Ellenberger C Jr: Structural factors in the development of ischemic optic neuropathy. *Am J Ophthalmol 1984;98:105–108.*

80. Beck RW, Savino PJ, Repka M, et al: Optic disc structure in anterior ischemic optic neuropathy. *Ophthalmology 1984;91:1334–1337.*

81. Doro S, Lessell S: Cup–disc ratio and ischemic optic neuropathy. *Arch Ophthalmol 1985;103:1143–1144.*

82. Katz B, Weinreb RN, Wheeler D: Ischemic optic neuropathy and intraocular pressure (abstr). *Ophthalmology 1987;94(suppl 10):92.*

83. Katz B, Weinreb RN, Wheeler DT, et al: Anterior ischaemic optic neuropathy and intraocular pressure. *Br J Ophthalmol 1990;74(2):99–102.*

84. Sergott RC, Cohen MS, Boseley TM, et al: Optic nerve decompression may improve the progressive form of nonarteritic ischemic optic neuropathy. *Arch Ophthalmol 1989;107:1743–1754.*

85. Beri M, Klugman MR, Kohler JA, et al: Anterior ischemic optic neuropathy. VII. Instances of bilaterality and various influencing factors. *Ophthalmology 1987;94:1020–1028.*

86. McLeod D, Marshall J, Kohner EM: Role of axoplasmic transport in the pathophysiology of ischaemic disc swelling. *Br J Ophthalmol 1980;64: 247–261.*

87. Anderson DR, Davis EB: Retina and optic nerve after posterior ciliary artery occlusion. *Arch Ophthalmol 1974;92:422–426.*

88. Ellenberger C, Netsk MD: Infarction of the optic nerve. *J Neurol Neurosurg Psychiatr 1968;31:606–611.*

89. Lieberman MF, Shahi A, Green WR: Embolic ischemic optic neuropathy. *Am J Ophthalmol 1978;86:206–210.*

90. Cullen JF: Ischemic optic neuropathy. *Trans Ophthalmol Soc UK 1967; 87:759–774.*

91. Klein RG, Campbell RJ, Hunder GG, et al: Skip lesions in temporal arteritis. *Mayo Clin Proc 1976;51:504–510.*

92. Katz B: Disc swelling in an adult diabetic. *Surv Ophthalmol 1990;35: 158–163.*

93. Carroll FD: Optic nerve complications of cataract extraction. *Trans Am Acad Ophthalmol Otolaryngol 1973;77:623–629.*

94. Hayreh SS: Anterior ischemic optic neuropathy IV. Occurrence after cataract extraction. *Arch Ophthalmol 1980;98:1410–1416.*

95. Tomsak R: Ischemic optic neuropathy associated with retinal emboli. *Am J Ophthalmol 1985;99:590–592.*

96. Guyer DR, Miller NM, Auer CL, et al: The risk of cerebrovascular disease in patients with anterior ischemic optic neuropathy. *Arch Ophthalmol 1985;103:1136–1142.*

97. Durcan FJ, Corbett JJ, Wall M: The incidence of pseudotumor cerebri. Population studies in Iowa and Louisiana. *Arch Neurol 1988;45:875–877.*

98. Wall M, George D: Idiopathic intracranial hypertension (pseudotumor cerebri): A prospective study of 50 patients. *Brain 1991;14:155–180.*

99. Corbett JJ, Savino PJ, Thompson HS, et al: Visual loss in pseudotumor cerebri. Follow-up of 57 patients from five to 41 years and a profile of 14 patients with permanent severe visual loss. *Arch Neurol 1982; 39:461–474.*

100. Giuseffi V, Wall M, Rojas PB, Siegel PZ: Symptoms and disease associations in idiopathic intracranial hypertension: A case-control study. *Neurology 1991;41:239–244.*

101. Wall M: Sensory visual testing in idiopathic intracranial hypertension: Measures sensitive to change. *Neurology 1990;40:1859–1864.*

102. Frisén L: Swelling of the optic nerve head: A staging scheme. *J Neurol Neurosurg Psychiatr 1982;45:13–18.*

103. Verplanck M, Kaufman DI, Parsons T, et al: Electrophysiology versus psychophysics in the detection of visual loss in pseudotumor cerebri. *Neurology 1988;38:1789–1792.*

104. Wall M: Contrast sensitivity testing in pseudotumor cerebri. *Ophthalmology 1986;93:4–7.*

105. Digre KB, Corbett JJ: Pseudotumor cerebri in men. *Arch Neurol 1988; 45:866–872.*

106. Corbett JJ, Thompson HS: The rational management of idiopathic intracranial hypertension. *Arch Neurol 1989;46:1049–1051.*

107. Wall M: Idiopathic intracranial hypertension, in Breen L (ed): *Neurology Clinics of North America.* Philadelphia: WB Saunders, 1991, 73–95.

108. Ireland B, Corbett JJ, Wallace RB: The search for causes of pseudotumor cerebri: A preliminary case-control study. *Arch Neurol 1990;47:315–320.*

109. Digre KB, Varner MW, Corbett JJ: Pseudotumor cerebri and pregnancy. *Neurology 1984;34:721–729.*

110. Sergott RC, Savino PJ, Bosley TM: Modified optic nerve sheath decompression provides long-term visual improvement for pseudotumor cerebri. *Arch Ophthalmol 1988;106:1391–1397.*

111. Corbett JJ, Nerad JA, Tse DT, Anderson RL: Results of optic nerve sheath fenestration for pseudotumor cerebri. The lateral orbitotomy approach. *Arch Ophthalmol 1988;106:1391–1397.*

112. Sergott RC, Brown MJ: Current concepts of the pathogenesis of optic neuritis associated with multiple sclerosis. *Surv Ophthalmol 1988; 33:108–116.*

113. Bradley WG, Whitty CMW: Acute optic neuritis: Its clinical features and their relation to prognosis for recovery of vision. *J Neurol Neurosurg Psychiatr 1967;30:531–538.*

114. Hess RF, Plant GT: *Optic Neuritis.* Cambridge: Cambridge University Press, 1986.

115. Kupersmith MJ, Burde RM, Warren FA, et al: Autoimmune optic neuropathy: Evaluation and treatment. *1988;51:1381–1386.*

116. Lightman S, McDonald WI, Bird AC, et al: Retinal venous sheathing in optic neuritis. *Brain 1987;110:405–414.*

117. Arnold AC, Pepose JS, Hepler RS, Foos RY: Retinal periphlebitis and retinitis in multiple sclerosis. *Ophthalmology 1984;91:255–262.*

118. Graham EM, Francis DA, Sanders MD, Rudge P: Ocular inflammatory changes in established multiple sclerosis. *J Neurol Neurosurg Psychiatr 1989;52:1360–1363.*

119. Bachman DM, Rosenthal AR, Beckingsale AB: Granulomatous uveitis in neurological disease. *Br J Ophthalmol 1985;69:192–196.*

120. Wall M: Loss of P retinal ganglion cell function in resolved optic neuritis. *Neurology 1990;40:649–652.*

121. Parmley VC, Schiffman JS, Maitland CG, et al: Does neuroretinitis rule out multiple sclerosis. *1987;44:1045–1048.*

122. Rizzo JF, Lessell S: Risk of developing multiple sclerosis after uncomplicated optic neuritis: A long-term prospective study. *Neurology 1988; 38:185–190.*

123. Compston DAS, Batchelor JR, Earl CJ, McDonald WI: Factors influencing the risk of multiple sclerosis developing in patients with optic neuritis. *Brain 1978;101:495–511.*

124. Sandberg-Wollheim M: Optic neuritis: Studies on the cerebrospinal fluid in relation to clinical course in 61 patients. *Acta Neurol Scand 1975;52:167–178.*

125. Beck RW, Cleary PA, Anderson MM, et al: A randomized controlled trial of corticosteroids in the treatment of acute optic neuritis. *N Engl J Med 1992;326:581–588.*

126. Hackett EH, Martinez RD, Larson PL, Paddison RM: Optic neuritis in systemic lupus erythematosus. *Arch Neurol 1974;31:9–11.*

127. Frohman L, Bielory L, Warren F, Kupersmith M: Skin biopsies in the evaluation of a typical optical neuropathy (abstr). *Invest Ophthalmol Vis Sci 1991;(suppl 32):951.*

128. Dutton JJ, Burde RM, Klingle TG: Autoimmune retrobulbar optic neuritis. *Am J Ophthalmol 1982;94:11–17.*

129. Zion V: Optic disc hypoplasia. *Ophthalmol Semin 1976;1:171–196.*

130. Lambert SR, Hoyt CS, Narahara MH: Optic nerve hypoplasia. *Surv Ophthalmol 1987;32:1–9.*

131. Novakovic P, Taylor DSI, Hoyt WF: Localising patterns of optic nerve hypoplasia—retina to occipital lobe. *Br J Ophthalmol 1988;72:176–182.*

132. Strömland K: Ocular involvement in the fetal alcohol syndrome. *Surv Ophthalmol 1987;31:277–284.*

133. Strömland K: Ocular abnormalities in the fetal alcohol syndrome. *Acta Ophthalmol 1985;63(suppl):1–50.*

134. Nelson M, Lessell S, Sadun AA: Optic nerve hypoplasia and maternal diabetes mellitus. *Arch Neurol 1986;43:20–25.*

135. Mann I: *The Developmental Anomalies of the Human Eye.* London: Butler & Tanner, 1964, 42.

136. Apple DJ, Raab MF, Walsh PM: Congenital anomalies of the optic disc. *Surv Ophthalmol 1982;27:3–41.*

137. Haik BG, Greenstein SH, Smith ME, et al: Retinal detachment in the morning glory anomaly. *Ophthalmology 1984;91:1638–1647.*

138. Sobol WM, Blodi CF, Folk JC, Weingiest TA: Long-term visual outcome in patients with optic nerve pit and serous retinal detachment of the macula. *Ophthalmology 1990;97:1539–1542.*

139. Rosenberg MA, Savino PJ, Glaser JS: A clinical analysis of pseudopapilledema: I. Population, laterality, acuity, refractive error, ophthalmoscopic characteristics, and coincident disease. *Arch Ophthalmol 1979;97:65–70.*

140. Savino PJ, Glaser JS, Rosenberg MA: A clinical analysis of pseudopapilledema: II. Visual field defects. *Arch Ophthalmol 1979;97:71–75.*

141. Lorentzen SE: Drusen of the optic disc. *Acta Ophthalmol 1966;(suppl 90):9–19.*

142. Friedman DH, Henkind P, Gartner S: Drusen of the optic disc: A histopathological study. *Trans Ophthalmol Soc UK 1975;95:4–9.*

143. Beck RW, Corbett JJ, Thompson HS, Sergott RC: Decreased visual acuity from optic disc drusen. *Arch Ophthalmol 1985;103;1155–1159.*

144 Sanders TE, Gay AJ, Newman M: Hemorrhagic complications of drusen of the optic disc. *Am J Ophthalmol 1971;71:204–217.*

145. Brown GC, Shields JA: Tumors of the optic nerve head. *Surv Ophthalmol 1985;29:239–264.*

146. Zimmerman LE, Garron LK: Melanocytoma of the optic disc. *Int Ophthalmol Clin 1962;2:431–440.*

147. Wyburn-Mason R: Arteriovenous aneurysm of the mid-brain and retina, facial naevi and mental changes. *Brain 1943;66:163–203.*

148. Knight CL, Hoyt WF, Wilson CB: Syndrome of incipient prechiasmal optic nerve compression. *Arch Ophthalmol 1972;87:1–11.*

149. Sibony P, Krauss H, Kennerdal J, et al: Optic nerve sheath meningiomas. Clinical manifestations. *Ophthalmology 1984;91:1313–1326.*

150. Schrell UMH, Adams EF, Fahlbusch R, et al: Hormonal dependency of cerebral meningiomas. Part 1: Female sex steroid receptors and their significance as specific markers for adjuvant medical therapy. *J Neurosurg 1990;73:743–749.*

151. Zimmerman CF, Schatz NJ, Glaser JG: Magnetic resonance imaging of optic nerve meningiomas. *Ophthalmology 1990;97:585–591.*

152. Kennerdell JS, Maroon JC, Malton M, Warren F: The management of optic nerve sheath meningiomas. *Am J Ophthalmol 1988;106;450–457.*

153. Albright AL, Scalabassi RJ, Slamovits TL, Bergman I: Spasmus nutans associated with optic gliomas in infants. *J Pediatr 1984;105:778–780.*

154. Hoyt WF, Baghdassarian SA: Optic glioma of childhood. Natural history and rationale for conservative management. *Br J Ophthalmol 1969; 53:793–798.*

155. Borit A, Richardson EP: The biological and clinical behavior of pilocytic astrocytomas of the optic pathways. *Brain 1982;105:161–187.*

156. Imes RK, Hoyt WF: Childhood chiasmal gliomas. An update on the fate of patients in the 1969 San Francisco study. *Br J Ophthalmol 1986;70:179–182.*

157. Alvord EC, Lofton S: Gliomas of the optic nerve or chiasm. Outcome by patients' age, tumor site, and treatment. *J Neurosurg 1988;68:85–98.*

158. Albers GW, Hoyt WF, Forno LS, Shratter LA: Treatment response in malignant optic glioma of adulthood. *Neurology 1988;38:1071–1074.*

159. Haik BG, Saint Louis L, Bierly J, et al: Magnetic resonance imaging in the evaluation of optic nerve gliomas. *Ophthalmology 1987;94:709–717.*

160. Packer RJ, Sutton LN, Bilaniuk LT, Radcliffe J: Treatment of chiasmatic/hypothalamic gliomas of childhood with chemotherapy: An update. *Ann Neurol 1988;23:79–85.*

161. Neigl JM, Rootman J, Belkin RI, Nugent RA: Dysthyroid optic neuropathy. The crowded orbital apex syndrome. *Ophthalmology 1988;95: 1515–1521.*

162. Feldon SE, Lee CP, Muramatsu SK, Weiner JM: Quantitative computerized tomography of Graves' ophthalmopathy. Extraocular muscle and orbital fat in development of optic neuropathy. *Arch Ophthalmol 1985;103:213–215.*

163. Neigel JM, Rootman J, Belkin RI, et al: Dysthyroid optic neuropathy. The crowded orbital apex. *Ophthalmology: 1988;95:1515–1521.*

1. Kirkham TH: The ocular symptomatology of pituitary tumours. *Proc R Soc Med 1972;65:517–518.*

2. Nachtigaller H, Hoyt WF: Storungen des Seheindruckes bei Bitemporaler Hemianopsie und Verschiebung der Sehachsen. *Klin Monatsbl Augenheilk 1970;156:821–836.*

3. Schaeffer JP: Some points in the regional anatomy of the optic pathway, with especial reference to tumors of the hypophysis cerebri and resulting ocular changes. *Anat Rec 1924;28:243–279.*

4. Bergland RM, Ray BS, Torack RM: Anatomical variations in the pituitary gland and adjacent structures in 225 human autopsy cases. *J Neurosurg 1968;28:93–99.*

5. Traquair HM: *An Introduction to Clinical Perimetry,* ed 4. St. Louis: CV Mosby, 1944.

6. Hoyt WF, Luis O: Visual fiber anatomy in the infrageniculate pathway of the primate: Uncrossed and crossed retinal quadrant fiber projections studied with Nauta silver stain. *Arch Ophthalmol 1962;68:94.*

7. Hoyt WF, Luis O: The primate chiasm: Details of visual fiber organization studied by silver impregnation techniques. *Arch Ophthalmol 1963;70:69–85.*

8. Hoyt WF, Tudor RC: The course of the parapapillary temporal retinal axons through the anterior optic nerve: A Nauta degeneration study in the primate. *Arch Ophthalmol 1963;69:503–507.*

9. Hoyt WF: Correlative functional anatomy of the optic chiasm—1969. *Clin Neurosurg 1970;17:189–208.*

CHAPTER 4

CHIASM, PARACHIASMAL SYNDROMES, RETROCHIASM, AND DISORDERS OF HIGHER VISUAL FUNCTION

10. Chamlin M, Davidoff LM: The 1/2000 field in chiasmal interference. *Arch Ophthalmol 1950;44:53–70.*

11. Gutman I, Behrens M, Odel J: Bilateral central and centrocaecal scotomata due to mass lesions. *Br J Ophthalmol 1984;68:336–342.*

12. Hoyt WF, Rios-Montenegro EN, Behrens MM, et al: Homonymous hemioptic hypoplasia. Fundoscopic features in standard and red-free illumination in three patients with congenital hemiplegia. *Br J Ophthalmol 1972;56:537–545.*

13. Fein JM, Williams RDB: See-saw nystagmus. *J Neurol Neurosurg Psychiatry 1969;32:202–207.*

14. Williams TM, Dickinson P, Ramsay RJ, Thomas L: See-saw nystagmus. *Aust J Ophthalmol 1982;10:19–25.*

15. Kanter DS, Ruff RL, Leigh RJ, Modic M: Seesaw nystagmus and brainstem infarction. MRI findings. *J Clin Neuro-Ophthalmol 1987;7:279–283.*

16. Gittinger JW Jr: Ophthalmological evaluation of pituitary adenomas, in Post KD, Jackson IMD, Reichlin S (eds): *The Pituitary Adenoma.* New York: Plenum, 1980, 259–286.

17. Hollenhorst RW, Younge BR: Ocular manifestations produced by adenomas of the pituitary gland: Analysis of 1000 cases, in Kohler PO, Ross GT (eds): *Diagnosis and Treatment of Pituitary Tumor.* Amsterdam: Excerpta Medica, 1973, 53–68.

18. Hollenhorst RW, Younge BR: Ocular manifestations of intrasellar and suprasellar tumors, in Burde RM (ed): *Symposium on Neuroophthalmology: Transactions of the New Orleans Academy of Ophthalmology.* St. Louis: CV Mosby, 1976.

19. Brougham D, Heusner AP, Adams RD: Acute degenerative changes of adenomas of the pituitary body with special reference to pituitary apoplexy. *J Neurosurg 1950;7:421–439.*

20. Meadows SP: Unusual clinical features and modes of presentation in pituitary adenoma, including pituitary apoplexy, in Smith JL (ed): *Neuro-Ophthalmology IV.* St. Louis: CV Mosby, 1968, 178.

21. Rovit RL, Fein JM: Pituitary apoplexy: A review and reappraisal. *J Neurosurg 1972;37:280–288.*

22. David NH, Gargano FP, Glaser JS: Pituitary apoplexy in clinical perspective, in Smith JL, Glaser JS (eds): *Neuro-Ophthalmology VIII.* St. Louis: CV Mosby, 1975, 140.

23. Wakai S, Fukushima T, Teramoto A, et al: Pituitary apoplexy: Its incidence and clinical significance. *J Neurosurg 1981;55:187–193.*

24. Neetens A, Selosse P: Oculomotor anomalies in sellar and parasellar pathology. *Ophthalmologica 1977;175:80–104.*

25. Bartlett JR: Craniopharyngiomas: A summary of 85 cases. *J Neurol Neurosurg Psychiatr 1971;34:37–41.*

26. Kennedy HB, Smith RJS: Eye signs in craniopharyngioma. *Br J Ophthalmol 1975;59:689–695.*

27. Finn JE, Mount LA: Meningiomas of the tuberculum sellae and planum sphenoidale. A review of 83 cases. *Arch Ophthalmol 1974;92:23–27.*

28. Miller NR, Iliff WJ, Green WR: Evaluation and management of gliomas of the anterior visual pathways. *Brain 1974;97:743–754.*

29. Glaser JS, Hoyt WF, Corbett J: Visual morbidity with chiasmal glioma. Long-term studies of visual fields in untreated and irradiated cases. *Arch Ophthalmol 1971;85:3–12.*

30. Hoyt WF, Meshel LG, Lessell S, et al: Malignant optic glioma of adulthood. *Brain 1973;96:121–132.*

31. Harper CG, Stewart–Wynne EG: Malignant optic gliomas in adults. *Arch Neurol 1978;35:731–735.*

32. Cohen MM, Lessell S: Chiasmal syndrome due to metastasis. *Arch Neurol 1979;36:565–567.*

33. Weyand RD, Rucker CW: Unusual lesions involving the optic chiasm. *Mayo Clin Proc 1952;27:505–511.*

34. Gittinger JW Jr: Ophthalmological evaluation of pituitary adenomas, in Post KD, Jackson IMD, Reichlin S (eds): *The Pituitary Adenoma.* New York: Plenum, 1980, 263.

35. Walsh FB: Visual field defects due to aneurysms at the circle of Willis. *Arch Ophthalmol 1964,71:15–27.*

36. Matsuo K, Kobayashi S, Sugita K: Bitemporal hemianopsia associated with sclerosis of the intracranial internal carotid arteries. *J Neurosurg 1980;53:566–569.*

37. Fermaglich J, Kattah J, Manz H: Venous angioma of the optic chiasm. *Ann Neurol 1978;4:470–471.*

38. Manz HJ, Klein LH, Fermaglich J, et al: Cavernous hemangiomas of optic chiasm, optic nerves and right optic nerves and right optic tract. *Virchows Arch [Pathol Anat] 1979;383:225–231.*

39. Segall HD, Hassan G, Ling SM, et al: Suprasellar cysts associated with isosexual precocious puberty. *Radiology 1974;111:607–616.*

40. Dominque JN, Wilson CB: Pituitary abscesses. Report of seven cases and a review of the literature. *J Neurosurg 1977;46:601–608.*

41. Lindholm J, Rasmussen P, Korsgaard O: Intrasellar or pituitary abscess. *J Neurosurg 1973;38:616–619.*

42. Alper MG: Mucoceles of the sphenoid sinus: Neuro-ophthalmic manifestations. *Trans Am Ophthalmol Soc 1977;74:53–81.*

43. Goodwin JA, Glaser JS: Chiasmal syndrome in sphenoid sinus mucocele. *Ann Neurol 1978;4:440–444.*

44. Walsh TJ, Smith JL: Sarcoidosis and suprasellar mass, in Smith JL (ed): *Neuro-Ophthalmology IV.* St. Louis: CV Mosby, 1968, 167–177.

45. Gudeman SK, Selhorst JB, Susac JO, et al: Sarcoid optic neuropathy. *Neurology 1982;32:597–603.*

46. Bruetsch WL: Etiology of optochiasmatic arachnoiditis. *Arch Neurol Psychiatr 1948;59:215–228.*

47. Coyle JT: Chiasmatic arachnoiditis. *Am J Ophthalmol 1969;68:345–349.*

48. Lee KF, Schatz NJ, Savino PJ: Ischemic chiasmal syndrome, in Glaser JS, Smith JL (eds): *Neuro-Ophthalmology VIII.* St. Louis: CV Mosby, 1975, 115.

49. Savino PJ, Glaser JS, Schatz NJ: Traumatic chiasmal syndrome. *Neurology 1980;30:963–970.*

50. Sacks JG, Melen O: Bitemporal visual field defects in presumed multiple sclerosis. *JAMA 1975;234:69–72.*

51. Spector RH, Glaser JS, Schatz NJ: Demyelinative chiasmal lesions. *Arch Neurol 1980;37:757–762.*

52. Newman NJ, Lessell S, Winterkorn JM: Optic chiasmal neuritis. *Neurology 1991;41:1203–1210.*

53. Schatz NJ, Schlezinger NS: Noncompressive causes of chiasmal disease, in Burde RM (ed): *Symposium on Neuro-Ophthalmology: Transactions of the New Orleans Academy of Ophthalmology.* St. Louis: CV Mosby, 1976, 90.

54. Schatz NJ, Lichtenstein S, Corbett JJ: Delayed radiation necrosis of the optic nerves and chiasm, in Glaser JS, Smith JL (eds): *Neuro-Ophthalmology VII.* St. Louis: CV Mosby, 1975, 131–139.

55. Neelon FA, Goree J, Lebovitz H: The primary empty sella: Clinical and radiographic characteristics and endocrine function. *Medicine 1973;52:73–92.*

56. Berke JP, Buxton LF, Kokmen E: The "empty" sella. *Neurology 1975;25:1137–1143.*

57. Osher RH, Corbett JJ, Schatz NJ, et al: Neuro-ophthalmological complications of enlargement of the third ventricle. *Br J Ophthalmol 1978;62:536–542.*

58. Streletz LJ, Schatz NJ: Transsphenoidal encephalocele associated with colobomas of the optic disc and hypopituitary dwarfism, in Smith JL, Glaser JS (eds): *Neuro-Ophthalmology VII.* St. Louis: CV Mosby, 1975.

59. Laws ER Jr, Kern EB: Complications of transsphenoidal surgery, in Tindall GT, Collins WF (eds): *Clinical Management of Pituitary Disorders.* New York: Raven Press, 1979, 435.

60. Wilson CB, Dempsey LC: Transsphenoidal microsurgical removal of 250 pituitary adenomas. *J Neurosurg 1978;48:13–22.*

61. George SR, Burrow GN, Zinman B, et al: Regression of pituitary tumors, a possible effect of bromergocryptine. *Am J Med 1979;66:697–702.*

62. McGregor AM, Scanlon MF, Hall R, et al: Effects of bromocriptine in pituitary tumor size. *Br Med J 1979;2:700–703.*

63. McGregor AM, Scanlon MF, Hall K, et al: Reduction of size of a pituitary tumor by bromocriptine therapy. *N Engl J Med 1979;300:291–293.*

64. Thorner MO, Martin WH, Rogol AD, et al: Rapid regression of pituitary prolactinomas during bromocriptine treatment. *J Clin Endocrinol Metab 1980;51:438–445.*

65. Lesser RL, Zheutlin JD, Boghen D, et al: Visual function improvement in patients with macroprolactinomas treated with bromocriptine. *Am J Ophthalmol 1990;109:535–543.*

66. Vance ML, Lipper M, Klibanski A, et al: Treatment of prolactin-secreting pituitary macroadenomas with the long-acting nonergot dopamine agonist CV 205–502. *Ann Intern Med 1990;112:668–673.*

67. Savino PJ, Paris M, Schatz NJ, et al: Optic tract syndrome: a review of 21 patients. *Arch Ophthalmol 1978;96:656–663.*

68. Bender MB, Bodis–Wollner I: Visual dysfunctions in optic tract lesions. *Ann Neurol 1978;3:187–193.*

69. Frisen L: The neurology of visual acuity. *Brain 1980;103:639–670.*

70. Burde RM: The pupil. *Int Ophthalmol Clin 1967;7:839–855.*

71. Bell RA, Thompson HS: Relative afferent pupillary defect in optic tract hemianopias. *Am J Ophthalmol 1978;85:538–540.*

72. O'Connor PS, Kasdon D, Tredici TJ, et al: The Marcus Gunn pupil in experimental tract lesions. *Ophthalmology 1982;89:160–164.*

73. Hoyt WF: Geniculate hemianopias: Incongruous visual field defects from partial involvement of the lateral geniculate nucleus. *Proc Aust Assoc Neurol 1975;12:7–16.*

74. Gunderson CH, Hoyt WF: Geniculate hemianopia: Incongruous homonymous field defects in two patients with partial lesions of the lateral geniculate nucleus. *J Neurol Neurosurg Psychiatr 1971;34:1-6.*

75. Frisen L, Holmegaard L, Rosencrantz M: Sectorial optic atrophy and homonymous, horizontal sectoranopia: A lateral choroidal artery syndrome? *J Neurol Neurosurg Psychiatr 1978;41:374–380.*

76. Frisen L: Quadruple sectoranopia and sectorial optic atrophy. A syndrome of the distal anterior choroidal artery. *J Neurol Neurosurg Psychiatr 1979;42:590–594.*

77. Marino R, Rasmussen T: Visual field changes after temporal lobectomy in man. *Neurology 1968;18:825–835.*

78. Bjork A, Kugelberg E: Visual field defects after temporal lobectomy. *Acta Ophthalmol 1957;35:210–216.*

79. Falconer MA, Wilson JL: Visual field changes following anterior temporal lobectomy: Their significance in relation to "Meyer's loop" of the optic radiation. *Brain 1958;81:1–14.*

80. Van Buren JM, Baldwin M: The architecture of the optic radiation in the temporal lobe in man. *Brain 1958;81:15–40.*

81. Goodglass H, Quadfasel FA: Language laterality in left-handed aphasics. *Brain 1954;77:521–548.*

82. Gloning K: Handedness and aphasia. *Neuropsychologia 1977;15:355–358.*

83. Subirana A: Handedness and cerebral dominance, in Vinker PJ, Bruyn GW (eds): *Handbook of Clinical Neurology: Disorders of Speech, Perception and Symbolic Behavior,* Vol 4. Amsterdam: North-Holland, 1969, 284–292.

84. Baloh RW, Yee RD, Honrubia V: Optokinetic nystagmus and parietal lobe lesions. *Ann Neurol 1980;7:269–276.*

85. Leigh RJ, Zee DS: *The Neurology of Eye Movements.* Philadelphia: FA Davis, 1983, 79–80.

86. Leigh RJ, Zee DS: *The Neurology of Eye Movements.* Philadelphia: FA Davis, 1983, 81.

87. Smith JL: *Optokinetic Nystagmus.* Springfield, IL: Charles C Thomas, 1963, 55–67.

88. Gerstmann J: Syndrome of finger agnosia, disorientation for right and left, agraphia and acalculia. *Arch Neurol Psychiatr 1940;44:398–408.*

89. Morax V: Discussion des hypotheses faites sures connexions corticales des faisceaux maculaires. *Ann Ocul 1919;156:103–107.*

90. Dubois–Poulsen A, Magis C, de Ajuriaguerra J, et al: Les consequences visuelles de les lobectomies occipitalles chez l'homme. *Ann Ocul 1952;185:305–347.*

91. Gramberg-Danielsen B: Die doppelversorgung der Macula. *Graefes Arch Ophthalmol 1959;160:534–539.*

92. Huber A: Homonymous hemianopia after occipital lobectomy. *Am J Ophthalmol 1962;54:623–629.*

93. Stone J: The naso-temporal division of the cat's retina. *J Comp Neurol 1966;126:585–599.*

94. Stone J, Leicester J, Sherman SM: The naso-temporal division of the monkey's retina. *J Comp Neurol 1973;150:333–348.*

95. Bunt AH, Minckler DS: Foveal sparing. *Arch Ophthalmol 1977;95: 1445–1447.*

96. Bunt AH, Minckler DS, Johnson GW: Demonstration of bilateral projection of the central retina of the monkey with horseradish peroxidase neuronography. *J Comp Neurol 1977;171:619–630.*

97. Hoyt WF, Newton TH: Angiographic changes with occlusion of arteries that supply the visual cortex. *NZ Med J 1970;72:310–317.*

98. Benton S, Levy I, Swash M: Vision in the temporal crescent in occipital infarction. *Brain 1980;103:83–97.*

99. Walsh TJ: Temporal crescent or half-moon syndrome. *Ann Ophthalmol 1974;6:501–505.*

100. Daroff RB, Hoyt WF: Supranuclear disorders of ocular control systems in man: Clinical, anatomical, and physiological correlations, in Bach-y-Rita P, Collins CC, Hyde JE (eds): *The Control of Eye Movements.* New York: Academic Press, 1971, 175–236.

101. Bogousslavsky J, Regli F, Van Melle G: Unilateral occipital infarction: Evaluation of the risk of developing bilateral loss of vision. *J Neurol Neurosurg Psychiatr 1983;46:78–80.*

102. Anton G: Über die Selbstwahrnehmung der Herderkrankungen des Gehirns durch den Kranken bie rindenblindheitund Rindentaubheit. *Arch Psychiatr Nervenkr 1899;32:86–127.*

103. Lessell S, Lessell IM, Glaser JS: Topical diagnosis: Retrochiasmal visual pathways and higher cortical function, in Duane TD, Jaeger EA (eds): *Clinical Ophthalmology,* Vol 2. New York: JB Lippincott, 1988, 1–24.

104. Smith JL: Homonymous hemianopia: A review of one hundred cases. *Am J Ophthalmol 1962;54:616–622.*

105. Fujino T, Kigazawa K, Yamada R: Homonymous hemianopia. A retrospective study of 140 cases. *Neuroophthalmology 1986;6:17–21.*

106. Trobe JD, Lorber ML, Schlezinger NS: Isolated homonymous hemianopia: A review of 104 cases. *Arch Ophthalmol 1973;89:377–381.*

107. Goto K, Tagawa K, Uemura K, et al: Posterior cerebral artery occlusion: Clinical, computed tomographic, and angiographic correlation. *Radiology 1979;132:357–368.*

108. Pessin MS, Lathi ES, Cohen MB, et al: Clinical features and mechanism of occipital infarction. *Ann Neurol 1987;21:290–299.*

109. Koroshetz WJ, Ropper AH: Artery-to-artery embolism causing stroke in the posterior circulation. *Neurology 1987;37:292–296.*

110. Helgason C, Caplan LR, Goodwin J, et al: Anterior choroidal artery-territory infarction. Report of cases and review. *Arch Neurol 1986; 43:681–686.*

111. Anderson DR, Trobe JD, Hood TW, et al: Optic tract injury after anterior temporal lobectomy. *Ophthalmology 1989;96:1065–1070.*

112. Hoyt WF: Transient bilateral blurring of vision: Considerations of an episodic ischemic symptom of vertebrobasilar insufficiency. *Arch Ophthalmol 1963;70:746–751.*

113. Dennis MS, Sandercock PAG, Bamford JM, et al: Lone bilateral blindness: A transient ischaemic attack. *Lancet 1989;1:185–188.*

114. Parkinson D, Craig WM: Tumours of the brain, occipital lobe: Their signs and symptoms. *Can Med Assoc J 1951;64:111–113.*

115. So YT, Beckstead JH, Davis RL: Primary central nervous system lymphoma in acquired immune deficiency syndrome. A clinical and pathologic study. *Ann Neurol 1986;20:566–572.*

116. Stern BJ, Krumholz A, Johns C, et al: Sarcoidosis and its neurological manifestations. *Arch Neurol 1985;42:909–917.*

117. Graf CJ, Perret GE, Torner JC: Bleeding from cerebral arteriovenous malformations as part of their natural history. *J Neurosurg 1983;58:331–337.*

118. Spalding JMK: Wounds of the visual pathway: Part II. The striate cortex. *J Neurol Neurosurg Psychiatr 1952;15:169–183.*

119. Koerner F, Teuber HL: Visual field defects after missile injuries to the geniculostriate pathway in man. *Exp Brain Res 1973;18:88–113.*

120. Holmes G, Lister WT: Disturbances of vision from cerebral lesions with special reference to the cortical representation of the macula. *Brain 1916;39:34–73.*

121. Holmes G: Disturbance of vision by cerebral lesions. *Br J Ophthalmol 1918;2:353–384.*

122. Teuber HL, Battersby WS, Bender MB: *Visual Field Defects After Penetrating Missile Wounds in the Brain.* Cambridge, MA: Harvard University Press, 1960, 104–105.

123. Greenblatt SH: Posttraumatic transient cerebral blindness: Association with migraine and seizure diatheses. *JAMA 1973;225:1073–1076.*

124. Griffith JF, Dodge PR: Transient blindness following head injury in children. *N Engl J Med 1968;278:648–651.*

125. Gjerris F, Mellemgaard L: Transitory cortical blindness in head injury. *Acta Neurol Scand 1969;45:623–631.*

126. Eldridge PR, Punt JA: Transient traumatic cortical blindness in children. *Lancet 1988;1:815–816.*

127. Sedwick LA, Klingele TG, Burde RM, et al: Schilder's (1912) disease. Total cerebral blindness due to acute demyelination. *Arch Neurol 1986; 43:85–87.*

128. Astrom KE, Mancall EL, Richardson EP: Progressive multifocal leukoencephalopathy. A hitherto unrecognized complication of chronic lymphatic leukemia and Hodgkin's disease. *Brain 1958;81:93–111.*

129. Johnson RT: *Viral Infections of the Nervous System.* New York: Raven Press, 1982.

130. Krupp LB, Lipton RB, Swerdlow ML, et al: Progressive multifocal leukoencephalopathy: Clinical and radiographic features. *Ann Neurol 1985;17:344–349.*

131. Blum LW, Chambers RA, Schwartzman RJ, et al: Progressive multifocal leukoencephalopathy in acquired immune deficiency syndrome. *Arch Neurol 1985;42:137–139.*

132. Hawkins K, Behrens MM: Homonymous hemianopia in multiple sclerosis: With report of bilateral case. *Br J Ophthalmol 1975;59:334–337.*

133. Katz B, Rimmer S: Ophthalmologic manifestations of Alzheimer's disease. *Surv Ophthalmol 1989;34:31–43.*

134. Mendez MF, Mendez MA, Martin R, et al: Complex visual disturbances in Alzheimer's disease. *Neurology 1990;40:439–443.*

135. Benson DF, Davis RJ, Snyder BD: Posterior cortical atrophy. *Arch Neurol 1988;45:789–793.*

136. Siedler H, Malamud N: Creutzfeldt–Jakob's disease: Clinicopathologic report of 15 cases and review of the literature (with special reference to a related disorder designated as subacute spongiform encephalopathy). *J Neuropathol Exp Neurol 1963;22:381–402.*

137. Fisher CM: The clinical picture in Creutzfeldt–Jakob disease. *Trans Am Neurol Assoc 1960;85:147–150.*

138. Heidenhain A: Klinische und anatomische Untersuchungen über eine eigenartige organische Erkrankung des Zentralnervensystems im Praesenium. *Zentralbl Ges Neurol Psychiatr 1928;118:49.*

139. Bergman PS: Cerebral blindness. *Arch Neurol Psychiatr 1957;78:568–584.*

140. Magitot A, Hartmann E: La cecite corticale. *Rev Otoneuroóculo 1927; 5:81–114. Bull Soc Ophthalmol Fr 1926;427–545.*

141. Heran F, Defer G, Brugieres P, et al: Cortical blindness during chemotherapy: Clinical, CT, and MR correlations. *J Comput Assist Tomogr 1990;14:262–266.*

142. Wilson SE, deGroen PC, Aksamit AJ, et al: Cyclosporin A-induced reversible cortical blindness. *J Clin Neuro-Ophthalmol 1988;8:215–220.*

143. Barnet AB, Manson JI, Wilner E: Acute cerebral blindness in childhood. *Neurology 1970;20:1147–1156.*

144. Kupersmith MJ, Nelson JI: Preserved visual evoked potential in infancy cortical blindness. Relationship to blindsight. *Neuroophthalmology 1986;6:85–94.*

145. Lantos G: Cortical blindness due to osmotic disruption of the blood-brain barrier by angiographic contrast material: CT and MRI studies. *Neurology 1989;39:567–571.*
146. Salmon JH: Transient postictal hemianopsia. *Arch Ophthalmol 1968; 79:523–525.*
147. Ashby H, Stephenson S: Acute amaurosis following infantile convulsions. *Rep Soc Study Dis Child 1903;3:197–209. Lancet 1903;1:1294–1296.*
148. Pritchard E: Case of amaurosis following violent convulsions. *Proc R Soc Med 1918;11:1–2.*
149. Sadeh M, Goldhammer Y, Kuritsky A: Postictal blindness in adults. *J Neurol Neurosurg Psychiatry 1983;46:566–569.*
150. Lessell S: Higher disorders of visual function: Negative phenomena, in Glaser JS, Smith JL (eds): *Neuro-Ophthalmology VIII.* St. Louis: CV Mosby, 1975, 1–26.
151. Aldrich MS, Vanderzant CW, Alessi AG, Abou-Khalil B, et al: Cortical blindness as an ictal manifestation. *Electoencephalogr Clin Neurophysiol 1985;61:37.*
152. Aldrich MS, Vanderzant CW, Alessi AG, et al: Ictal cortical blindness with permanent visual loss. *Epilepsia 1989;30:116–120.*
153. Roos KL, Tuite PJ, Below ME, et al: Reversible cortical blindness (Anton's syndrome) associated with bilateral occipital EEG abnormalities. *Clin Electroencephalogr 1990;21:104–109.*
154. Lance JW, Smee RI: Partial seizures with visual disturbance treated by radiotherapy of cavernous hemangioma. *Ann Neurol 1989;26:782–785.*
155. Jaffe SJ, Roach ES: Transient cortical blindness with occipital lobe epilepsy. *J Clin Neuro-Ophthalmol 1988;8:221–224.*
156. Lessell S: Higher disorders of visual function: Positive phenomena, in Glaser JS, Smith JL (eds): *Neuro-Ophthalmology VIII.* St. Louis: CV Mosby, 1975, 27–44.
157. Lepore FE: Spontaneous visual phenomena with visual loss: 104 patients with lesions of retinal and neural afferent pathways. *Neurology 1990;40:444–447.*
158. Cummings JL, Miller BL: Visual hallucinations—clinical occurrence and use in differential diagnosis. *West J Med 1987;146:46–51.*
159. Bender MB, Kanzer MG: Metamorphopsia and other psychovisual disturbances in a patient with tumor of the brain. *Arch Neurol Psychiatr 1941;45:481–485.*
160. van Bogaert L: L'hallucinose pedonculaire. *Rev Neurol 1927;47:608–617.*
161. L'hermitte J: Syndrome de la calotte du pedoncule cérébral: Les troubles psychosensoriels dans les lesions du mésocephale. *Rev Neurol (Paris) 1922;38:1359–1365.*
162. McKee AC, Levine DN, Kowall NW, et al: Peduncular hallucinosis associated with isolated infarction of the substantia nigra pars reticulata. *Ann Neurol 1990;27:500–504.*
163. Cogan DG: Visual hallucinations as release phenomena. *Graefes Arch Clin Exp Ophthalmol 1973;188:139–150.*
164. Bender MB, Feldman M, Sobin AJ: Palinopsia. *Brain 1968;91:321–338.*
165. Michel EM, Troost BT: Palinopsia. Cerebral localization with computed tomography. *J Neurology 1980;30:887–889.*
166. Meadows JC, Munro SSF: Palinopsia. *J Neurol Neurosurg Psychiatr 1977;40:5–8.*
167. Hughes MS, Lessell S: Trazodone-induced palinopsia. *Arch Ophthalmol 1990;108:399–400.*
168. Purvin V, Bonnin J, Goodman J: Palinopsia as a presenting manifestation of Creutzfeldt–Jakob disease. *J Clin Neuro-Ophthalmol 1989; 9:242–246.*
169. Johnson SF, Loge RV: Palinopsia due to nonketotic hyperglycemia. *West J Med 1988;148:331–332.*
170. Wilson SAK: Dysmetropsia and its pathogenesis. *Trans Ophthalmol Soc UK 1916;36:412–444.*
171. Bender MB, Savitsky N: Micropsia and teleopsia limited to the temporal fields of vision. *Arch Ophthalmol 1943;29:904–908.*
172. Critchley M: Metamorphopsia of central origin. *Trans Ophthalmol Soc UK 1949;69:111–121.*

173. Bender MD: Polyopia and monocular diplopia of cerebral origin. *Arch Neurol Psychiatr 1945;54:323–338.*
174. Meadows JC: Observations of a case of monocular diplopia of cerebral origin. *J Neurol Sci 1973;18:249–253.*
175. Klee A, Willanger R: Disturbances of visual perception in migraine. *Acta Neurol Scand 1966;42:400–414.*
176. Meadows JC: Disturbed perception of colours associated with localized cerebral lesions. *Brain 1974;97:615–632.*
177. Green GJ, Lessell S: Acquired cerebral dyschromatopsia. *Arch Ophthalmol 1977;95:121–128.*
178. Damasio A, Yamada T, Damasio H, et al: Central achromatopsia: Behavioral, anatomic, and physiologic aspects. *Neurology 1980;30:1064–1071.*
179. Damasio AR, Damasio H: The anatomic basis of pure alexia. *Neurology 1983;33:1573–1583.*
180. Mendez MF: Visuoperceptual function in visual agnosia. *Neurology 1988;38:1754–1759.*
181. Rubens A, Benson DF: Associative visual agnosia. *Arch Neurol 1987; 24:305–316.*
182. Damasio AR, Damasio H, Van Hoesen GW: Prosopagnosia: Anatomic basis and behavioral mechanisms. *Neurology 1982;32:331–341.*
183. Critchley M: The problem of visual agnosia. *J Neurol Sci 1964;1:274–290.*
184. Bender MB, Feldman M: The so-called visual agnosias. *Brain 1972; 95:173–186.*
185. Geschwind N: Disconnexion syndromes in animals and man. *Brain 1965;88:237–297, 585–644.*
186. Albert ML, Reches A, Silverberg R: Associative visual agnosia without alexia. *Neurology 1975;25:322–326.*
187. Warrington EK, James M: Visual apperceptive agnosia—a clinico-anatomical study of three cases. *Cortex 1988;24:13–32.*
188. Damasio AR, Tranel D, Damasio H: Face agnosia and the neural substrates of memory. *Annu Rev Neurosci 1990;13:89–109.*
189. Levine DN, Calvanio R: Prosopagnosia: A defect in visual configural processing. *Brain Cog 1989;10:149–170.*
190. Allen IM: Unilateral visual inattention. *NZ Med J 1948;47:605–617.*
191. Bender MB, Furlow LT: Phenomenon of visual extinction in homonymous fields and psychologic principles involved. *Arch Neurol Psychiatr 1945;53:29–33.*
192. Mesulam MM: A cortical network for directed attention and unilateral neglect. *Ann Neurol 1981;10:309–325.*
193. Corin MS, Bender MB: Mislocalization in visual space. *Arch Neurol 1972;27:252–262.*
194. Hannay HJ, Varney NR, Benton AL: Visual localization in patients with unilateral brain disease. *J Neurol Neurosurg Psychiatr 1976;39:307–313.*
195. Holmes G: Pure word blindness. *Folia Psychiatr Neurol Neurochir Neerl 1950;53:279–288.*
196. Balint R: Seelenahmung des Schauens, optische Ataxie, raumliche Storung der Aufmerksamkeit. *Monatsschr Psychiatr Neurol 1909; 25:51–71.*
197. Pierrot-Deseilligny C, Gray F, Brunet P: Infarcts of both inferior parietal lobules with impairment of visually guided eye movements, peripheral visual inattention and optic ataxia. *Brain 1986;109:81–97.*
198. Brain WR: Visual disorientation with special reference to lesions of the right cerebral hemisphere. *Brain 1941;64:244–272.*
199. Jacobs L: Visual allesthesia. *Neurology 1980;30:1059–1063.*
200. Morgan RK, Nugent B, Harrison JM, et al: Voluntary alteration of pattern visual evoked responses. *Ophthalmology 1985;92:1356–1363.*
201. Bumgartner J, Epstein CM: Voluntary alteration of visual evoked potentials. *Ann Neurol 1982;12:475–478.*
202. Aldrich MS, Alessi AG, Beck RW, et al: Cortical blindness: Etiology, diagnosis, and prognosis. *Ann Neurol 1987;21:149–158.*

1. Hogan MJ, Alvarado JA, Weddell JE: *Histology of the Human Eye: An Atlas and Textbook.* Philadelphia: WB Saunders, 1971, 344–357.

2. Hada J, Hayashi Y: Retinal X-afferents bifurcate to lateral geniculate X-cells and to the pretectum or superior colliculus in cats. *Brain Res 1990;515:149–154.*

3. Perry VH, Cowey A: Retinal ganglion cells that project to the superior colliculus and pretectum in the macaque monkey. *Neuroscience 1984;12:1125–1137.*

4. Pierson R, Carpenter MB: Anatomical analysis of pupillary reflex pathways in the rhesus monkey. *J Comp Neurol 1974;158:121–144.*

5. Carpenter MB, Pierson RJ: Pretectal region and the pupillary light reflex: An anatomical analysis in the monkey. *J Comp Neurol 1973;149: 271–300.*

6. Burde RM: The visceral nuclei of the oculomotor complex. *Trans Am Ophthalmol Soc 1983;81:532–548.*

7. Jampel RS, Mindel J: The nucleus for accommodation in the midbrain of the macaque. *Invest Ophthalmol 1967;6:40–50.*

8. Taylor P: Cholinergic agonists, in Gilman AG, Goodman LS, Rall TW, Murad F (eds): *Goodman and Gilman's: The Pharmacological Basis of Therapeutics,* ed 7. New York: MacMillan, 1985.

9. Havener WH (ed): *Ocular Pharmacology,* ed 5. St. Louis, Toronto: CV Mosby, 1983, 314–402.

10. Mindel JS: Cholinergic pharmacology, in Duane TD, Jaeger EA (eds): *Biomedical Foundations of Ophthalmology,* Vol 3. Philadelphia: Harper & Row, 1986, 28–32.

11. Kalyanaraman S: Some observations during stimulation of the human hypothalmus. *Confin Neurol 1975;37:189–192.*

12. Kerr FWL, Brown JA: Pupillomotor pathways in the spinal cord. *Arch Neurol 1964;10:262–270.*

13. Williams PL, Warwick R: *Functional Neuroanatomy of Man,* ed 35 (British). Philadelphia: WB Saunders, 1975, 1068–1074.

14. Palumbo LT: A new concept of the sympathetic pathways to the eye. *Ann Ophthalmol 1976;8:947–954.*

15. Parkinson D, Johnston J, Chaudhuri A: Sympathetic connections to the fifth and sixth cranial nerves. *Anat Rec 1978;191:221–226.*

16. Weinstein JM, Zweifel TJ, Thompson HS: Congenital Horner's syndrome. *Arch Ophthalmol 1980;98:1074–1078.*

17. Forman AR: A new low-concentration preparation for mydriasis and cycloplegia. *Ophthalmology 1980;87:213–215.*

18. Sindell BD, Baker MD, Maisels MJ, Weinstein JM: A comparison of the pupillary and cardiovascular effects of various mydriatic agents in preterm infants. *J Pediatr Ophthalmol Strabismus 1987;23:273–276.*

19. Kardon RH, Denison CE, Brown CK, Thompson HS: Critical evaluation of the cocaine test in the diagnosis of Horner's syndrome. *Arch Ophthalmol 1990;108:834–837.*

20. Cremer SA, Thompson HS, Digre KB, Kardon RH: Hydroxyamphetamine mydriasis in Horner's syndrome. *Am J Ophthalmol 1990; 110:66–70.*

21. Loewenfeld IE: Simple, central anisocoria: A common condition, seldom recognized. *Trans Am Acad Ophthalmol Otolaryngol 1977;83; OP832–839.*

22. Thompson JS, Pilley SFJ: Unequal pupils. A flow chart for sorting out anisocorias. *Surv Ophthalmol 1976;21:45–48.*

23. Thompson BM, Corbett JJ, Kline LB, Thompson HS: Pseudo-Horner's syndrome. *Arch Neurol 1982;39:108–111.*

24. Gunn RM: Discussion on retro–ocular neuritis. *Lancet 1904;4:412.*

25. Thompson HS, Corbett JJ, Cox TA: How to measure the relative afferent pupillary defect. *Surv Ophthalmol 1981;26:39–42.*

26. Rizzo JF: Pupillodynamic study of the swinging flashlight test: *Intensity of Stimulating Light Variably Affects Components of the Pupil Response.* Abstract presented at the North American Neuro-Ophthalmology Society Meeting, Park City, UT, Feb 24–28, 1991.

CHAPTER 5
THE PUPIL

27. Cox TA: Pupillographic characteristics of simulated relative afferent pupillary defects. *Invest Ophthalmol Vis Sci 1989;30:1127–1131.*

28. Thompson HS, Corbett JJ: Swinging flashlight test: Letter to the editor. *Neurology 1989;39:154–157.*

29. Bell RA, Thompson HS: Relative afferent pupillary defect in optic tract hemianopias. *Am J Ophthalmol 1978;85:538–540.*

30. Cox TA: Relative afferent pupillary defects in multiple sclerosis. *Can J Ophthalmol 1989;24:207–210.*

31. Bovino JA, Burton TC: Measurement of the relative afferent pupillary defect in retinal detachment. *Am J Ophthalmol 1980;90:19–21.*

32. Newsome DA, Milton RC, Gass ID: Afferent pupillary defect in macular degeneration. *Am J Ophthalmol 1981;92:396–402.*

33. Thompson HS, Watzke RA, Weinstein JM: Afferent pupil defects in macular disease. *Trans Am Ophthalmol Soc 1980;78:311–317.*

34. Servais GE, Thompson HS, Hayreth SS: Relative afferent pupillary defect in central retinal vein occlusion. *Ophthalmology 1986;93:301–303.*

35. Portnoy JZ, Thompson HS, Lennarson L, et al: Pupillary defects in amblyopia. *Am J Ophthalmol 1983;96:609–614.*

36. Sadun AA, Bassi CJ, Lessell S: Why cataracts do not produce afferent pupillary defects. *Am J Ophthalmol 1990;110(6):712–714.*

37. Thompson HS: Pupillary light near dissociation: A classification. *Surv Ophthalmol 1975;19:290–292.*

38. Loewenfeld IE: The Argyll–Robertson pupil, 1869–1969. A critical survey of the literature. *Surv Ophthalmol 1969;14:199–299.*

39. Hopf HC, Gutman L: Diabetic 3rd nerve palsy: Evidence for a mesencephalic lesion. *Neurology 1990;40:1041–1045.*

40. Breen LA, Hopf HC, Farris BK, Gutmann L: Pupil-sparing oculomotor nerve palsy due to midbrain infarction. *Arch Neurol 1991;48:105–106.*

41. Dreyfus PM, Hakim S, Adams RD: Diabetic ophthalmoplegia: Report of case with postmortem study and comments on vascular supply of human oculomotor nerve. *Arch Neurol Psychiatr 1975;77:337–349.*

42. Asbury AK, Aldridge H, Hersberg R, Fisher CM: Oculomotor palsy in diabetes mellitus: A clinico-pathological study. *Brain 1970;93:555–556.*

43. Weber RB, Daroff RB, Mackey EA: Pathology of oculomotor nerve palsy in diabetics. *Neurology 1970;20:835–838.*

44. Daroff R: Discussion of paper by Asbury, et al. *Trans Am Neurol Assoc 1969;94:66–67.*

45. Nadeau SE, Trobe JD: Pupil sparing in oculomotor palsy: A brief review. *Ann Neurol 1983;13:143–149.*

46. Kissell JT, Burde RM, Kingele TG, et al: Pupil-sparing oculomotor palsies with internal carotid–posterior communicating artery aneurysms. *Ann Neurol 1983;13:149–154.*

47. Burde RM, Savino PJ, Trobe JD: *Clinical Decision in Neuro-ophthalmology.* St. Louis, Toronto, Princeton: CV Mosby, 1985, 178–185.

48. Czarnecki JC, Thompson HS: The iris sphincter in aberrant regeneration of the third nerve. *Arch Ophthalmol 1978;96:1606–1610.*

49. Trobe JD, Glaser JS, Post JD: Meningiomas and aneurysms of the cavernous sinus. Neuro-ophthalmic features. *Arch Ophthalmol 1978; 96:457–467.*

50. Harr DL, Quencer RM: Acute cavernous sinus syndrome. *J Clin Neuro Ophthalmol 1981;1:291–294.*

51. Thompson HS: A classification of tonic pupils, in Thompson HS, Daroff RB, Frisen L, et al (eds): *Topics in Neuro–Ophthalmology.* Baltimore: Williams & Wilkins, 1979, 95–96.

52. Thompson HS: Adie's syndrome: Some new observations. *Trans Am Ophthalmol Soc 1977;75:587–626.*

53. Bell RA, Thompson HS: Ciliary muscle dysfunction in Adie's syndrome. *Arch Ophthalmol 1978;96:638–642.*

54. Harriman DGF, Garland H: The pathology of Adie's syndrome. *Brain 1968;91:401–418.*

55. Purcell JJ Jr, Drachmer JH, Thompson HS: Corneal sensation in Adie's syndrome. *Am J Ophthalmol 1977;84:496–500.*

56. Jacobson DM: Pupillary responses to dilute pilocarpine in third nerve disorders. *Neurology 1990;40:804–808.*

57. Slamovits TL, Miller NR, Burde RM: Intracranial oculomotor nerve paresis with anisocoria and pupillary parasympathetic hypersensitivity. *Am J Ophthalmol 1987;104:401–406.*
58. Horner JF: Über eine Form von Ptosis. *Klin Monatsbl Augenheilk 1869;7:193–198.*
59. Pilley SFJ, Thompson HS: Pupillary dilatation lag in Horner syndrome. *Br J Ophthalmol 1975;50:731–735.*
60. Maloney WF, Younge BR, Moyer NJ: Evaluation of the causes and accuracy of pharmacologic localization in Horner's syndrome. *Am J Ophthalmol 1980;90:394–402.*
61. Bougouslavsky J, Despland PA, Regli F: Spontaneous carotid dissection with acute stroke. *Arch Neurol 1987;44:137–140.*
62. Kline LB, Vitek JJ, Raymon BC: Painful Horner's syndrome due to spontaneous carotid artery dissection. *Ophthalmology 1987;94:226–230.*
63. Raeder JG: Paratrigeminal paralysis of oculo-pupillary sympathetic. *Brain 1924;47:149–158.*
64. Woodruff G, Buncic JR, Morin JD: Horner syndrome in children. *J Pediatr Ophthalmol Strabismus 1988;25:41–44.*
65. Barricks ME, Flynn JT, Kushner BJ: Paradoxical pupillary responses in congenital stationary night blindness. *Arch Ophthalmol 1977;95: 1800–1804.*
66. Flynn JT, Kazarian E, Barricks ME: Paradoxical pupil in congenital achromatopsia. *Int Ophthalmol 1981;3:91–96.*
67. Frank JW, Kushner BJ, France TD: Paradoxic pupillary phenomena: A review of patients with pupillary constriction to darkness. *Arch Ophthalmol 1988;106:1564–1566.*
68. Loewenfeld IE, Thompson HS: Oculomotor paresis with cyclic spasms. A critical review of the literature and a new case. *Surv Ophthalmol 1975;20:81–144.*
69. Edelson RN, Levy DE: Transient benign unilateral pupillary dilation in young adults. *Arch Neurol 1974;31:12–14.*
70. Woods D, O'Connor PS, Fleming R: Episodic unilateral mydriasis and migraine. *Am J Ophthalmol 1984;98:229–234.*
71. Thompson HS, Zackon DH, Czarnecki JSC: Tadpole-shaped pupils caused by segmental spasm of the iris dilator muscle. *Am J Ophthalmol 1983;96:467–477.*

CHAPTER 6
THE EFFERENT VISUAL SYSTEM

1. Keane JR, Zaias B, Itabashi HH: Levator-sparing oculomotor nerve palsy caused by a solitary midbrain metastasis. *Arch Neurol 1984;41:210–212.*
2. Pusateri TJ, Sedwick LA, Margo CE: Isolated inferior rectus muscle palsy from a solitary metastasis to the oculomotor nucleus. *Arch Ophthalmol 1987;105:675–677.*
3. Nadeau SE, Trobe JD: Pupil sparing in oculomotor palsy: A brief review. *Ann Neurol 1983;13:143–148.*
4. Castro O, Johnson LN, Mamourian AC: Isolated inferior oblique paresis from brain-stem infarction. *Arch Neurol 1990;47:235–237.*
5. Shuaib A, Israelian G, Lee MA: Mesencephalic hemorrhage and bilateral pupillary defect. *J Clin Neuro Ophthalmol 1989;9:47–49.*
6. Shuaib A, Murphy W: Mesencephalic hemorrhage and third nerve palsy. *J Comput Tomogr 1987;11:385–388.*
7. Ksiazek SM, Repka MX, Maguire A, et al: Divisional oculomotor nerve paresis caused by intrinsic brainstem disease. *Ann Neurol 1989; 26:714–718.*
8. Antworth MV, Beck RW: Third nerve palsy as a presenting sign of acquired immune deficiency syndrome. *J Clin Neuro Ophthalmol 1987;7:125–128.*
9. Guy J, Day AL, Mickle JP, Schatz NJ: Contralateral trochlear nerve paresis and ipsilateral Horner's syndrome. *Am J Ophthalmol 1989;107:73–76.*
10. Keane JR: Ocular skew deviation: Analysis of 100 cases. *Arch Neurol 1975;32:185–190.*
11. Miller NR, Kiel SM, Green WR, Clark AW: Unilateral Duane's retraction syndrome (Type I). *Arch Ophthalmol 1982;100:1468–1472.*

12. Wall M, Wray SH: The one-and-a-half syndrome. A unilateral disorder of the pontine tegmentum. A study of 20 cases and review of the literature. *Neurology 1983;33:971–980.*

13. Johnson LN, Hepler RS: Isolated abducens nerve paresis from intrapontine, fascicular abducens nerve injury. *Am J Ophthalmol 1989;108: 459–461.*

14. Stern RM, Tomsak RL: Magnetic resonance images in a case of "divergence paralysis." *Surv Ophthalmol 1986;30:397–401.*

15. Miller NR: *Walsh and Hoyt's Clinical Neuro-Ophthalmology, Vol 2,* ed 4. Baltimore: Williams & Wilkins, 705.

CHAPTER 7
DISORDERS OF
OCULAR MOTILITY

1. Rubin SE, Wagner RS: Ocular torticollis. *Surv Ophthalmol 1966; 30:366–375.*

2. Gutman I, Levartovski S, Goldhammer Y, et al: Sixth nerve palsy and unilateral Horner's syndrome. *Ophthalmology 1986;93:913–916.*

3. Striph GG, Burde RM: Abducens nerve palsy and Horner's syndrome revisited. *J Clin Neuro Ophthalmol 1988;8:13–17.*

4. Gamblin GT, Galentine PG III, Eil C: Intraocular pressure and thyroid disease, in Gorman CA, Waller RR, Dyer JA (eds): *The Eye and Orbit in Thyroid Disease.* New York: Raven Press, 1984, 155–166.

5. Rosenberg ML, Glaser JS: Superior oblique myokymia. *Ann Neurol 1983;13:667–669.*

6. Tyler TD, Ruiz RS: Propranolol in the treatment of superior oblique myokymia. *Arch Ophthalmol 1990;108:175–176.*

7. Shults WT, Hoyt WF, Behrens M, et al: Ocular neuromyotonia. A clinical description of six patients. *Arch Ophthalmol 1986;104:1028–1034.*

8. Lessell S, Lessell IM, Rizzo JF III: Ocular neuromyotonia after radiation therapy. *Am J Ophthalmol 1986;102:766–770.*

9. Donaldson D, Rosenberg NL: Infarction of abducens nerve fascicle as cause of isolated sixth nerve palsy related to hypertension. *Neurology 1988;38:1654.*

10. Stein R, Regenbogen L, Romano A, et al: Orbital apex syndrome due to cranial arteritis. *Ann Ophthalmol 1980;12:708–713.*

11. Koorey DJ: Cranial arteritis. A twenty-year review of cases. *Aust NZ J Med 1984;14:143–147.*

12. Rosenstein ED, Sobelman J, Kramer N: Isolated, pupil-sparing third nerve palsy as initial manifestation of systemic lupus erythematosus. *J Clin Neuro Ophthalmol 1989;9:285–288.*

13. Newton TH, Hoyt WF: Dural arteriovenous shunts in the region of the cavernous sinus. *Neuroradiology 1970;1:71–81.*

14. Werner DB, Savino PJ, Schatz NJ: Benign recurrent sixth nerve palsies in childhood. Secondary to immunization or viral illness. *Arch Ophthalmol 1983;101:607–608.*

15. Fisher M: An unusual variant of acute idiopathic polyneuritis (syndrome of ophthalmoplegia, ataxia and areflexia). *N Engl J Med 1956;255:57–65.*

16. Keane JR, Finstead BA: Upward gaze paralysis as the initial sign of Fisher's syndrome. *Arch Neurol 1982;39:781–782.*

17. Meienberg O, Ryffel E: Supranuclear eye movement disorders in Fisher's syndrome of ophthalmoplegia, ataxia, and areflexia. *Arch Neurol 1983;40:402–405.*

18. Swaminathan TR, Kalyanaraman S, Narendran P: Ocular manifestations of central nervous system tuberculosis correlated with CT scan findings, in Henkind P (ed): *ACTA: XXIV International Congress of Ophthalmology,* Vol 2. Philadelphia: JB Lippincott, 1982, 841–845.

19. Currie JN, Coppeto JR, Lessell S: Chronic syphilitic meningitis resulting in superior orbital fissure syndrome and posterior fossa gumma. A report of two cases followed for 20 years. *J Clin Neuro Ophthalmol 1988;8:145–155.*

20. Stern BJ, Krumholz A, Johns C, et al: Sarcoidosis and its neurological manifestations. *Arch Neurol 1985;49:909–917.*

21. Clifford–Jones RE, Ellis CJK, Stevens JM, Turner A: Cavernous sinus thrombosis. *J Neurol Neurosurg Psychiatr 1982;45:1092–1097.*

22. Antworth MV, Beck RW: Third nerve palsy as presenting sign of acquired immune deficiency syndrome. *J Clin Neuro Ophthalmol 1987; 7:125–128.*

23. Freeman WR, Lerner CW, Mines JA, et al: A prospective study of the ophthalmologic findings in the acquired immune deficiency syndrome. *Am J Ophthalmol 1984;97:133–142.*

24. Rush JA, Younge BR: Paralysis of cranial nerves III, IV, and VI. Cause and prognosis in 1000 cases. *Arch Ophthalmol 1981;99:76–79.*

25. Thomas JE, Yoss RE: The parasellar syndrome: Problems in determining etiology. *Mayo Clin Proced 1970;45:617–623.*

26. Robertson DM, Hines JD, Rucker CW: Acquired sixth-nerve paresis in children. *Arch Ophthalmol 1970;83:574–579.*

27. Godtfredsen E, Lederman M: Diagnostic and prognostic roles of ophthalmoneurologic signs and symptoms in malignant nasopharyngeal tumors. *Am J Ophthalmol 1965;59:1063–1069.*

28. Hotchkiss MG, Miller NR, Clark AW, Green WR: Bilateral Duane's retraction syndrome. A clinical-pathologic case report. *Arch Ophthalmol 1980;98:870–874.*

29. Miller NR, Kiel SM, Green WR, Clark AW: Unilateral Duane's retraction syndrome (Type I). *Arch Ophthalmol 1982;100:1468–1472.*

30. Pitner SE, Edwards JE, McCormick WF: Observations on the pathology of the Moebius syndrome. *J Neurol Neurosurg Psychiatr 1965;28:362–374.*

31. Towfighi J, Marks K, Palmer E, Vannucci R: Möbius syndrome. Neuropathologic observations. *Acta Neuropathol 1979;48:11–17.*

32. Beerbower J, Chakeres DW, Larsen PD, Kapila A: Radiographic findings in Moebius and Moebius-like syndromes. *AJNR 1986;7:364–365.*

33. Traboulsi EI, Maumenee IH: Extraocular muscle aplasia in Moebius syndrome. *J Pediatr Ophthalmol Strabismus 1986;23:120–122.*

34. Miller NR: Solitary oculomotor nerve palsy in childhood. *Am J Ophthalmol 1977;83:106–111.*

35. Victor DI: The diagnosis of congenital unilateral third-nerve palsy. *Brain 1976;99:711–718.*

36. Loewenfeld IE, Thompson HS: Oculomotor paresis with cyclic spasms. A critical review of the literature and a new case. *Surv Ophthalmol 1975;20:81–124.*

37. Insel TR, Kalin NH, Risch SC, et al: Abducens palsy after lumbar puncture. *N Engl J Med 1980;303:703.*

38. McCammon A, Kaufman HH, Sears ES: Transient oculomotor paralysis in pseudotumor cerebri. *Neurology 1981;31:182–184.*

39. Sunderland S: The tentorial notch and complications produced by herniations of the brain through that aperture. *Br J Surg 1958;45:422–438.*

40. Harley RD: Paralytic strabismus in children. Etiologic incidence and management of the third, fourth, and sixth nerve palsies. *Ophthalmology 1980;86:24–43.*

41. Moster ML, Savino PJ, Sergott RC, Bosley TM, Schatz NJ: Isolated sixth-nerve palsies in younger adults. *Arch Ophthalmol 1984;102:1328–1330.*

42. Henn V, Lang W, Hepp K, Reisine H: Experimental gaze palsies in monkeys and their relation to human pathology. *Brain 1984;107:619–636.*

43. Kellen RI, Burde RM, Hodges FJ III, Roper–Hall G: Central bilateral sixth nerve palsy associated with a unilateral preganglionic Horner's syndrome. *J Clin Neuro Ophthalmol 1988;8:179–184.*

44. Keane JR: Trochlear nerve pareses with brainstem lesions. *J Clin Neuro Ophthalmol 1986;6:242–246.*

45. Gradenigo G: A special syndrome of endocranial otitic complications (paralysis of the motor oculi externus of otitic origin). *Ann Otol Rhinol Laryngol 1904;13:637.*

46. Savino PJ, Hilliker JK, Casell GH, Schatz NJ: Chronic sixth nerve palsies. Are they really harbingers of serious intracranial disease? *Arch Ophthalmol 1982;100:1442–1444.*

47. Sharf B, Hyams S: Oculomotor palsy following varicella. *J Pediatr Ophthalmol 1972;9:245–247.*

48. McKinna AJ: Eye signs in 611 cases of posterior fossa aneurysms: Their diagnostic and prognostic value. *Can J Ophthalmol 1983;18:3–6.*

49. Kennerdell JS, Dresner SC: The nonspecific orbital inflammatory syndromes. *Surv Ophthalmol 1984;29:93–103.*
50. Krohel GB, Tobin DR, Hartnett ME, Barrows NA: Divergence paralysis. *Am J Ophthalmol 1982;94:506–510.*
51. Stern RM, Tomsak RL: Magnetic resonance images in a case of "divergence paralysis." *Surv Ophthalmol 1986;30:397–401.*
52. Trobe JD: Cyclodeviation in acquired vertical strabismus. *Arch Ophthalmol 1984;102:717–720.*
53. Hedges TR III, Hoyt WF: Ocular tilt reaction due to an upper brainstem lesion: Paroxysmal skew deviation, torsion, and oscillation of the eyes with head tilt. *Ann Neurol 1982;11:537–540.*
54. Younge BR, Sutula F: Analysis of trochlear nerve palsies. Diagnosis, etiology, and treatment. *Mayo Clin Proc 1977;52:11–18.*
55. Guy J, Day AL, Mickle JP, Schatz NJ: Contralateral trochlear nerve paresis and ipsilateral Horner's syndrome. *Am J Ophthalmol 1989;107:73–76.*
56. Guy JR, Friedman WF, Mickle JP: Bilateral trochlear nerve paresis in hydrocephalus. *J Clin Neuro Ophthalmol 1989;9:105–111.*
57. Wolf JK: *The Classical Brain Stem Syndromes. Translations of the Original Papers with Notes on the Evolution of Clinical Neuroanatomy.* Springfield, Il: Charles C. Thomas, 1971.
58. Biller J, Shapiro R, Evans LS, et al: Oculomotor nuclear complex infarction. Clinical and radiological correlation. *Arch Neurol 1984;41:985–987.*
59. Nadeau SE, Trobe JD: Pupil sparing in oculomotor palsy: A brief review. *Ann Neurol 1983;13:143–148.*
60. Kissel JT, Burde RM, Klingele TG, Zeiger HE: Pupil-sparing oculomotor palsies with internal carotid-posterior communicating artery aneurysms. *Ann Neurol 1983;13:149–154.*
61. Trobe JD, Glaser JS, Post JD: Meningiomas and aneurysms of the cavernous sinus. Neuro-ophthalmologic features. *Arch Ophthalmol 1978;96:457–467.*
62. Bohgen D: Pupil sparing oculomotor palsy. *Ann Neurol 1983;14:698.*
63. Keane JR: Aneurysms and third nerve palsies. *Ann Neurol 1983;14:696–697.*
64. Trobe JD: Isolated pupil-sparing third nerve palsy. *Ophthalmology 1985;92:58–61.*
65. Leunda G, Vaquero J, Cabezudo J, et al: Schwannoma of the oculomotor nerves. A report of four cases. *J Neurosurg 1982;57:563–565.*
66. Ksiazek SM, Repka MX, Maguire A, et al: Divisional oculomotor nerve paresis caused by intrinsic brainstem disease. *Ann Neurol 1989;26:714–718.*
67. Hriso E, Masdeu JC, Miller A: Monocular elevation weakness and ptosis: An oculomotor fascicular syndrome? *J Clin Neuro Ophthalmol 1991;11:111–113.*
68. Bregman DK, Harbour R: Diabetic superior division oculomotor nerve palsy. *Arch Ophthalmol 1988;106:1169–1170.*
69. Siboney PA, Lessell S, Gittenger JW Jr: Acquired oculomotor synkinesis. *Surv Ophthalmol 1984;28:382–390.*
70. Hepler RS, Cantu RC: Aneurysms and third nerve palsies. Ocular status of survivors. *Arch Ophthalmol 1967;77:604–608.*
71. Schatz NJ, Savino PJ, Corbett JC: Primary aberrant oculomotor regeneration. A sign of intracavernous meningioma. *Arch Neurol 1977;34:29–32.*
72. Lam S, Margo CE, Beck R, et al: Cavernous sinus syndrome as the initial manifestation of multiple myeloma. *J Clin Neuro Ophthalmol 1987;7:135–138.*
73. Nugent GR, Sprinkle P, Bloor BM: Sphenoid sinus mucoceles. *J Neurosurg 1970;32:443–451.*
74. Alper MG: Mucoceles of the sphenoid sinus: Neuro-ophthalmologic manifestations. *Trans Am Ophthalmol Soc 1976;74:53–81.*
75. Moore CE, Hoyt WF, North JB: Painful ophthalmoplegia following treated squamous cell carcinoma of the forehead. Orbital apex involvement from centripetal spread via the supraorbital nerve. *Med J Aust 1976;1:657–659.*

76. Kosmorsky GS, Tomsak RL: Ischemic ("diabetic") cavernous sinus syndrome. *J Clin Neuro Ophthalmol 1986;6:96–99.*

77. Babel J: Ophthalmological aspects of myotonic dystrophy, in Huber A, Klein D (eds): *Neurogenetics and Neuro-Ophthalmology.* Amsterdam: Elsevier/North-Holland, 1981, 19–30.

78. Lessell S, Coppeto J, Samet S: Ophthalmoplegia in myotonic dystrophy. *Am J Ophthalmol 1971;71:1231–1235.*

79. Burian HM, Burns CA: Ocular changes in myotonic dystrophy. *Am J Ophthalmol 1967;63:22–34.*

80. Johnson CC, Kuwabara T: Oculopharyngeal muscular dystrophy. *Am J Ophthalmol 1974;77:872–879.*

81. Bourée P, Bouvier JB, Passeron J, et al: Outbreak of trichinosis near Paris. *Br Med J 1979;1:1047–1049.*

82. Rootman J, Nugent R: The classification and management of acute orbital pseudotumors. *Ophthalmology 1982;89:1040–1048.*

83. Trokel SL, Hilal SK: Recognition and differential diagnosis of enlarged extraocular muscles in computed tomography. *Am J Ophthalmol 1979; 87:503–512.*

84. Moraes CT, DiMauro S, Zeviani M, et al: Mitochondrial DNA deletions in progressive external ophthalmoplegia and Kearns-Sayre syndrome. *N Engl J Med 1989;320:1293–1299.*

85. Drachman DA: Ophthalmoplegia plus. The neurodegenerative disorders associated with progressive external ophthalmoplegia. *Arch Neurol 1968;18:654–674.*

86. Kearns TP: External ophthalmoplegia, pigmentary degeneration of the retina, and cardiomyopathy: A newly recognized syndrome. *Trans Am Ophthalmol Soc 1965;63:559–625.*

87. Mullie MA, Harding AE, Petty RKH, et al: Retinal manifestations of mitochondrial myopathy. A study of 22 cases. *Arch Ophthalmol 1985; 103:1825–1830.*

88. Vincent A, Newsom–Davis J: Anti-acetylcholine receptor antibodies. *J Neurol Neurosurg Psychiatr 1980;43:590–600.*

89. Bever CT, Aquino AV, Penn AS, et al: Prognosis of ocular myasthenia. *Ann Neurol 1983;14:516–519.*

90. Grob D, Arsura EL, Brunner NG, Namba T: The course of myasthenia gravis, and therapies affecting outcome. *Ann NY Acad Sci 1987;505: 472–499.*

91. Cogan DG: Myasthenia gravis. A review of the disease and a description of lid twitch as a characteristic sign. *Arch Ophthalmol 1965;74:217–221.*

92. Pestronk A, Drachman DB, Self SG: Measurement of junctional acetylcholine receptors in myasthenia gravis: Clinical correlates. *Muscle Nerve 1985;8:245–251.*

93. Kelly JJ Jr, Daube JR, Lennon VA, et al: The laboratory diagnosis of mild myasthenia gravis. *Ann Neurol 1982;12:238–242.*

94. Vincent A, Newsom–Davis J: Acetylcholine receptor antibody characteristics in myasthenia gravis. I. Patients with generalized myasthenia or disease restricted to ocular muscles. *Clin Exp Immunol 1982;49:257–265.*

95. Stalberg E: Clinical electrophysiology in myasthenia gravis. *J Neurol Neurosurg Psychiatr 1980;43:622–633.*

96. Seybold ME: The office Tensilon test for ocular myasthenia gravis. *Arch Neurol 1986;43:842–843.*

97. Miller NR, Morris JE, Maguire M: Combined use of neostigmine and ocular motility measurements in the diagnosis of myasthenia gravis. *Arch Ophthalmol 1982;100:761–763.*

98. Downes JM, Greenwood BM, Wray SH: Auto-immune aspects of myasthenia gravis. *Q J Med 1966;35:85–105.*

99. Seybold ME, Drachman DB: Gradually increasing doses of prednisone in myasthenia gravis. Reducing the hazards of treatment. *N Engl J Med 1974;290:81–84.*

100. Mulder DG, Herrmann C Jr, Keesey J, Edwards H: Thymectomy for myasthenia gravis. *Am J Surg 1983;146:61–66.*

101. Howard BD, Gundersen CB Jr: Effects and mechanisms of polypeptide neurotoxins that act presynaptically. *Ann Rev Pharmacol Toxicol 1980;20:307–336.*

102. Terranova W, Palumbo JN, Breman JG: Ocular findings in botulism type B. *JAMA 1979;241:475–477.*

103. Hedges TR III, Jones A, Stark L, Hoyt WF: Botulin ophthalmoplegia. Clinical and oculographic observations. *Arch Ophthalmol 1983; 101:211–213.*

104. Miller NR, Moses H: Ocular involvement in wound botulism. *Arch Ophthalmol 1977;95:1788–1789.*

105. Cooper BJ, Spence I: Temperature-dependent inhibition of evoked acetylcholine release in tick paralysis. *Nature 1976;263:693–695.*

106. Smith B, Regan WF: Blowout fracture of the floor of the orbit. Mechanism and correction of internal orbital fracture. *Am J Ophthalmol 1957;44:733–739.*

107. Lyon DB, Newman SA: Evidence of direct damage to extra-ocular muscles as a cause of diplopia following orbital trauma. *Ophthalmol Plast Reconstruct Surg 1989;5:81–91.*

108. Trokel SL, Jakobiec FA: Correlation of CT scanning and pathologic features of ophthalmic Graves' disease. *Ophthalmology 1981;88:553–564.*

109. Sergott RC, Glaser JS: Graves' ophthalmopathy. A clinical and immunologic review. *Surv Ophthalmol 1981;26:1–21.*

109. Harley RD, Rodrigues MM, Crawford JS: Congenital fibrosis of the extraocular muscles. *Trans Am Ophthalmol Soc 1978;76:197–222.*

110. Metz HS: Double elevator palsy. *Arch Ophthalmol 1979;97:901–903.*

111. Helveston EM, Giangiacomo JG, Ellis FD: Congenital absence of the superior oblique tendon. *Trans Am Ophthalmol Soc 1981;79:123–135.*

112. Diamond GR, Katowitz JA, Whitaker LA, et al: Variations in extraocular muscle number and structure in craniofacial dysostosis. *Am J Ophthalmol 1980;90:416–418.*

113. Brown HW: True and simulated superior oblique tendon sheath syndrome. *Doc Ophthalmol 1973;34:123–136.*

114. Pinchoff BS, Spahlinger DA, Bergstrom TJ, Sandall GS: Extraocular muscle involvement in Wegener's granulomatosis. *J Clin Neuro Ophthalmol 1983;3:163–168.*

115. Barricks ME, Traviesa DB, Glaser JS, Levy IS: Ophthalmoplegia in cranial arteritis. *Brain 1977;100:209–222.*

116. Beck M, Hickling P: Treatment of bilateral superior oblique tendon sheath syndrome complicating rheumatoid arthritis. *Br J Ophthalmol 1980;64:358–361.*

117. Blanchard CL, Young LA: Acquired inflammatory superior oblique tendon sheath (Brown's) syndrome. *Arch Otolaryngol 1984;110:120–122.*

118. Katz B, Leja S, Melles RB, Press GA: Amyloid ophthalmoplegia. Ophthalmoparesis secondary to primary systemic amyloidosis. *J Clin Neuro Ophthalmol 1989;9:39–42.*

119. Slamovits TL, Burde RM, Sedwick L, et al: Bumpy muscles. *Surv Ophthalmol 1988;33:189–199.*

120. Kohn R, Hepler R: Management of limited rhino-orbital mucormycosis without exenteration. *Ophthalmology 1985;92:1440–1444.*

121. Grimson BS, Thompson HS: Raeder's syndrome. A clinical review. *Surv Ophthalmol 1980;24:199–210.*

122. Vijayan N: Ophthalmoplegic migraine: Ischemic or compressive neuropathy? *Headache 1980;20:300–304.*

123. Grimson BS, Glaser JS: Isolated trochlear nerve palsies in herpes zoster ophthalmicus. *Arch Ophthalmol 1978;96:1233–1235.*

124. Marsh RJ, Dulley B, Kelly V: External ocular motor palsies in ophthalmic zoster: A review. *Br J Ophthalmol 1977;61:677–682.*

125. Archambault P, Wise JS, Rosen J, et al: Herpes zoster ophthalmoplegia. Report of six cases. *J Clin Neuro Ophthalmol 1988;8:185–191.*

126. Palestine AG, Rodrigues MM, et al: Ophthalmic involvement in acquired immunodeficiency syndrome. *Ophthalmology 1984;91:1092–1099.*

127. Tolosa E: Periarteritic lesions of the carotid siphon with the clinical features of a carotid infraclinoidal aneurysm. *J Neurol Neurosurg Psychiatr 1954;17:300–302.*

128. Hunt WE, Meagher JN, LeFever HE, Zeman W: Painful ophthalmoplegia. Its relation to indolent inflammation of the cavernous sinus. *Neurology 1961;11:56–62.*

129. Kline LB: The Tolosa-Hunt syndrome. *Surv Ophthalmol* 1982;27:79–95.

130. Smith JL, Taxdal DSR: Painful ophthalmoplegia. The Tolosa-Hunt syndrome. *Am J Ophthalmol* 1966;61:1466–1472.

131. Marmor M, Wertenbaker C, Berstein L: Delayed ophthalmoplegia following head trauma. *Surv Ophthalmol* 1982;27:126–132.

132. Hawke SHB, Mullie MA, Hoyt WF, et al: Painful oculomotor nerve palsy due to dural-cavernous sinus shunt. *Arch Neurol* 1989;46:1252–1255.

133. Currie J, Lubin JH, Lessell S: Chronic isolated abducens paresis from tumors at the base of the brain. *Arch Neurol* 1983;40:226–229.

134. Abdul-Rahim AS, Savino PJ, Zimmerman RA, et al: Cryptogenic oculomotor nerve palsy. The need for repeated neuroimaging studies. *Arch Ophthalmol* 1989;107:387–390.

135. Wasserstrom WR, Glass JP, Posner JB: Diagnosis and treatment of leptomeningeal metastases from solid tumors: Experience with 90 patients. *Cancer* 1982;49:759–772.

136. Fitzsimmons R, Fraco, Lee JP, Elston J: Treatment of sixth nerve palsy in adults with combined botulinum toxin chemodenervation and surgery. *Ophthalmology* 1988;95:1535–1542.

137. Murray ADN: Early and late botulinum toxin treatment of acute sixth nerve palsy. *Aust NZ J Ophthalmol* 1989;17:239–245.

138. Knapp P: Treatment of unilateral fourth nerve paralysis. *Trans Ophthalmol Soc UK* 1981;101:273–275.

139. Lee DA, Dyer JA, O'Brien PC, Taylor JZ: Surgical treatment of lateral rectus muscle paralysis. *Am J Ophthalmol* 1984;97:511–518.

1. Muskens LJJ: An anatomico-physiological study of the posterior longitudinal bundle in its relation to forced movements. *Brain* 1914; 36:356–426.

2. Robinson DA: Control of eye movements, in *Handbook of Physiology, Section 1: The Nervous System,* Vol II. Bethesda: American Physiological Society, 1981, 1275–1319.

3. Baloh R, Yee R, Honrubia V: Eye movements in patients with Wallenberg's syndrome. *Ann NY Acad Sci* 1981;374:600–613.

4. Cox T, Corbett J, Thompson H, Lennarson L: Upbeat nystagmus changing to downbeat nystagmus with convergence. *Neurology* 1981; 31:891–892.

5. Furman JMR, Becker JT: Vestibular responses in Wernicke's encephalopathy. *Ann Neurol* 1989;26:669–674.

6. Furman JM, Perlman S, Baloh RW: Eye movements in Friedreich's ataxia. *Arch Neurol* 1983;40:343–346.

7. Sharpe JA, Fletcher WA: Saccadic intrusions and oscillations. *Can J Neurol Sci* 1984;11:426–433.

8. Digre KB: Opsoclonus in adults. *Arch Neurol* 1986;43:1165–1175.

9. Troost BT, Daroff RB: The ocular motor defects in progressive supranuclear palsy. *Ann Neurol* 1977;2:397–403.

10. Leigh RJ, Zee DS: *The Neurology of Eye Movements,* ed 2. Philadelphia: FA Davis, 1991.

11. Schwartz MA, Selhorst JB, Ochs AL, et al: Oculomasticatory myorhythmia: A unique movement disorder occurring in Whipple's disease. *Ann Neurol* 1986;20:677–683.

12. Baloh RW, Furman JM, Yee RD: Dorsal midbrain syndrome: Clinical and oculographic findings. *Neurology* 1985;35:54–60.

13. Pierrot–Deseilligny C, Chain F, Gray F, et al: Parinaud's syndrome: Electro-oculographic and anatomical analyses of six vascular cases with deductions about vertical gaze organization in the premotor structures. *Brain* 1982;105:667–696.

14. White OB, Saint-Cyr JA, Tomlinson RD, Sharpe JA: Ocular motor deficits in Parkinson's Disease. II. Control of the saccadic and smooth pursuit systems. *Brain* 1983;106:571–587.

15. Collewijn H, Went LN, Tamminga EP, Vegter–Van der Vlis M: Oculomotor defects in patients with Huntington's disease and their offspring. *J Neurol Sci* 1988;86:307–320.

CHAPTER 8
SUPRANUCLEAR
DISORDERS

16. Kirkham TH, Guitton D: A quantitative study of abnormal eye movements in Huntington's chorea using the scleral search coil technique. *Neuro-Ophthalmology 1984;4:27–38.*
17. Lasker AG, Zee DS, Hain TC, et al: Saccades in Huntington's disease: Initiation defects and distractibility. *Neurology 1987;37:364–370.*
18. Lasker AG, Zee DS, Hain TC, Folstein SE, Singer HS: Saccades in Huntington's disease: Slowing and dysmetria. *Neurology 1988;38:427–431.*
19. Oepen G, Clarenbach P, Thoden U: Disturbance of eye movements in Huntington's chorea. *Arch Psychiatr Nervenkr 1981;229:205–213.*
20. Morrow MJ, Sharpe JA: Cerebral hemispheric localization of smooth pursuit asymmetry. *Neurology 1990;40:284–292.*
21. Sharpe JA, Lo AW, Rabinovitch HE: Control of the saccadic and smooth pursuit systems after cerebral hemidecortication. *Brain 1979; 102:387–403.*

CHAPTER 9
NYSTAGMUS AND THE VESTIBULAR SYSTEM

1. Leigh RJ, Zee DS: *The Neurology of Eye Movements,* ed 2. Philadelphia: FA Davis, 1991.
2. Baloh RW, Yee RD, Honrubia V: Eye movements in patients with Wallenberg's syndrome. *Ann NY Acad Sci 1981;374:600–614.*
3. Baloh RW, Spooner JW: Downbeat nystagmus: A type of central vestibular nystagmus. *Neurology 1981;31:304–310.*
4. Medhorn E, Kommerell G, Meienberg O: Primary position vertical nystagmus directional preponderence of the pursuit system. *Graefes Arch Clin Exp Ophthalmol 1979;209:209-217.*
5. Zee DS, Friendlich A, Robinson D: The mechanism of downbeat nystagmus. *Arch Neurology 1974;30:227–337.*
6. Robinson DA: A quantitative analysis of extraocular muscle cooperation and squint. *Invest Ophthalmol 1975;14:801–825.*
7. Cannon S, Robinson D: The final common integrator is in the prepositus and vestibular nuclei, in Keller EL, Zee DS (eds): *Adaptive Processes in Visual and Oculomotor Systems.* New York: Pergamon Press, 1985, 307–311.
8. Takemori S, Cohen B: Loss of visual suppression of vestibular nystagmus after flocculus lesions. *Brain Res 1974;72:213–224.*
9. Zee DS, Yamazaki A, Butler P, Gucer G: Effects of ablation of flocculus and paraflocculus on eye movements in primate. *J Neurophysiol 1981; 46:878–899.*
10. Hood J: Further observations on the phenomenon of rebound nystagmus. *Ann NY Acad Sci 1981;374:532–539.*
11. Jung R, Kornhuber H: Results of electronystagmography in man: The value of optokinetic, vestibular, and spontaneous nystagmus for neurologic diangosis and research, in Bender E (ed): *The Oculomotor System.* New York: Harper and Row, 1964, 428–488.
12. Waespe W, Cohen B, Raphan T: Dynamic modification of the vestibulo-ocular reflex by the nodulus and uvula. *Science 1985;228: 199–202.*
13. Furman JMR, Wall C III, Pang D: Vestibular function in periodic alternating nystagmus. *Brain 1990;113:1425–1439.*
14. Pierrot–Deseilligny C, Chain F, Gray F, et al: Parinaud's syndrome electro-oculographic and anatomical analyses of six vascular cases with deductions about vertical gaze organization in the premotor structures. *Brain 1982;105:667–696.*
15. Ochs AL, Stark L, Hoyt WF, D'Amico D: Opposed adducting saccades in convergence-retraction nystagmus. *Brain 1979;102:497–508.*
16. Ranalli PJ, Sharpe JA: Upbeat nystagmus and the ventral tegmental pathway of the upward vestibulo-ocular reflex. *Neurology 1988; 38:1329–1330.*
17. Sharpe JA, Fletcher WA: Saccadic intrusions and oscillations. *Can J Neurol Sci 1984;11:426–433.*
18. Zee DS, Robinson DA: A hypothetical explanation of saccadic oscillations. *Ann Neurol 1979;5:405–414.*

1. Ellingson FT: The uveitis-glaucoma-hyphema syndrome associated with Mark VIII anterior chamber lens implant. *Am Intraocul Implant Soc J 1978;4:50–53.*
2. Sadun AA, Currie JN, Lessell S: Transient visual obscurations with elevated optic discs. *Ann Neurol 1984;16:489–494.*
3. Seybold M, Rosen PN: Peripapillary staphyloma and amaurosis fugax. *Ann Ophthalmol 1977;9:1139–1141.*
4. Manor RS, Sira IB: Amaurosis fugax at downward gaze. *Surv Ophthalmol 1987;31:411–416.*
5. Cogan DG: Blackouts not obviously due to carotid occlusion. *Arch Ophthalmol 1961;66:180–187.*
6. Fisher CM: Observations of the fundus oculi in transient monocular blindness. *Neurology 1959;9:333–347.*
7. Hoyt WF: Ocular symptoms and signs, in Wylie ES, Ehrenfeld WK (eds): *Extracranial Occlusive Cerebrovascular Disease: Diagnosis and Management.* Philadelphia: WB Saunders, 1970, 64–95.
8. Hollenhorst RW: Significance of bright plaques in the retinal arterioles. *JAMA 1961;178:23–29.*
9. Inkeles DM, Walsh JB: Retinal fat emboli as a sequela to acute pancreatitis. *Am J Ophthalmol 1975;80:935–938.*
10. Shapiro I, Jacob HS: Leukoembolization in ocular vascular occlusion. *Ann Ophthalmol 1982;14:60–62.*
11. Rosenfeld S, Kosmorsky G, Klingele T, Burde R: Treatment of temporal arteritis with ocular involvement. *Am J Med 1986;80:143–145.*
12. Burger SK, Saul RF, Selhorst JD, Thurston SE: Transient blindness caused by vasospasm. *N Engl J Med 1991;325:870–873.*
13. Winterkorn JMS, Teman AJ: Recurrent attacks of amaurosis fugax treated with calcium channel blocker. *Ann Neurol 1991;30:423–425.*
14. Winterkorn JMS, Kupersmith MJ, Wirtschafter JD, Forman S: Treatment of vasospastic amaurosis fugax with calcium channel blockers. *N Engl J Med, in press.*
15. Hupp SL, Kline LB, Corbett JJ: Visual disturbances of migraine. *Surv Ophthalmol 1989;33:221–236.*
16. Hayreh SS: Vasospasm and transient monocular blindness. *N Engl J Med 1992;326:837–838.*
17. Troost BT, Newton TH: Occipital lobe arteriovenous malformation: Clinical and radiologic features in 26 cases with comments on differentiation from migraine. *Arch Ophthalmol 1975;93:250–256.*
18. Polyak S: *The Vertebrate Visual System.* Chicago: University of Chicago Press, 1957, 735–747.
19. Brandt KD, Lessell S: Migrainous phenomena in systemic lupus erythematosus. *Arthritis Rheum 1978;21:7–16.*
20. Cohen GR, Harbison JW, Blair CJ, Ochs AL: Clinical significance of transient visual phenomena in the elderly. *Ophthalmology 1984;91: 436–441.*
21. Kearns TP, Hollenhorst RW: Venous stasis retinopathy of occlusive disease of the carotid artery. *Neurol Clin Proc 1963;38:304–312.*
22. Kearns TP: Differential diagnosis of central retinal vein obstruction. *Ophthalmology 1983;90:475–480.*
23. Hayreh SS: Occlusion of the central retinal vessels. *Br J Ophthalmol 1965;49:626–645.*
24. Hayreh SS: Classification of central retinal vein occlusion. *Ophthalmology 1983;90:458–474.*
25. Ellenberger C, Epstein AD: Ocular complications of atherosclerosis: What do they mean? *Semin Neurol 1986;6:185–193.*
26. North American Symptomatic Carotid Endarterectomy Trial Collaborators: Beneficial effect of carotid endarterectomy in symptomatic patients with high-grade carotid stenosis. *N Engl J Med 1991;325:445–453.*
27. Carroll FD: Nutritional amblyopia. *Arch Ophthalmol 1966;76:406–411.*
28. Grant WM: *Toxicology of the Eye.* Springfield, Il: CC Thomas, 1986, 405–410.

CHAPTER 10
VISUAL LOSS, DIPLOPIA, AND OSCILLOPSIA AS NEURO-OPHTHALMIC CLUES TO SYSTEMIC DISEASE

29. Grunwald GB, Klein R, Simmonds MA, Kornguth SE: Autoimmune basis for visual paraneoplastic syndrome in patients with small cell lung carcinoma. *Lancet 1985;1:658–661.*
30. Thirkill CE, Roth AM, Keltner JL: Cancer associated retinopathy. *Arch Ophthalmol 1987;105:372–375.*
31. Klingele TG, Burde RM, Rappazzo JA, et al: Paraneoplastic retinopathy. *J Clin Neuro-Ophthalmol 1984;4:239–245.*
32. Sawyer RA, Selhorst JB, Zimmerman LE, Hoyt WF: Blindness caused by photoreceptor degeneration as a remote effect of cancer. *Am J Ophthalmol 1986;81:606–613.*
33. Keltner JL, Thirkill CE, Tyler NK, Roth AM: Management and monitoring of cancer-associated retinopathy. *Arch Ophthalmol 1991; 11:48–53.*
34. Finelli PF, McEntee WJ, Lessell S, et al: Whipple's disease with predominantly neuro-ophthalmic manifestations. *Ann Neurol 1977;1:247–252.*
35. Hausser–Hauw C, Roullet E, Robert R, et al: Oculo-facial-skeletal myorhythmia as a cerebral complication of systemic Whipple's disease. *Movement Disorders 1988;3:179–184.*
36. Relman DA, Schmidt TM, MacDermott RP, Falkow S. Identification of the uncultured bacillus of Whipple's disease. *N Engl J Med 1992; 327:293–348.*
37. Cherington M: Botulism: Ten years experience. *Arch Neurol 1974; 30:432–437.*
38. Victor M, Adams RD, Collins GH: *The Wernicke–Korsakoff Syndrome: A Clinical and Pathological Study of 245 Patients.* Philadelphia: Davis, 1971.
39. Henson RA, Urich H: *Cancer and the Nervous System. The Neurological Manifestations of Systemic Malignant Disease.* Oxford: Blackwell, 1982.
40. Cunningham J, Graus F, Anderson N, Posner JB: Partial characterization of the Purkinje cell antigens in paraneoplastic cerebellar degeneration. *Neurology 1986;36:1163–1168.*
41. Furneaux HM, Rosenblum MK, Wong E, et al: Selective expression of Purkinje neuron antigens in ovarian and breast tumors of patients with paraneoplastic cerebellar degeneration. *Neurology 1989;(suppl):260.*
42. Anderson NE, Rosenblum MK, Posner JB: Paraneoplastic cerebellar degeneration: Clinical-immunological correlations. *Ann Neurol 1988; 24:559–567.*
43. Anderson NE, Rosenblum MK, Graus F, et al: Autoantibodies in paraneoplastic syndromes associated with small-cell lung cancer. *Neurology 1988;38:1391–1398.*
44. Cogan DG: Ocular dysmetria, flutter-like oscillopsia of the eye, and opsoclonus. *Arch Ophthalmol 1954;51:318–335.*
45. Hoyt CS: Neonatal opsoclonus. *J Pediatr Ophthalmol 1977;14:274.*

INDEX